Biology in Time and Space

A Partial Differential Equation Modeling Approach

The Sally SERIES

Pure and Applied
UNDERGRADUATE TEXTS · 50

Biology in Time and Space

A Partial Differential Equation Modeling Approach

James P. Keener

AMS AMERICAN MATHEMATICAL SOCIETY

Providence, Rhode Island USA

2020 *Mathematics Subject Classification.* Primary 35-XX, 92-XX;
Secondary 34-XX, 60-XX, 65-XX.

Cover description: Depiction of a biased random walk
performed by the run and tumble motion of bacteria
in order to chemotactically locate a food source.
Image credit: Johanna Bossart.

For additional information and updates on this book, visit
www.ams.org/bookpages/amstext-50

Library of Congress Cataloging-in-Publication Data

Names: Keener, James P., author.
Title: Biology in time and space : a partial differential equation modeling approach / James P. Keener.
Description: Providence, Rhode Island : American Mathematical Society, [2021] | Series: Pure and applied undergraduate texts, 1943-9334 ; Volume 50 | Includes bibliographical references and index.
Identifiers: LCCN 2020041397 | ISBN 9781470454289 (paperback) | ISBN 9781470464141 (ebook)
Subjects: LCSH: Biomathematics. | Differential equations, Partial. | AMS: Partial differential equations. | Biology and other natural sciences. | Ordinary differential equations. | Probability theory and stochastic processes. | Numerical analysis.
Classification: LCC QH323.5 .K455 2021 | DDC 570.1/51–dc23
LC record available at https://lccn.loc.gov/2020041397

For since the creation of the world His invisible attributes,
His eternal power and divine nature, have been clearly seen,
being understood through what has been made. — St. Paul, AD 57

Contents

Preface

Mathematical biology is, broadly speaking, the use of mathematics to study how biological objects do what they do. And what they do is characterized by change. If nothing is changing it is not alive. For any living organism, dormant seeds notwithstanding, there is always something that is changing. Something is being created and something is being destroyed. And when a living organism dies, it does not stop changing quite yet, but the change is characterized by degradation, as complex molecules and structures that required energy and specialized information to construct, degrade and deteriorate.

What this means is that life must be thought of as a *process*, and to understand what is happening, one must think about how to describe processes and things that are changing. That is why to begin the study of how to use mathematics to study biology it makes sense to talk about change—that is, objects or collections of objects that vary in time and are created or destroyed—and to study these using dynamical descriptions. The natural mathematical language for this is the language of differential and/or difference equations where the natural independent variable is time. Indeed, there are a number of excellent books that introduce their readers to mathematical biology using the language of time varying dynamical systems. There is a lot of insight that can be gained from these studies of dynamical descriptions of biological processes. (For example, see [2],[3],[8],[11],[15],[16],[18],[50].)

However, this perspective is limited when it comes to understanding most real biological situations, because biological objects are essentially *never* homogeneously distributed in space, or well-mixed, even in a test tube or in a Petrie dish, let alone inside the human body or on a mountain slope. In fact, it is a primary feature of biological objects that there are spatial differences and, correspondingly, movement of objects from one place to another. So, whether one is studying the spread of an infectious disease or an invasive species, or the movement of an electrical signal along a nerve axon, it is crucially important to include the effects of spatial differences.

The ultimate goal of this book, then, is to use mathematics to begin to tell the story of how biological objects do what they do, such as communicate, make structures, make measurements and decisions, search for food, etc., all things necessary for survival. But this story can be told using mathematics only if certain mathematical tools are understood. The first of these tools is mathematical modeling, i.e., the ability to turn a verbal description of some process into quantifiable terms and equations that can be studied. Back in the day, when I was still a student, we called these "word problems". Second, because we are dealing with processes that evolve in both space and time, we use multivariable dynamical systems. Consequently, a subplot of this story is the study of partial differential equations, primarily diffusion reaction equations. So part of what is hoped for is that this text will expand your mathematical toolbox to include multivariable differential equations, i.e., partial differential equations and their approximations.

There are two broad areas of biology that are discussed here, namely population level and cellular level, i.e., physiology. Biology at the population level is relatively easy to discuss because it does not require an extensive biological background to understand the issues involved. Many of the issues involved are part of our everyday experience, or at least our internet newsfeed reading. For this reason population level modeling is a popular entry point for mathematical biology modeling. However, the models that are used tend to be highly qualitative and difficult to use to make specific quantitative predictions or observations. Cell biology and physiology, on the other hand, require more biological background, but have the advantage that the mechanisms involved are much more readily quantifiable and testable, lending themselves to more specific and detailed predictions and observations. In my experience, very few mathematics students have had an introduction to cell biology, and so processes at the cellular level are less familiar to them. My hope is that these topics are presented in a way that a person with only a modest background of biology can understand. (Or, consult Wikipedia or [35] when my introductions here are lacking.) It is useful, but not absolutely necessary, to have studied more introductory mathematical biology material.

This book is intended for an advanced undergraduate audience, with no previous background in partial differential equations, although beginning graduate students should also find this useful. Prerequisites for this exploration include multivariable calculus, ordinary differential equations and basic aspects of probability theory and stochastic processes. However, to make sure that we are all on the same page, Chapter 1 is devoted to a quick review or introduction of these topics. So, in Chapter 1, you will find summaries of the mathematical background that is needed from multivariable calculus, from ordinary differential equations, and from probability theory, stochastic processes and stochastic simulations, because these are used a lot.

Since understanding the solutions of partial differential equations is generally rather difficult, and analytical approaches are quite limited, numerical simulation is a must. Consequently, this material is presented from a heavily computational perspective, using Matlab to compute solutions and to make plots. So, in Appendix A you will find a primer for Matlab and a list of all of the Matlab codes that were used for the simulations and to make the plots. All of these codes are available for download at

http://www.ams.org/bookpages/amstext-50

The hope is that these codes can be readily used and easily modified for Exercises and projects, and that this will facilitate the process of hands-on learning to understand this material.

The content of the book is organized pedagogically around mathematical material, starting simply and adding mathematical complexity as we proceed. We start with basic diffusion processes, then move to diffusion with reaction, then to advection with reaction, then advection with diffusion, and finally combinations of all three advection, diffusion, and reaction. However, all of the equations studied here are derived with specific biological processes in mind. Specifically, the first ten chapters of this text each introduce new mathematical ideas or techniques, while Chapters 11 through 14 do not introduce any new mathematics but use what has been described earlier to study interesting and important biological processes.

The specific content of the book is as follows: As already described, Chapter 1 contains an introduction/review of the three main tools that are used extensively in this book. These are multivariable calculus, the qualitative theory of ordinary differential equations (especially phase plane analysis), and stochastic processes and their simulation. Chapter 2 introduces the main tool of mathematical modeling, namely, counting, or more formally, conservation laws and how to write equations that keep track of things. In Chapters 3, 4, and 5 we describe diffusion, derivations of diffusion equations, simulation of diffusion processes, and solution techniques for equations describing diffusion. In Chapter 6, we begin to include what happens when there are chemical reactions as well as diffusion, focussing on Fisher's equation for the spread of a growing, but limited population. Here we include discussion of populations whose dynamics are similar to those of Fishers's equation, including sustainability on an animal preserve, spatial spread of an epidemic, glucose consumption by bacteria in a Petrie dish, the spread of rabies in foxes in England, and the role of myoglobin in enhancing the delivery of oxygen to muscle tissue. Then, in Chapter 7, we introduce the bistable equation, with four examples of dynamics (spread of spruce budworm in northeastern forests, spread of *wolbachia* infection in mosquitoes, spread of the electrical action potential in nerve axons, and spread of calcium release in frog eggs following fertilization) whose mathematical description is that of the bistable equation. This chapter illustrates my long-held belief in the importance of transferable principles. That is, it is often the case as illustrated here that processes transpire according to the same principles and therefore their mathematical descriptions have common features that can inform each other even though the vocabulary describing the details is vastly different. Chapter 8 provides a study of the bistable equation, and examples of propagation of signals via travelling waves, as well as causes for propagation failure. Some of these are spatial inhomogeneities in the medium, including damage to neurons from traumatic brain injury, or effects from the discrete nature of the medium, such as in cardiac tissue or calcium release sites in muscle cells. Chapter 9 introduces advection-reaction equations and the important technique of the method of characteristics. Some of the problems included here include the dynamics of age-structured epidemics, dynamics of red blood cell production, the counter-current mechanism for delivery of oxygen to muscle tissue, and protein-mediated friction and the contraction of muscle fibers. Included also is a discussion of Burgers' equation, but from a perspective and with an application (formation of gels) different than that found in most introductory books on partial differential equations. Finally, Chapter 10 introduces diffusion-advection equations, including a discussion of the Ornstein–Uhlenbeck process.

No new mathematical ideas are introduced in the remaining chapters, as these are dedicated to the description of interesting processes which we are now fully prepared to study. These include chemotaxis, i.e., the bacterial search for food (Chapter 11), pattern formation including the famous Turing mechanism, formation of tiger bush stripes in semi-arid climates, and cell polarization (Chapter 12), dispersal-renewal processes and the spread of invasive species (Chapter 13), and collective behavior of organisms, including quorum sensing by bacteria, and swarming of flying birds or insects or swimming fish (Chapter 14).

As with any new topic of study, it is important to do the exercises. Here I have tried to provide a gamut of exercises, from fairly routine to more challenging. However, many of the exercises involve simulation, and for these the Matlab codes presented with the main text can be modified to carry out the requested computation. Some, but not nearly all, of the answers to exercises are provided at the end of this book (in Appendix C), in order to help students know if they are getting the right answer. However, instructors who are working through this material for the first time may want a little more guidance. For those of you in this situation, a fairly extensive solution manual is available from the AMS at textbooks@ams.org.

As you can see from the above description, the mathematical focus of this book is diffusion reaction equations. However, this constitutes only the most basic introduction to this topic and does not explore its more theoretical aspects. Consequently, for those who are interested in pursuing the more theoretical aspects of this subject matter, I recommend books such as [7],[9],[19],[26],[58],[66]. A book with a similar philosophy for studying biological processes using partial differential equations, but at a more advanced level, is [49].

The material described here is drawn from a course in Mathematical Biology that I and my colleagues have taught at the University of Utah for many years. I owe a debt of gratitude to colleagues Fred Adler, Alla Borisyuk, Aaron Fogelson, and Sean Lawley, from whom I have taken course notes and homework exercises that have been used in the development of this text. I am also very appreciative of the hard work of Alex Beams and Amanda Alexander who did the Herculean task of reading this text and making numerous invaluable suggestions. Thanks to all of you.

Finally, I owe a tremendous debt of gratitude to the staff of clinic 2E at the Huntsman Cancer Center, including the aides and nurses, APRNs Mary Steinbach, Jan Weidner and Heidi Nielson, and especially Dr. Douglas Sborov. It is no exaggeration to say that without their gracious and expert care, this book would not have been written.

As with any work such as this, there are bound to be errors that have not yet been found. As you work through this text and exercises, please let me know those that you find, and I will post an updated list of these on my website.

And now that this project is finished, hopefully I will have more time for "poisson processing".

Jim Keener

Chapter 1

Background Material

To explore the biological world in both space and time, several mathematical tools are necessary. We need to be facile with multivariable calculus, with the qualitative theory of ordinary differential equations and their numerical simulation, and with basic stochastic processes. These are the topics to which we now give our attention.

1.1. Multivariable Calculus

1.1.1. Partial Derivatives. In what is to come, we will be dealing with functions of both space and time. We may be interested in the electrolyte balance within muscle tissue, or the distribution of microorganisms occupying a lake; either way, we are studying how something occupying a region in space evolves over time. We often describe position in this space by using the Cartesian coordinates x, y, and z, and time by the variable t (although other coordinate representations like polar or spherical coordinates are sometimes useful).

The quantity of interest may be the concentration (= number per unit volume) of calcium ions in a cell or the concentration of microorganisms in the lake, but it is typically denoted by some scalar function $u = u(x, y, z, t)$. If u changes smoothly in time, then it has a time derivative $\frac{\partial u}{\partial t}$ defined by[1]

$$(1.1) \qquad \frac{\partial u}{\partial t} = \lim_{\Delta t \to 0} \frac{u(x, y, z, t + \Delta t) - u(x, y, z, t)}{\Delta t}.$$

The fundamental theorem of calculus states that

$$(1.2) \qquad u(x, y, z, b) - u(x, y, z, a) = \int_a^b \frac{\partial u}{\partial t} dt.$$

In words, the cumulative change in u over an interval of time can be measured by observing the difference between u at the end and the beginning of the interval.

---

[1] For notation, the objects $\frac{\partial u}{\partial t}$ and u_t are exactly the same thing, as are $\frac{\partial u}{\partial x}$ and u_x.

Similarly, if u varies smoothly in space, spatial derivatives can be defined, such as

$$(1.3) \qquad \frac{\partial u}{\partial x} = \lim_{\Delta x \to 0} \frac{u(x + \Delta x, y, z, t) - u(x, y, z, t)}{\Delta x},$$

and this is one component of the *gradient* of u, the vector-valued function

$$(1.4) \qquad \nabla u = (\frac{\partial u}{\partial x}, \frac{\partial u}{\partial y}, \frac{\partial u}{\partial z}).$$

The gradient holds all of the information we need about how u changes in space, but since there are an infinite number of directions in which we could move from a particular point, to find the derivative of u in a particular direction, $\mathbf{v}$, where $\mathbf{v}$ is a unit vector, we define the *directional derivative*,

$$(1.5) \qquad \frac{\partial u}{\partial \mathbf{v}} = \nabla u \cdot \mathbf{v}.$$

One important object that uses the gradient is

$$(1.6) \qquad \mathbf{n} = \frac{\nabla u}{|\nabla u|},$$

which, provided $|\nabla u| \neq 0$, is a unit vector pointing in the direction of the greatest increase of the function u. The importance of this to a skier or snowboarder is obvious, pointing in the direction parallel to the "fall-line". It is also noteworthy that $\mathbf{n}$ is perpendicular (orthogonal) to level surfaces of the function u. We can verify this by noting that if $(x(s), y(s), z(s))$ is a curve in space parametrized by s, the tangent direction of the curve is the vector $(\dot{x}(s), \dot{y}(s), \dot{z}(s))$. If the function $u(x, y, z)$ is a constant on this curve, $u(x(s), y(s), z(s)) = C$, then differentiating this with respect to s, we find that

$$(1.7) \qquad 0 = \frac{\partial u}{\partial x}\dot{x}(s) + \frac{\partial u}{\partial y}\dot{y}(s) + \frac{\partial u}{\partial z}\dot{z}(s) \equiv \nabla u \cdot \begin{pmatrix} \dot{x}(s) \\ \dot{y}(s) \\ \dot{z}(s) \end{pmatrix},$$

as claimed.

1.1.2. Vector Fields. It could be that the quantity of interest is a vector valued function, for example, the velocity of the water in a river or the velocity of the blood in an artery, given by $\mathbf{v} = (v_1, v_2, v_3)$ where each of the components of the vector $\mathbf{v}$ is a function of x, y, z, and t. Of course, this vector valued function could be the gradient of some scalar function u. One important quantity for any vector valued function is its *divergence*, denoted

$$(1.8) \qquad \nabla \cdot \mathbf{v} = \frac{\partial v_1}{\partial x} + \frac{\partial v_2}{\partial y} + \frac{\partial v_3}{\partial z}.$$

The most important theorem regarding the divergence, called the *divergence theorem*, is stated as

$$(1.9) \qquad \int_{\Omega} \nabla \cdot \mathbf{v} dV = \int_{\partial \Omega} \mathbf{v} \cdot \mathbf{n} dS,$$

where Ω is a region of interest with dimension $d = 1, 2$ or 3, $\partial \Omega$ is its $(d-1)$-dimensional boundary, and $\mathbf{n}$ is the unit outward normal vector to the boundary. Here dV is the volume element for the space, with units $(\text{length})^d$ and dS is its surface element, with units (length)$^{d-1}$. This theorem gives an understanding to the physical meaning of divergence. If $\mathbf{v}$ represents a flow field of some material, then $\int_{\partial\Omega} \mathbf{v} \cdot \mathbf{n} dS$ represents the total flux of that material across the boundary out of the region Ω. The divergence of $\mathbf{v}$ represents the source density (sink, if negative) of the material at each point inside the domain Ω. The divergence theorem states that the net flux of material across the boundary is the cumulation (i.e., the integral) of all the sources in the interior. Consequently, if the net flux is outward, it is because there are more sources inside than there are sinks, and vice versa.

The divergence theorem is valid for one, two, or three dimensional regions Ω. In one-dimensional space, the divergence theorem is the same as the fundamental theorem of calculus

$$(1.10) \qquad v(b) - v(a) = \int_a^b \frac{dv}{dx} dx.$$

The divergence theorem can be used to derive another important identity, namely,

$$(1.11) \qquad \int_\Omega \nabla u dV = \int_{\partial\Omega} u \mathbf{n} dS,$$

where u is a scalar quantity. The proof follows from the identity

$$(1.12) \qquad \int_{\partial\Omega} (u\mathbf{v}) \cdot \mathbf{n} dS = \int_\Omega \nabla \cdot (u\mathbf{v}) dV = \int_\Omega u \nabla \cdot \mathbf{v} dV + \int_\Omega \mathbf{v} \cdot \nabla u dV,$$

which, if $\mathbf{v}$ is a constant vector, reduces to

$$(1.13) \qquad \mathbf{v} \cdot \int_{\partial\Omega} u \mathbf{n} dS = \mathbf{v} \cdot \int_\Omega \nabla u dV.$$

Since $\mathbf{v}$ is arbitrary, (1.11) follows.

Notice that the gradient operator produces a vector quantity from a scalar quantity, and the divergence operator produces a scalar quantity from a vector quantity. These operations can be composed to form the *Laplacian operator* $\nabla \cdot \nabla u$, which in Cartesian coordinates is

$$(1.14) \qquad \nabla^2 u \equiv \nabla \cdot \nabla u = \frac{\partial^2 u}{\partial x^2} + \frac{\partial^2 u}{\partial y^2} + \frac{\partial^2 u}{\partial z^2}.$$

The Laplacian operator has important physical significance, in that $\nabla^2 u$ is a measure of the "average" convexity of u. To see this, suppose that $x = x_0$ is a local minimum for the function $u(x)$. This means that for all x in some neighborhood of x_0, $u(x) \geq u(x_0)$. Thus, the second derivative of u with respect to x at x_0 is

$$\frac{\partial^2 u}{\partial x^2} = \lim_{\Delta x \to 0} \frac{u(x_0 + \Delta x) - 2u(x_0) + u(x_0 - \Delta x)}{\Delta x^2}$$

$$(1.15) \qquad = \lim_{\Delta x \to 0} \frac{(u(x_0 + \Delta x) - u(x_0)) + (u(x_0 - \Delta x) - u(x_0))}{\Delta x^2} \geq 0.$$

Similarly, $\frac{\partial^2 u}{\partial y^2} \geq 0$ and $\frac{\partial^2 u}{\partial z^2} \geq 0$. Therefore $\nabla^2 u \geq 0$ at a point which is a local minimum for u.

An important identity involving the Laplacian is

$$(1.16) \qquad \int_{\partial\Omega} v\nabla u \cdot \mathbf{n} dS = \int_{\Omega} \nabla \cdot (v\nabla u) dV = \int_{\Omega} \nabla v \cdot \nabla u dV + \int_{\Omega} v\nabla^2 u dV,$$

which has use as an integration by parts formula. Setting $v = 1$, we find that

$$(1.17) \qquad \int_{\Omega} \nabla^2 u dV = \int_{\Omega} \nabla \cdot \nabla u dV = \int_{\partial\Omega} \nabla u \cdot \mathbf{n} dS,$$

another very useful identity.

There are some other facts from vector calculus needed for this book, namely, what gradient, divergence, and Laplacian operators look like in different coordinate systems. The two most important coordinate systems here, other than Cartesian coordinates, are polar and spherical coordinates.

The relationship between polar and Cartesian coordinates is given by

$$(1.18) \qquad x = r\cos\theta, \qquad y = r\sin\theta.$$

In polar coordinates, the Laplacian operator is

$$(1.19) \qquad \nabla^2 u = \frac{1}{r}\frac{\partial}{\partial r}\left(r\frac{\partial u}{\partial r}\right) + \frac{1}{r^2}\frac{\partial^2 u}{\partial\theta^2}.$$

The relationship between spherical and Cartesian coordinates is given by

$$(1.20) \qquad x = r\cos\theta\sin\phi, \qquad y = r\sin\theta\sin\phi, \qquad z = r\cos\phi.$$

In spherical coordinates, the Laplacian operator is

$$(1.21) \qquad \nabla^2 u = \frac{1}{r^2}\frac{\partial}{\partial r}\left(r^2\frac{\partial u}{\partial r}\right) + \frac{1}{r^2\sin^2\phi}\frac{\partial^2 u}{\partial\theta^2} + \frac{1}{r^2\sin\phi}\frac{\partial}{\partial\theta}\left(\sin\phi\frac{\partial u}{\partial\phi}\right).$$

1.1.3. Taylor's Theorem. A second result from calculus that is used often in this book is Taylor's theorem. For a function $f(x)$ of a single variable x which has N continuous derivatives in the vicinity of a point, say x_0, Taylor's theorem states that

$$(1.22) \qquad f(x) = \sum_{j=0}^{N} \frac{d^j f(x_0)}{dx^j}\frac{(x-x_0)^j}{j!} + O\left((x-x_0)^{N+1}\right)$$

in some open neighborhood of $x = x_0$. It is possible to let N be large and even let $N \to \infty$, however, in this book we almost never (see Exercise 1.24) use Taylor's theorem for N larger than four.[2]

---

[2]The "Big-Oh" notation $O(x^n)$ carries the meaning that $f(x) = O(x^n)$ if

$$(1.23) \qquad\qquad |f(x)| \leq K|x|^n,$$

for some positive constant K in some nonzero neighborhood of $x = 0$. In words, $f(x)$ goes to zero at least as fast as the monomial x^n as x goes to zero.

1.2. Ordinary Differential Equations

1.2.1. First Order Equations.
An ordinary differential equation specifies a relationship between the (time) derivative of some quantity u and its values through, say,

$$(1.24) \qquad \frac{du}{dt} = f(u, t).$$

This equation is *autonomous* if f is independent of t, so that

$$(1.25) \qquad \frac{du}{dt} = f(u).$$

Many of the problems discussed in this book are autonomous in time.

If u is a scalar quantity, the solution of equation (1.25) can be readily understood using graphical means, i.e., by plotting $\frac{du}{dt}$ vs. u. An example is shown in Figure 1.1.

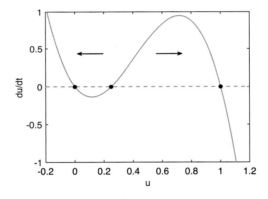

Figure 1.1. Plot of $\frac{du}{dt}$ vs. u for the bistable function $f(u) = au(1 - u)(u - \alpha)$ with $\alpha = 0.25, a = 10$.

The first things to notice are the zeros of $f(u)$, i.e., the *equilibria*. For the example $f(u) = au(u - 1)(\alpha - u)$, shown in Figure 1.1, the equilibria are at $u_0 = 0$, $u_0 = \alpha$, and $u_0 = 1$. Next, one can determine the direction of movement if u is not at an equilibrium. These are shown with arrows in Figure 1.1. For example, if $0 < u < \alpha$, $\frac{du}{dt} < 0$ indicating that u is decreasing there, while if $\alpha < u < 1$, $\frac{du}{dt} > 0$ so that u is increasing there. This is our first indication that $u_0 = 0$ and $u_0 = 1$ are *stable* equilibria, while $u_0 = \alpha$ is *unstable*.

The next thing to do is to linearize the equations about the equilibria. Linearization is a very important procedure by which one reduces a nonlinear equation to a linear equation.[3] It is a good idea to understand it thoroughly, because it is used often in this text.

---

[3]A linear operator is an operator L for which $L(u + v) = Lu + Lv$ and $L(au) = aL(u)$ for any scalar quantity a. In words, the operation on the sum of operands is the same as the sum of the operation on the operands and the operation on a scalar times an operand is the same as the scalar times the operation on the operand. A linear equation is one consisting only of the sum of linear operators. For example, both $\frac{\partial u}{\partial t}$ and $\frac{\partial^2 u}{\partial x^2}$ are linear operators.

The linearization of any differentiable function or operator $G(u)$ about u_0 is defined as

$$(1.26) \qquad \lim_{\epsilon \to 0} \frac{\partial}{\partial \epsilon} G(u_0 + \epsilon U),$$

so the linearization of the differential equation (1.25) about any of its equilibria is

$$(1.27) \qquad \lim_{\epsilon \to 0} \frac{\partial}{\partial \epsilon} \left(\frac{d}{dt}(u_0 + \epsilon U) - f(u_0 + \epsilon U) \right),$$

which reduces to

$$(1.28) \qquad \frac{dU}{dt} = f'(u_0)U.$$

The solution of the linearized problem is the exponential function

$$(1.29) \qquad U(t) = U_0 \exp(f'(u_0)t),$$

and it is now obvious that $U(t)$ grows if $f'(u_0) > 0$ and decays if $f'(u_0) < 0$. Hence, for our example here, the equilibria $u_0 = 0$ and $u_0 = 1$ are *linearly stable* while the equilibrium $u_0 = \alpha$ is unstable. This agrees with our graphical stability analysis.

Finally, it is noteworthy that the equation (1.25) is *separable* and can be rewritten as

$$(1.30) \qquad \frac{du}{f(u)} = dt,$$

which, after integrating both sides of the equation, enables us to write

$$(1.31) \qquad F(u) - F(u(0)) = t,$$

where $F(u) = \int^u \frac{du}{f(u)}$ and $u = u(0)$ at $t = 0$. In most situations, this is not a particularly useful representation of the solution, since analytical inversion of the function $F(u)$ to find $u(t)$ explicitly is usually impossible. However, through the wonders of Matlab, it is easy to graph this solution. That is, plot t as a function of u and then reverse the axes.

As an example, for the function $f(u) = au(1-u)(u-\alpha)$,

$$(1.32) \qquad F(u) = \frac{1}{a\alpha(\alpha-1)} (\alpha \ln(1-u) - \ln(|u-\alpha|) + (1-\alpha)\ln(u)),$$

a plot of which is shown in Figure 1.2(a), and then, reversing the axes gives the plot of $u(t)$ as a function of t, shown in Figure 1.2(b). This plot illustrates the fact that the solution has a different outcome as $t \to \infty$ depending on the initial condition. Clearly (as we already knew), if $0 < u(0) < \alpha$, $u(t) \to 0$ as $t \to \infty$, whereas, if $\alpha < u(0) < 1$, then $u(t) \to 1$ as $t \to \infty$. Only if $u(0) \equiv \alpha$ does $u(t) \to \alpha$ as $t \to \infty$, since then $u(t)$ is identically equal to α for all time.

This "trick" to invert functions by plotting the function and then reversing the axes is extremely useful and is used many times in this book.

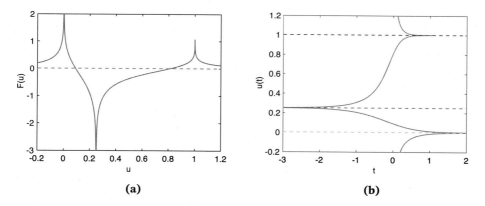

Figure 1.2. (a) Plot of $F(u)$ from (1.32)vs. u, and (b) plot of $u(t)$ as a function of t, for the function (1.32), with $\alpha = 0.25$.

1.2.2. Systems of first order equations.

We now turn our attention to systems of first order equations, which can still be written in the form of (1.24) provided we recognize that u is a vector, rather than a scalar, quantity. The most important example for this text is when there are two unknown scalar functions $u(t)$ and $v(t)$ and the equations describing their evolution are in the form

$$(1.33) \qquad \frac{du}{dt} = f(u, v),$$

$$(1.34) \qquad \frac{dv}{dt} = g(u, v).$$

As with first order equations, a useful way to proceed is with a graphical, or *phase plane*, analysis. The first step of this analysis is to plot the *nullclines*, the curves in the $u - v$ plane along which either u or v do not change, i.e., $\frac{du}{dt} = 0$ or $\frac{dv}{dt} = 0$.

There are many examples of this procedure in this book, however, for purposes of illustration, let's look at solutions of the second order differential equation

$$(1.35) \qquad \frac{d^2u}{dt^2} + f(u) = 0,$$

where $f(u) = au(1-u)(u-\alpha)$, the same function as used above. To write this equation as a first order system, we set $v = \frac{du}{dt}$, and then the equations are

$$(1.36) \qquad \frac{du}{dt} = v,$$

$$(1.37) \qquad \frac{dv}{dt} = -f(u).$$

The nullclines for this system are easily determined, being the line $v = 0$ for the u nullcline, and $f(u) = 0$ for the v nullclines, i.e., the lines $u = 0$, $u = \alpha$, and $u = 1$. These are shown plotted in Figure 1.3 as dashed lines.

The next step is to identify all the *critical points*, i.e., the points at which $\frac{du}{dt}$ and $\frac{dv}{dt}$ are simultaneously zero, hence, points of equilibrium. These are, of course, all the

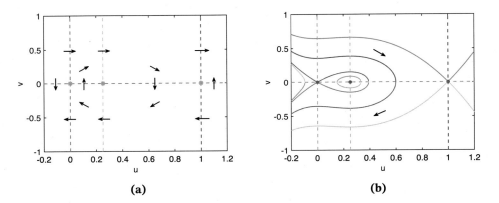

Figure 1.3. Phase portrait for the equations (1.36)–(1.37), showing nullclines and direction arrows in (a) and trajectories in (b).

intersections of the u and v nullclines. For this example, they are the points with $v = 0$ and $u = 0, \alpha$ and 1.

Next, we determine the direction of the flow in regions bounded by the nullclines. For this example, u increases if $v > 0$ and decreases if $v < 0$, while v increases if $0 < u < \alpha$ and decreases if $\alpha < u < 1$. It is also possible at this point to sketch a few typical trajectories by following the vector of flow directions. It quickly becomes apparent that the equilibria at $u = 0$ and $u = 1$ are saddle points, but the nature of the critical point at $u = \alpha$ cannot be decided by graphical means alone.

How do we classify critical points in general? The answer is using linear stability analysis, which proceeds as follows: one considers the linear system that approximates the full system of equations in the vicinity of a given point in phase space, and studies how that linear system behaves.

For the general system (1.33)–(1.34), the linearization is (in all of its glory)

$$\lim_{\epsilon \to 0} \frac{\partial}{\partial \epsilon} \left(\begin{array}{c} \frac{d}{dt}(u_0 + \epsilon U) - f(u_0 + \epsilon U, v_0 + \epsilon V) \\ \frac{d}{dt}(v_0 + \epsilon V) - g(u_0 + \epsilon U, v_0 + \epsilon V) \end{array} \right)$$

(1.38)
$$= \frac{d}{dt} \left(\begin{array}{c} U \\ V \end{array} \right) - \left(\begin{array}{cc} \frac{\partial f_0}{\partial u} & \frac{\partial f_0}{\partial v} \\ \frac{\partial g_0}{\partial u} & \frac{\partial g_0}{\partial v} \end{array} \right) \left(\begin{array}{c} U \\ V \end{array} \right).$$

Consequently, the linearized system is

(1.39)
$$\frac{d}{dt} \left(\begin{array}{c} U \\ V \end{array} \right) = A \left(\begin{array}{c} U \\ V \end{array} \right),$$

where the matrix A is the *Jacobian matrix* for this system,

(1.40)
$$A = \left(\begin{array}{cc} \frac{\partial f_0}{\partial u} & \frac{\partial f_0}{\partial v} \\ \frac{\partial g_0}{\partial u} & \frac{\partial g_0}{\partial v} \end{array} \right),$$

and f_0, g_0 denote evaluation at the equilibria u_0, and v_0.

To find the solutions of the linearized system (1.39), we try an exponential solution of the form

(1.41)
$$\left(\begin{array}{c} U \\ V \end{array} \right) = \left(\begin{array}{c} U_0 \\ V_0 \end{array} \right) \exp(\lambda t),$$

and determine that it must be that

(1.42)
$$(A - \lambda I) \left(\begin{array}{c} U_0 \\ V_0 \end{array} \right) = \left(\begin{array}{c} 0 \\ 0 \end{array} \right),$$

where I is the 2×2 identity matrix. The values of λ for which this equation has a solution are known as the eigenvalues of A, satisfying $\det(A - \lambda I) = 0$. For the 2×2 case at hand, this is the quadratic polynomial (also known as the *characteristic polynomial*) $\lambda^2 - \text{Tr}(A)\lambda + \det(A) = 0$, with $\text{Tr}(A)$ and $\det(A)$ representing the trace and determinant of A, respectively.

For this text, it is assumed that you have some basic familiarity with linear algebra, including what is a matrix, and what is the determinant of a square matrix. Also, for Exercise 1.29, you will need to know how to use row reduction (i.e., Gaussian elimination) to reduce a matrix equation to an upper triangular system. As a reminder, the eigenvalues and eigenvectors of an $n \times n$ matrix A are defined as the numbers λ and vectors ϕ for which $A\phi = \lambda\phi$. Necessarily, the eigenvalues are roots of the characteristic polynomial $\det(A - \lambda I) = 0$, an nth order polynomial. Thus, there are always n eigenvalues, counting possible multiplicities. The *algebraic multiplicity* of an eigenvalue is the multiplicity with which that eigenvalue is a root of the characteristic polynomial, and the number of linearly independent eigenvectors associated with that eigenvalue is its *geometric multiplicity*. The geometric multiplicity is always less than or equal to the algebraic multiplicity, but never less than one. Thus, if the eigenvalues of a matrix are distinct, it has n linearly independent eigenvectors.

If $\det(A) < 0$, then there are two real roots, of opposite sign; the equilibrium is a *saddle point*. A typical phase portrait for a saddle point is shown in Figure 1.4. A saddle point has four special trajectories, two of which leave the saddle point, i.e., approach the saddle point in backwards time, as $t \to -\infty$, and two of which approach the saddle point as $t \to \infty$. These are identified as the unstable and stable manifolds, respectively. The unstable manifold has the same direction as the eigenvector of A corresponding to the positive eigenvalue, and the stable manifold has the same direction as the eigenvector of A corresponding to the negative eigenvalue.

If $\det(A) > 0$, there are four possible outcomes, depending on the sign of the discriminant, disc $= \text{Tr}(A)^2 - 4\det(A)$, and the sign of $\text{Tr}(A)$. If disc > 0, the two roots are real both with the same sign as $\text{Tr}(A)$, and if disc < 0, the two roots are a complex conjugate pair with the sign of the real part the same as the sign of $\text{Tr}(A)$. If the roots are real, the equilibrium is called a *node*, and if the roots are complex, it is called a *spiral point*. If the real parts are positive, the equilibrium is unstable, while if they are negative, the equilibrium is stable. The intermediate case with $\text{Tr}(A) = 0$ has neutral stability and is called a *center*. Thus, the four cases with $\det(A) > 0$ are stable node, stable spiral, unstable node, unstable spiral. These four are summarized in Table 1.1.

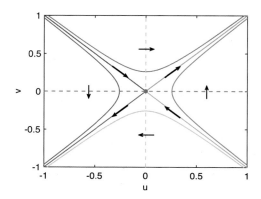

Figure 1.4. Typical phase portrait for a saddle point.

Table 1.1. Summary of stability criteria for $\det(A) > 0$.

$\mathrm{Tr}(A)$\\ disc	< 0 (complex roots)	> 0 (real roots)
> 0	unstable spiral	unstable node
< 0	stable spiral	stable node

Typical phase portraits for a stable node and a stable spiral are shown in Figure 1.5.

For the example problem (1.36)–(1.37), the Jacobian matrix is

$$A = \begin{pmatrix} 0 & 1 \\ -f'(u_0) & 0 \end{pmatrix},$$

(1.43)

and since $\mathrm{Tr}(A) = 0$, the determining feature is the sign of $f'(u_0)$. In particular, the critical points at $u_0 = 0$ and $u_0 = 1$ are both saddle points, while the critical point at $u_0 = \alpha$ is a neutral center.

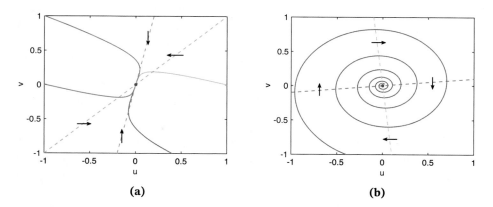

(a)   **(b)**

Figure 1.5. Typical phase portraits for (a) a stable node and (b) a stable spiral.

With this information, it is now usually possible to get an understanding of the behavior of the solutions. However, there are situations where this information is not sufficient to tell the whole story, and one such case is when there are isolated, closed orbits, i.e., limit cycles. We do not discuss limit cycles any further here.

Another important feature of these equations is that sometimes, but not often, it is possible to find expressions for some of the solution curves. For the current example problem, the slope of trajectories in the phase plane is given by

$$(1.44) \qquad \frac{dv}{du} = -\frac{f(u)}{v},$$

which is separable, yielding

$$(1.45) \qquad -f(u)du = vdv.$$

Integrating both sides of this equation, we find that

$$(1.46) \qquad F(u) + \frac{1}{2}v^2 = F(u_0),$$

where $F(u) = \int^u f(u)du$, and $u_0, v_0 = 0$ is a point on the trajectory. The expression (1.46) is called an integral of the motion. These trajectories can easily be plotted in the $u-v$ phase plane by plotting v as a function of u, wherever it is defined. Some examples are shown in Figure 1.3(b).

1.2.2.1. *Higher Order Systems.* Consider now the first order system of differential equations

$$(1.47) \qquad \frac{d\mathbf{u}}{dt} = \mathbf{f}(\mathbf{u}),$$

where $\mathbf{u} \in R^n$, and $\mathbf{f} : R^n \to R^n$. Although we cannot readily draw it for $n > 2$, according to (1.47) the flow of $\mathbf{u}$ is in the direction of the vector field $\mathbf{f}$. Equilibria are any points $\mathbf{u_0}$ for which $\mathbf{f}(\mathbf{u_0}) = 0$. The stability of an equilibrium $\mathbf{u_0}$ is determined by the linearized system

$$(1.48) \qquad \frac{d\mathbf{u}}{dt} = A\mathbf{u},$$

where $A = \frac{\partial \mathbf{f}(\mathbf{u_0})}{\partial \mathbf{u}}$ is the Jacobian matrix. Solutions of (1.48) are linear combinations of exponentials $\exp(\lambda t)$ where λ are eigenvalues of A, roots of the characteristic polynomial $\det(A - \lambda I) = 0$. Then, an equilibrium solution $\mathbf{u_0}$ is linearly stable if all the eigenvalues have negative real part, but unstable if any of the eigenvalues have positive real part.

1.2.3. Numerical Simulation. It is extremely important to be able to numerically simulate differential equations efficiently and accurately. A number of algorithms to do this have been devised and implemented in Matlab, so that it is rarely necessary to write your own differential equation numerical solver. However, there are a few basic ideas of numerical simulation that are useful for this text, which are summarized here.

Suppose we wish to simulate the differential equation

$$(1.49) \qquad \frac{du}{dt} = f(u).$$

We set $u^n = u(n\Delta t)$ where Δt is the discrete time step. The simplest discretization of the derivative is

(1.50)
$$\frac{du}{dt} \approx \frac{1}{\Delta t}(u^{n+1} - u^n),$$

and this suggests the algorithm

(1.51)
$$\frac{1}{\Delta t}(u^{n+1} - u^n) = f(u^n).$$

With this algorithm, we can determine u^{n+1} if u^n is known using

(1.52)
$$u^{n+1} = u^n + \Delta t f(u^n).$$

This method is called the *forward Euler method.*

Other possibilities exist. For example, we could try

(1.53)
$$\frac{1}{\Delta t}(u^{n+1} - u^n) = f(u^{n+1}),$$

called the *backward Euler method.* This method is implicit, because to find u^{n+1} given u^n, we must solve the equation

(1.54)
$$u^{n+1} - \Delta t f(u^{n+1}) = u^n,$$

and this typically involves additional approximations. In spite of this additional complexity, this method is recommended for *stiff* differential equations, in which one or more of the variables changes rapidly compared to others.

Both of these methods are first order accurate, meaning that the error of the numerical solution vanishes at a rate that is linear in Δt. A more accurate approximation would be to use a centered difference such as

(1.55)
$$\frac{1}{\Delta t}(u^{n+1} - u^n) = f(u^{n+\frac{1}{2}}),$$

but this is more complicated than the backward Euler method as it involves the additional unknown $u^{n+\frac{1}{2}}$. However, the approximation

(1.56)
$$\frac{1}{\Delta t}(u^{n+1} - u^n) = \frac{1}{2}(f(u^n) + f(u^{n+1})),$$

avoids this complexity. For this, finding u^{n+1} given u^n requires solution of the equation

(1.57)
$$u^{n+1} - \frac{\Delta t}{2} f(u^{n+1}) = u^n + \frac{\Delta t}{2} f(u^n),$$

which, from a computational perspective is no more difficult than solving (1.54). The additional advantage of this algorithm is that it is second order accurate, meaning that the error of the numerical solution vanishes at a rate that is quadratic in Δt.

1.2.4. Modeling Chemical Reactions. One of the important uses of differential equations, at least in this book, is to model the dynamics of chemical reactions. The two elementary reactions that are of most importance here are conversion between species, denoted

(1.58)
$$A \underset{\beta}{\overset{\alpha}{\rightleftharpoons}} B,$$

called a first order reaction, and formation and degradation of a product from two component species, denoted

(1.59)
$$A + B \overset{\gamma}{\underset{\delta}{\rightleftharpoons}} C,$$

called a second order reaction.

The differential equations describing the first of these are

(1.60)
$$\frac{da}{dt} = \beta b - \alpha a, \qquad \frac{db}{dt} = -\beta b + \alpha a,$$

where $a = [A]$ and $b = [B]$, is the statement in math symbols that B is created from A at rate $\alpha[A]$ and A is created from B at rate $\beta[B]$. Of course, the total of A and B is a conserved quantity, since $\frac{d}{dt}(a + b) = 0$.

The second of these reactions is described by the three differential equations

(1.61)
$$\frac{da}{dt} = -\gamma ab + \delta c, \qquad \frac{db}{dt} = -\gamma ab + \delta c, \qquad \frac{dc}{dt} = \gamma ab - \delta c,$$

where $c = [C]$, which puts into math symbols the fact that C is created from the combination of A and B at a rate that is proportional to the product $[A][B]$, called the law of mass action. Notice that the units of γ are different $((\text{time})^{-1} (\text{concentration})^{-1})$ than those for first order reactions $((\text{time})^{-1})$. The degradation of C into A and B is a first order reaction. For this reaction there are two conserved quantities, namely $[A] + [C]$ and $[B] + [C]$.

An important example of reaction kinetics occurs in the study of epidemics, with the so-called SIR epidemic. Here S represents susceptible individuals, I represents infected individuals, and R represents recovered or removed individuals. We represent the disease process by the reaction scheme

(1.62)
$$S + I \overset{\alpha}{\longrightarrow} 2I, \quad I \overset{\beta}{\longrightarrow} R.$$

This implies that a susceptible individual can become infected following contact with an infected individual, and that infected individuals recover at an exponential rate.

Using the law of mass action described above, the deterministic differential equations for these reactions are

(1.63)
$$\frac{ds}{dt} = -\alpha si, \qquad \frac{di}{dt} = \alpha si - \beta i, \qquad \frac{dr}{dt} = \beta i.$$

Analysis of these equations is readily accomplished using the $s - i$ phase plane, shown in Figure 1.6(a). The lines $s = 0$ (vertical) and $i = 0$ (horizontal) are nullclines for s, while the vertical line $\frac{\alpha s}{\beta} = 1$, shown dashed, is the nullcline for i. s is everywhere decreasing, while i increases if $\frac{\alpha s}{\beta} > 1$ and decreases if $\frac{\alpha s}{\beta} < 1$.

It is clear from the phase portrait that there is a threshold phenomenon. That is, starting from a very small initial value of i, the infected population will grow only if $s(0)$, the initial susceptible population, is greater than $\frac{\beta}{\alpha}$. If the initial susceptible population is smaller than $\frac{\beta}{\alpha}$, the infection will die without spreading.

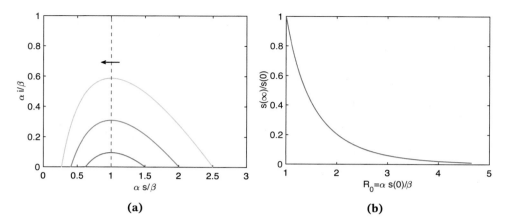

Figure 1.6. (a) Phase portrait for the SIR dynamics with $\frac{\alpha s}{\beta}$ on the horizontal axis and $\frac{\alpha i}{\beta}$ on the vertical axis. (b) Plot of $\frac{s(\infty)}{s(0)}$, the fraction of susceptible population remaining following an epidemic as a function of $R_0 = \frac{\alpha s(0)}{\beta}$.

We can find a relationship between the initial and final susceptible population as follows. Note that

$$(1.64) \qquad\qquad \frac{di}{ds} = -1 + \frac{\beta}{\alpha s},$$

which is separable, so that integral curves are given by

$$(1.65) \qquad\qquad i = s(0) - s + \frac{\beta}{\alpha} \ln\left(\frac{s}{s(0)}\right),$$

taking $i(0) = 0$. Thus,

$$(1.66) \qquad\qquad 0 = 1 - \frac{s(\infty)}{s(0)} + \frac{\beta}{\alpha s(0)} \ln\left(\frac{s(\infty)}{s(0)}\right),$$

specifies the relationship between the initial and final susceptible populations, $s(0)$ and $s(\infty)$. We cannot solve this explicitly for $s(\infty)$, but it is easy to solve for $\frac{\alpha s(0)}{\beta}$ as a function of $\frac{s(\infty)}{s(0)}$, i.e.,

$$(1.67) \qquad\qquad \frac{\alpha s(0)}{\beta} = \frac{\ln\left(\frac{s(\infty)}{s(0)}\right)}{\frac{s(\infty)}{s(0)} - 1},$$

and then use this to plot $\frac{s(\infty)}{s(0)}$ as a function of $\frac{\alpha s(0)}{\beta}$, as shown in Figure 1.6(b). The quantity $\frac{\alpha s(0)}{\beta}$ is usually referred to as R_0, the *basic reproduction number* in the epidemiology literature and is a measure of how easily spread a disease is. For example, $R_0 = 18$ for measles which implies that almost nobody will remain susceptible after a measles outbreak. For COVID-19, R_0 is estimated to be between 2 and 3, which implies that, without a vaccine, between 80% and 90% of the susceptible population will become infected before the epidemic runs its course.

Figure 1.6(b) confirms what we intuitively expect, namely, that the more easily spread a disease is (larger R_0), the more individuals will be infected during the course of an epidemic. It also suggests the effect of control measures, including vaccination which reduces the initial density of susceptibles $s(0)$, quarantine of infectives, which reduces the number of contacts of susceptibles with infectives (reduce α), social distancing and mask wearing, which reduces the infectiousness of a contact (reduce α), and shortening the recovery time with medical treatments (increase β).

The calculations to make these plots were done using the Matlab code SIR_pp.m.

1.3. Stochastic Processes

1.3.1. Decay Processes. Now that we have the review of differential equations behind us, we must face the fact that differential equation descriptions of biological processes are at best, highly idealized. This is because biological processes, and in fact many physical processes, are not deterministic, but noisy, or stochastic. This noise, or randomness, could be because, while the process actually is deterministic, we do not have the ability or the patience to accurately calculate the outcome of the process. For example, the flipping of a coin or the spin of a roulette wheel has a deterministic result, in that, if initial conditions were known with sufficient accuracy, an accurate calculation of the end result could be made. However, this is so impractical that it is not worth pursuing. Similarly, the motion of water vapor molecules in the air is by completely deterministic process (following Newton's Second Law, no quantum physics required) but determining the behavior of a gas by solving the governing differential equations for the position of each particle is completely out of the question.

There are other processes for which deterministic laws are not even known. This is because they are governed by quantum dynamics, having possible changes of state that cannot be described by a deterministic equation. For example, the decay of a radioactive particle and the change of conformation of a protein molecule, such as an ion channel, cannot, as far as we know, be described by a deterministic process. Similarly, the mistakes made by the reproductive machinery of a cell when duplicating its DNA (i.e., the mutations) cannot, as far as we currently know, be described by a deterministic process.

Given this reality, we are forced to come up with another way to describe interesting processes. And this is by keeping track of various *statistics* as time proceeds. For example, it may not be possible to exactly track the numbers of people who get the flu every year, but an understanding of how the average number changes over several years be sufficient for health care policy makers. Similarly, with carbon dating techniques, it is not necessary to know exactly how many carbon-14 molecules there are in a particular painting at a particular time, but an estimate of an average or expected number of molecules can be sufficient to decide if the painting is genuine or a forgery.

1.3.1.1. *Probability Theory*. To make some progress in this way of describing things, we must define some terms. First, there must be some object that we wish to measure or quantify, also called a *random variable*, and the collection of all possible outcomes of this measurement is called its *state space*, or *sample space*. For example, the flip of a coin can result in it landing with head or tail up, and these two outcomes constitute the state space. Similarly, an ion channel may at any given time be either open or closed, and this also constitutes its state space. The random variable could be a discrete or continuous variable taking on only integer values if it is discrete or a real valued number or vector if it is continuous.

The idea of a *probability* is intuitively clear, defined as the percentage of time a particular state occurs after a very large, i.e., infinite, number of observations of the state of the object have been made. Of course, this is a somewhat unsatisfactory definition, because no experiment can be repeated an infinite number of times. However, this definition is useful, even if it can never be checked. So, we easily understand that the probability that a coin toss will result in heads rather than tails should be one half. However, it is also clear that one should not expect the outcome of a large number of coin flips to result in *exactly* one half heads and one half tails. In fact, the probability that after 1,000 coin flips you will observe *exactly* 500 heads and 500 tails is rather small, at 0.025. (See Exercise 1.19). One goal of probability theory is to understand random variables by determining their *probability distribution functions* or *probability density functions*. For a discrete random variable, this would be some nonnegative quantity p_j which is the probability that the random variable is the value j, while for a continuous random variable x this is a nonnegative function $p(\xi)$ of the real variable ξ, having the feature that $P(x \in \Omega) = \int_\Omega p(\xi)d\xi$ is the probability that x is in the set Ω.

The two most famous and most commonly used probability distribution functions are the *binomial distribution* and the *normal distribution*. The binomial distribution answers the question of the probability of k successful outcomes in N independent experiments, denoted $p(k|N)$, where the probability of an individual successful outcome is p. The answer is

$$(1.68) \qquad p(k|N) = \left(\begin{array}{c} N \\ \kappa \end{array} \right) p^k (1-p)^{N-k},$$

where

$$(1.69) \qquad \left(\begin{array}{c} N \\ \kappa \end{array} \right) = \frac{N!}{k!\,(N-k)!}.$$

The normal distribution (also known as the Gaussian distribution) is given by

$$(1.70) \qquad p(\xi) = \frac{1}{\sqrt{2\pi}} \exp\left(\frac{-\xi^2}{2}\right),$$

and in this text, we also denote this as the distribution $\mathcal{N}(0, 1)$.[4]

An important measure of a probability density function is called an *expected value*. Specifically, if $f(x)$ is some function of the random variable x, then the expected value of f is defined as

$$(1.71) \qquad E(f) = \int f(\xi)p(\xi)d\xi,$$

---

[4]The notation $\mathcal{N}(\mu, \sigma^2)$ refers to the normal distribution with mean μ and variance σ^2, given by $p(\xi) = \frac{1}{\sqrt{2\pi}\sigma} \exp\left(\frac{-(\xi-\mu)^2}{2\sigma^2}\right)$.

if x is a continuous random variable, or

$$(1.72) \qquad\qquad E(f) = \sum f(k) p_k,$$

if it is a discrete random variable. In both cases, the integral or sum is taken over all possible values of the random variable.

This definition leads to three important measures of a random variable, namely its *mean value*, its *variance* and its *standard deviation*. The mean value of x is the expected value of x, i.e., the expected value of $f(x) = x$, $E(x)$. The variance of x is the expected value of the square of x minus its mean, i.e.,

$$(1.73) \qquad\qquad \sigma^2 = \mathrm{var}(x) = E((x - E(x))^2) = E(x^2) - (E(x))^2.$$

The standard deviation is $\sigma = \sqrt{\mathrm{var}(x)}$. Some obvious identities are that $E(ax) = aE(x)$ for any scalar a, and $\mathrm{var}(ax) = a^2 \mathrm{var}(x)$ for any scalar a.

It is a general fact that if y and z are independent random variables (meaning that their joint probability density function[5] $p(\xi, \eta)$ satisfies $p(\xi, \eta) = p_y(\xi) p_z(\eta)$, where $p_y(\xi)$ and $p_z(\eta)$ are the individual probability density functions for y and z, respectively), then

$$(1.74) \qquad\qquad \mathrm{var}(y + z) = \mathrm{var}(y) + \mathrm{var}(z).$$

(This is a statement that you, the reader, should verify. See Exercise 1.13.)

It is straightforward to verify that for the normal distribution, $E(x) = 0$ and $E(x^2) = 1$. One can also use Matlab[6] to determine that for a random variable x that is normally distributed, the probability that x is within one standard deviation of zero is

$$(1.77) \qquad\qquad P(-1 < x < 1) = \frac{1}{\sqrt{2\pi}} \int_{-1}^{1} \exp(\frac{-\xi^2}{2}) d\xi = 0.6827.$$

One can also calculate that $P(-1.96 < x < 1.96) = 0.95$ and $P(-2.576 < x < 2.576) = 0.99$. In the field of statistics, these are referred to as the 95% and 99% confidence intervals, respectively. In words, this means that 68% of the time a normally distributed random variable will be within one standard deviation of the mean, while 95% or 99% percent of the time it will be within 1.96 or 2.58 standard deviations, respectively, of the mean.

The normal distribution shows up often, as described by the

Central Limit Theorem. Suppose $m_1, m_2, \ldots$, are independent, identically distributed, random variables, with mean $\mu = E(m_i)$ and variance $\sigma^2 = \mathrm{var}(m_i)$. Then, the

---

[5]The joint probability density function has exactly the meaning one would expect, namely that the probability that the random variable ordered pair (y, z) is in some set Ω is $P((y, z) \in \Omega) = \int_\Omega p(\xi, \eta) d\xi d\eta$.

[6]The Matlab function $\mathrm{erf}(x)$ is defined as

$$(1.75) \qquad\qquad \mathrm{erf}(x) = \frac{2}{\sqrt{\pi}} \int_0^x \exp(-\xi^2) d\xi,$$

and this is known as the *error function*. It follows that for a normally distributed random variable x,

$$(1.76) \qquad P(-X < x < X) = \frac{1}{\sqrt{2\pi}} \int_{-X}^{X} \exp(-\frac{\xi^2}{2}) d\xi = \frac{2}{\sqrt{\pi}} \int_0^{\frac{X}{\sqrt{2}}} \exp(-\xi^2) d\xi = \mathrm{erf}(\frac{X}{\sqrt{2}}).$$

random variable

$$(1.78) \qquad\qquad\qquad s_N = \sum_{j=1}^{N} m_j$$

with N large, is approximately normally distributed with mean $\mu_N = N\mu$ and variance $\sigma_N^2 = N\sigma^2$. In other words, the distribution for x_N is well approximated by

$$(1.79) \qquad f_N(s) = \frac{1}{\sqrt{2\pi}\sigma_N} \exp\left(-\frac{(s-\mu_N)^2}{2\sigma_N^2}\right) = \frac{1}{\sqrt{2\pi N}\sigma} \exp\left(-\frac{(s-N\mu)^2}{2N\sigma^2}\right).$$

This distribution is also denoted as $\mathcal{N}(N\mu, N\sigma^2)$.

In a similar vein, the random variable,

$$(1.80) \qquad\qquad\qquad y_N = \frac{1}{N} \sum_{j=1}^{N} m_j$$

with N large, is approximately normally distributed with mean $\mu_N = \mu$ and variance $\sigma_N^2 = \frac{1}{N}\sigma^2$, i.e., the distribution for y_N is well approximated by

$$(1.81) \qquad\qquad f_N(y) = \frac{\sqrt{N}}{\sqrt{2\pi}\sigma} \exp\left(-\frac{N(y-\mu)^2}{2\sigma^2}\right),$$

denoted $\mathcal{N}(\mu, \frac{1}{N}\sigma^2)$.

A *stochastic process* or a random process is a collection of random variables, parametrized by some ordered index set. If the index set is continuous time it is a continuous time process, whereas if the index set consists of discrete points (of time) it is a discrete time stochastic process. For example, consider a carbon atom that can be in several isotopic states, including carbon-14, carbon-13 or carbon-12.[7] The state of carbon-14 can change at any time to nitrogen-14 by the process known as radioactive decay (or beta decay) in which one of the neutrons of carbon-14 becomes a proton. Or consider the state of an ion channel which can flip back and forth between its two states, open and closed, at different times.

Since the transitions between states may occur at any time, and those times cannot be known exactly, the best we can do is to track the probability that the object is in a particular state as a function of time. To study these processes, we need one more assumption, that the probability of the object changing its state in some small time interval is independent of how long it has been in its current state. Such a process is called a *Markov process*. For example, the probability that a carbon-14 atom decays to a nitrogen-14 atom in the next 30 seconds is completely independent of how long the carbon-14 molecule has been in existence. Similarly, suppose you have flipped a coin 1000 times and amazingly, it has come up heads every time. What is the probability that it will be heads on the 1001st time? Answer, one half: The probability of landing heads is independent of the history of previous flips (if it is a fair coin and unless someone is cheating).

---

[7]A carbon atom has 6 protons and 6 (carbon-12), 7 (carbon-13), or 8 (carbon-14) neutrons. Carbon-12 and carbon-13 are both stable. Nitrogen has 7 protons and 7 neutrons.

Let's consider first a discrete state space, continuous time process. To track the probability that the object is in a given state, we make use of the *law of total probability*. In words, the probability that the object is in a particular state at some time $t + \Delta t$ is equal to the probability that it was in the same state at time t *times* the probability of not switching out of that state in time Δt, *plus* the probability that it was *not* in that state at time t *times* the probability of switching into that state in time Δt. In mathematical language, if we denote the probability that the object is in state j at time t by $p_j(t)$, and the probability of switching from state i to state j in time Δt by $s_{ji}(\Delta t)$, then

$$(1.82) \qquad p_j(t + \Delta t) = p_j(t)(1 - \sum_{i \neq j} s_{ij}(\Delta t)) + \sum_{i \neq j} p_i(t) s_{ji}(\Delta t).$$

Now we also make the definition that

$$(1.83) \qquad \lambda_{ji} = \lim_{\Delta t \to 0} \frac{s_{ji}(\Delta t)}{\Delta t},$$

then we can divide the equation (1.82) by Δt and take the limit $\Delta t \to 0$ and find

$$(1.84) \qquad \frac{dp_j}{dt} = -\sum_{i \neq j} \lambda_{ij} p_j(t) + \sum_{i \neq j} \lambda_{ji} p_i(t).$$

It is useful to notice that (1.84) can be written in matrix form. That is, let $\mathbf{p}$ be the vector with elements $p_j(t)$. Then,

$$(1.85) \qquad \frac{d\mathbf{p}}{dt} = A\mathbf{p},$$

where the matrix A has elements $a_{j,k} = \lambda_{j,k}$ if $k \neq j$ and $a_{j,j} = -\sum_{k \neq j} \lambda_{k,j}$. Then, the matrix A has zero column sums, $\sum_j a_{j,k} = 0$ for all k.

As a first example, let's think about the obviously stochastic process of catching fish. Here the random variable is the number of fish caught at time t since you began fishing, and we suppose that at any given time the probability of catching a fish in a small window of time Δt is $\alpha \Delta t$, where α is a constant independent of time. This assumption is obviously not correct, as any fisherman can attest, but it is useful for this example. Following the above arguments, the equations describing the dynamics of $p_j(t)$, the probability of having caught exactly j fish at time t, are

$$(1.86) \qquad \frac{dp_j}{dt} = -\alpha p_j(t) + \alpha p_{j-1}(t),$$

for $j = 0, 1, 2, \ldots$, and $p_{-1} = 0$. This follows since there are only two ways that the state can change, namely from state $j - 1$ to state j by catching a fish, or from state j to state $j + 1$, also by catching a fish. And since the probability of catching a fish is independent of how many fish have been caught previously (in a big enough body of water), the rates for both of these events are the same, namely α.

How long will it be to catch the first fish? Since

$$(1.87) \qquad \frac{dp_0}{dt} = -\alpha p_0(t),$$

we find that

$$(1.88) \qquad p_0(t) = \exp(-\alpha t),$$

and the probability that you have caught at least one fish by time t is $1 - p_0(t) = 1 - \exp(-\alpha t)$. The function $-\frac{dp_0}{dt} = \alpha p_0(t) = \alpha \exp(-\alpha t)$ represents the *probability density function* (pdf) for the fish catching event and the function $1 - \exp(-\alpha t)$ is called the *cumulative distribution function* (cdf) because it represents the probability of having caught at least one fish in the time interval $[0, t]$. Accordingly, this event is said to be *exponentially distributed* and is identified as an exponential process.. The expected value of an exponential distribution is

$$(1.89) \qquad\qquad E(t) = \int_0^\infty \tau \alpha \exp(-\alpha\tau)d\tau = \frac{1}{\alpha},$$

and the expected value of t^2 is

$$(1.90) \qquad\qquad E(t^2) = \int_0^\infty \tau^2 \alpha \exp(-\alpha\tau)d\tau = \frac{2}{\alpha^2},$$

so that the variance is $\text{var}(t) = E(t^2) - E(t)^2 = \frac{1}{\alpha^2}$.

What more can we learn from these equations? We can check that total probability is conserved, since

$$(1.91) \qquad\qquad \frac{d}{dt}\sum_{j=0}^\infty p_j = -\alpha\sum_{j=0}^\infty p_j(t) + \alpha\sum_{j=1}^\infty p_{j-1}(t) = 0.$$

Of course, $\sum_{j=0}^\infty p_j = 1$, since at time zero you have caught no fish, $p_0(0) = 1$ and $p_j(0) = 0$ for all $j > 0$. We can also find that the expected value of j satisfies

$$
\begin{aligned}
\frac{d}{dt}E(j) &= \frac{d}{dt}\sum_{j=0}^\infty jp_j = -\alpha\sum_{j=0}^\infty jp_j(t) + \alpha\sum_{j=1}^\infty jp_{j-1}(t) \\
(1.92) \qquad &= -\alpha\sum_{j=0}^\infty jp_j(t) + \alpha\sum_{j=0}^\infty (j+1)p_j(t) = \alpha,
\end{aligned}
$$

so that $E(j) = \alpha t$. Similarly,

$$
\begin{aligned}
\frac{d}{dt}E(j^2) &= \frac{d}{dt}\sum_{j=0}^\infty j^2 p_j = -\alpha\sum_{j=0}^\infty j^2 p_j(t) + \alpha\sum_{j=1}^\infty j^2 p_{j-1}(t) \\
&= -\alpha\sum_{j=0}^\infty j^2 p_j(t) + \alpha\sum_{j=0}^\infty (j+1)^2 p_j(t) \\
(1.93) \qquad &= \alpha\sum_{j=0}^\infty (2j+1)p_j(t) = 2\alpha E(j) + \alpha,
\end{aligned}
$$

so that $E(j^2) = \alpha^2 t^2 + \alpha t$. It follows that $\text{var}(j) = \alpha t$.

These equations can be solved analytically (in Exercise 1.24), finding

$$(1.94) \qquad\qquad p_j(t) = \frac{(\alpha t)^j}{j!}\exp(-\alpha t),$$

and plots of the first five of these ($j = 0, 1, 2, 3, 4$) are shown in Figure 1.7. It is apparent from these plots and easily verified that the maximum of $p_j(t)$ occurs at $\alpha t = j$. Notice

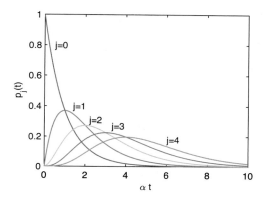

Figure 1.7. Plots of the Poisson distribution $p_j(t)$ for $j = 0, 1, 2, 3, 4$.

that α is a rate, having units of 1/time. Consequently, $\frac{1}{\alpha}$ is called the *time constant* for this process. Notice, also, that $p_4(t)$ looks similar to a normal distribution, which, according to the central limit theorem, it should. In fact, according to the central limit theorem, $p_j(t) \approx \mathcal{N}(\frac{j}{\alpha}, \frac{j}{\alpha^2})$ for j large.

This process is called a *Poisson process*, named after its inventor, French mathematician Siméon Denis Poisson, and not after the French meaning of his name (*poisson* means fish in French).

Now, let's consider the conversion of one chemical species to another. This we describe by a chemical reaction in which some species, S, is converted to a different species I at rate α, and this is denoted as

(1.95)
$$S \xrightarrow{\alpha} I.$$

For example, consider the decay of carbon-14 to nitrogen-14.

Suppose that at some time denoted $t = 0$, there is one molecule of carbon-14. What is the probability as a function of time that the carbon-14 molecule has not undergone decay by time $t > 0$? If we let $p_j(t)$ denote the probability of having exactly j molecules of carbon-14, then, following the same argument just given, the probability that there is exactly one carbon-14 molecule at time t satisfies the differential equation

(1.96)
$$\frac{dp_1}{dt} = -\alpha p_1,$$

where α is the *rate of decay*, known to be 1.21×10^{-4} per year for carbon-14. Since $p_1(0) = 1$, the solution of this equation is

(1.97)
$$p_1(t) = \exp(-\alpha t).$$

The function $1 - p_1(t) = 1 - \exp(-\alpha t)$ represents the probability that the decay event has taken place by time t, (i.e., the cdf) and $-\frac{dp_1}{dt} = \alpha p_1 = \alpha \exp(-\alpha t)$ represents the probability distribution function for the decay event. Accordingly, the decay event is *exponentially distributed*. As we learned from our fishing experience, the expected value of an exponential distribution is $E(t) = \frac{1}{\alpha}$, and the variance is $\text{var}(t) = \frac{1}{\alpha^2}$.

Now suppose we start with many, say n, carbon-14 molecules at time $t = 0$. What is the probability that we still have exactly n molecules at some time $t > 0$? Since the behavior of each atom of carbon-14 is independent of how many particles there are, it must be that $p_n(t)$ satisfies

$$(1.98) \qquad p_n(t) = (p_1(t))^n = \exp(-n\alpha t).$$

This follows from the law of independence, namely, that the probability of a collection of independent events is the product of the probabilities of the individual events. Consequently,

$$(1.99) \qquad \frac{dp_n}{dt} = -n\alpha p_n.$$

Now, suppose we start at time $t = 0$ with n molecules, but want to know the probability of having exactly $k < n$ molecules at some later time. For example, when will there be no molecules left, or, in mathematical language, what is $p_0(t)$?

Following the arguments given above (see (1.84)), we can write a differential equation for $p_k(t)$ as

$$(1.100) \qquad \frac{dp_k}{dt} = (k+1)\alpha p_{k+1} - k\alpha p_k.$$

This follows since the state with k molecules is entered from the state with $k + 1$ molecules at rate $(k + 1)\alpha$ when one of the $k + 1$ molecules decays and the state with k molecules is left at rate $k\alpha$ when one of the k molecules decays.

The equation for p_k is one of $n + 1$ equations (since $k = 0, 1, \ldots, n$), and while it is easy to determine $p_n(t)$ and not too hard to find $p_{n-1}(t)$, finding the general solution for $p_k(t)$ is more complicated (see Exercise 1.30). It is not difficult to simulate this system of equations, and this simulation is done in the Matlab code exponential_decay_via_Gillespie.m.

We can, however, get some information about this process without solving the full system of equations. For example, summing all of the equations, we find that

$$(1.101) \qquad \frac{d}{dt} \sum_{k=0}^{n} p_k(t) = 0.$$

In other words, the total probability does not change, that is, total probability is a conserved quantity. We can also find the expected value of k, which is defined as

$$(1.102) \qquad u = E(k) \equiv \sum_{k=0}^{n} k p_k(t),$$

by multiplying equation (1.100) by k and adding all the equations together. We find

$$(1.103) \qquad \frac{du}{dt} = -\alpha u,$$

and again, we find one of our favorite first order differential equations.

Notice that u is not an integer, even though it describes a process that only takes on integer values. In fact, u is a continuous function of time, and since the equation (1.103) is linear in u, the function u can be scaled to be the percentage of remaining molecules, or the concentration of molecules in a specified volume.

This equation has an important interpretation. If we were to watch a single particle to see when it decays, it would be extremely hard, essentially impossible, to predict when decay will occur. However, if we start with a large number of particles and record the times that each individual particle decays and then make a plot of the percentage of particles remaining at time t, we will see a curve that is quite close to the curve $\exp(-\alpha t)$. Further, if we make a histogram of the times that the individual decay events took place, it would be quite close to the curve $-\frac{du}{dt} = \alpha \exp(-\alpha t)$. This is to say that the decay times are distributed along the real number line, and the density with which they are distributed is the pdf.

Now let's use this information to numerically simulate this stochastic decay process. Suppose we start with n particles. When will the first decay event occur? We do not know this exactly, but we do know that this next reaction time should be distributed like $\exp(-n\alpha t)$, since the probability that decay occurs after time t is $\exp(-n\alpha t)$. The function $1 - \exp(-n\alpha t)$ is the cdf for the probability that at least one decay event has taken place in the interval $[0, t]$. In fact, the cdf $r = 1 - \exp(-n\alpha t)$ is a uniformly distributed random variable (see Exercise 1.28). So, we pick a uniformly distributed random number R between zero and one, $0 < R < 1$ (rather, let Matlab pick a number for you), and then take the next decay time increment δt_n to be the time at which the cdf is equal to $1 - R$, i.e., we invert the cdf to be such that

$$(1.104) \qquad\qquad R = \exp(-n\alpha \delta t_n),$$

or

$$(1.105) \qquad\qquad \delta t_n = \frac{-1}{n\alpha} \ln R.$$

Record this time increment, and repeat, next for $n - 1$ particles, and so on until all n particles have decayed.

The Matlab code that carries out this algorithm, called the *Gillespie algorithm*, or *next reaction time algorithm*, is titled exponential_decay_via_Gillespie.m, and an example of a simulation starting with 25 initial particles is shown in Figure 1.8.

There is an interesting and important observation to make about this decay process, and that is that the process always terminates in finite time, although the exponential curve that approximates it does not. To determine the expected time for the process to terminate, notice that the expected time to go from k to $k - 1$ molecules is

$$(1.106) \qquad\qquad t_k = \frac{1}{k\alpha},$$

and consequently, the expected time to go from n molecules to extinction is

$$(1.107) \qquad\qquad E(t) = \frac{1}{\alpha} \sum_{k=1}^{n} \frac{1}{k}.$$

Unfortunately, there is no closed form formula for this expression, although for large n it is well approximated by

$$(1.108) \qquad\qquad \sum_{k=1}^{n} \frac{1}{k} = \ln(n) + \gamma + O(\frac{1}{n}),$$

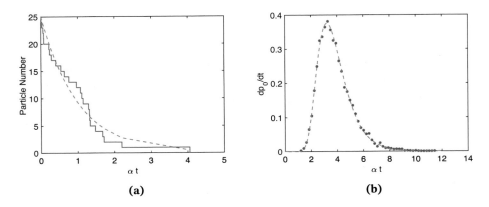

Figure 1.8. (a) Result of Gillespie simulation of decay (solid curve) compared to the function $N \exp(-\alpha t)$ (dashed curve), plotted as a function of αt, for $N = 25$ initial particles. (b) Histogram of extinction times for a simulation of 10,000 trials for decay of $N = 25$ initial particles, normalized to have total area one (shown with dots), compared with the function $\frac{dp_0}{dt}$ (dashed) coming from the numerical solution of the system (1.100).

where γ is the Euler–Mascheroni constant $\gamma = 0.57721 \cdots$. However, the validity of this formula can be verified by numerical simulation using the code exponential_decay_via_Gillespie.m. An example of this verification is shown in Figure 1.8(b) where a histogram of extinction times following 10,000 trials starting with 25 particles is shown. For this plot, the mean extinction time was computed to be 3.7969 and the theoretical value from (1.107) is $\alpha E(t) = 3.8160$.

This example of decay is only one of several possibilities. The death process could be *bimolecular*, as in

$$(1.109) \qquad\qquad S + S \overset{\beta}{\longrightarrow} S.$$

The differential equation describing this reaction is

$$(1.110) \qquad\qquad \frac{ds}{dt} = -\beta s^2,$$

and for a stochastic simulation, one takes

$$(1.111) \qquad\qquad \lambda_{k-1,k} = \frac{k(k-1)}{2} \frac{\beta}{\text{vol}}.$$

The motivation for this formula is that in a container with k S particles, the number of ways that a pair of particles can interact is $\frac{k(k-1)}{2}$. Then, the rate of interaction must be modified to take into account that the units of β for this reaction are $(\text{concentration})^{-1} \cdot (\text{time})^{-1}$, whereas $\lambda_{k-1,k}$ needs to be in units of $(\text{time})^{-1}$. The factor vol has units of volume, and is the conversion factor between concentration and particle numbers, so that the factor $\frac{\beta}{\text{vol}}$ has the correct units. Specifically, since concentration is number per volume, then the volume vol is number per concentration.

The spread of an infection might be described by the reaction

$$(1.112) \qquad\qquad S + I \overset{\gamma}{\longrightarrow} I + I,$$

in which case

(1.113)
$$\lambda_{k-1,k} = k(N-k)\frac{\gamma}{\text{vol}},$$

assuming the total number of particles $S + I$ is the constant N.

1.3.2. Several Reactions. In the example of particle decay there was only one reaction possible. However, this is not typical as most chemical reactions involve a range of possible reactions. For example, suppose a particle (like a bacterium) may reproduce at some rate or it may die at a different rate. The question addressed here is how to do a stochastic simulation of this process.

Suppose the state S_j can transition to the state S_k at rate λ_{kj}. To do a stochastic simulation of this process, we must decide when the next reaction takes place and which reaction it is that takes place.

To decide when the next reaction takes place, we use the fact that the probability that the next reaction has taken place by time t is 1 minus the probability that the next reaction has not taken place by time t. Furthermore, the probability that the reaction from state j to state k has not taken place by time t is $\exp(-\lambda_{kj}t)$. So, the probability that no reaction has taken place by time t (since these reactions are assumed to be independent) is

(1.114)
$$\prod_k \exp(-\lambda_{kj}t) = \exp(-\sum_k \lambda_{kj}t).$$

It follows that the cdf for the next reaction is

(1.115)
$$1 - \exp(-\sum_k \lambda_{kj}t) = 1 - \exp(-rt),$$

where $r = \sum_k \lambda_{kj}$. In other words, the next reaction is an exponential process with rate r.

Next, the probability that the next reaction is the ith reaction $S_j \to S_i$ is

(1.116)
$$p_{ij} = \frac{\lambda_{ij}}{\sum_k \lambda_{kj}} = \frac{\lambda_{ij}}{r}.$$

To be convinced of this, apply the results of Exercise 1.26 to the case where either the $S_j \to S_i$ reaction occurs first or another reaction occurs first.

With these facts in hand, as we did above, we pick the next reaction time increment to be

(1.117)
$$\delta t = \frac{-1}{r} \ln R_1,$$

where $0 < R_1 < 1$ is a uniformly distributed random number. Next, to decide which of the reactions to implement, construct the vector $x_k = \frac{1}{r}\sum_{i=1}^{k} \lambda_{ij}$, the scaled vector of cumulative sums of λ_{ij}. Notice that the vector x_k is ordered with $0 \le x_1 \le x_2 \le \cdots \le x_N = 1$, where N is the total number of states. Now, pick a second random number R_2, uniformly distributed between zero and one, and pick the next reaction to be $S_j \to S_k$ where

(1.118)
$$k = \min_j \{R_2 \le x_j\}.$$

With this formula, the proportion of the times the kth reaction is picked is $\frac{\lambda_{kj}}{r}$, as it must be.

Let's consider the specific example of the death and birth process with

$$(1.119) \qquad S \xrightarrow{\alpha} I, \quad S \xrightarrow{\beta} 2S.$$

The rate at which one particle is removed is

$$(1.120) \qquad \lambda_{k-1,k} = k\alpha,$$

and the rate at which one particle is added is

$$(1.121) \qquad \lambda_{k+1,k} = k\beta.$$

The deterministic differential equation governing the mean of the population is

$$(1.122) \qquad \frac{ds}{dt} = (\beta - \alpha)s,$$

and if $\alpha > \beta$, the population will go extinct. However, in contrast to the pure death process, the population will not decay monotonically. The equations governing the probability of having k particles at time t are

$$(1.123) \qquad \frac{dp_k}{dt} = -(\alpha k + \beta k)p_k + \alpha(k+1)p_{k+1} + \beta(k-1)p_{k-1},$$

and this is an infinite system of equations, since there is no a priori bound on the number of particles at any given time. Consequently, to solve this system numerically it must be truncated at some relatively large value of k. (For an analytical solution, see Exercise 9.9.)

The stochastic simulation for this process uses the Matlab code stochastic_birth_death.m and an example of a sample trajectory is shown plotted in Figure 1.9.

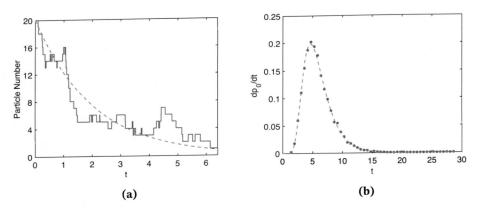

(a)   **(b)**

Figure 1.9. (a) Trajectory of a simulated birth-death process with death rate $\alpha = 1$ and birth rate $\beta = 0.5$ with the curve $N \exp(-(\alpha - \beta)t)$ (dashed line). (b) Histogram of extinction times for a simulation of 10,000 trials for decay of $N = 20$ initial particles, normalized to have total area one (shown with dots), compared with the function $\frac{dp_0}{dt}$ (dashed line) coming from the solution of the system (1.123).

1.3.3. Multiple Species. This method of simulation and analysis generalizes readily to the situation where there are multiple species and multiple reactions. At any given time, the state vector is the vector of integers $S = (n_1, n_2, \ldots, n_K)$, and there are J reactions with rates r_j that depend on the state of the system S. For each reaction there is a change in the state vector $c(j, k)$, meaning that if reaction j occurs, the kth integer n_k changes by the amount $c(j, k)$.

As an example, consider the SIR reactions

$$(1.124) \qquad S + I \xrightarrow{\alpha} 2I, \quad I \xrightarrow{\beta} R.$$

Here S represents susceptible individuals in a population, I represents the infected and contagious individuals, and R represents those individuals who are removed and no longer contagious. The deterministic differential equations for these reactions are given by (1.63), however, as we all know from experience with COVID-19, the evolution of an epidemic is highly stochastic.

An interesting question to ask is how many individuals have been infected and how many susceptibles remain (or survive) after an infection has run its course, and we can address this question using a stochastic simulation. The setup for this stochastic simulation is straightforward. The state space is identified by the three integers n_s, n_i, and n_r, and the two reactions are at rates

$$(1.125) \qquad r_1 = \alpha n_s n_i, \quad r_2 = \beta n_i,$$

and the change matrix $C = c(j, k)$ is

$$(1.126) \qquad C = \begin{pmatrix} -1 & 1 & 0 \\ 0 & -1 & 1 \end{pmatrix}.$$

This is easily implemented in Matlab code and in fact, the code that does this is titled stochastic_SIR.m.

Scatter plots of recovery times vs. number of survivors for the SIR stochastic process shown in Figure 1.10 are surprising, and are certainly different than what is predicted by the deterministic model. (Recovery time refers to the first time at which there are no more infected individuals.) The deterministic model predicts a unique outcome (recall (1.67)), with an epidemic spreading if $R_0 = \frac{\alpha s(0)}{\beta} > 1$ and not spreading if $R_0 = \frac{\alpha s(0)}{\beta} < 1$. However, in Figure 1.10(a), where $R_0 = 2.5$, the results of the stochastic simulation show a biphasic outcome, with many of the trials, as expected, having a large epidemic with few survivors and long recovery times, but also with a significant number of trials with little spread of the infection, a large percentage of survivors, and a short recovery time. Similarly, in Figure 1.10(b), where $R_0 = 0.9$, most of the trials result in a short-lived epidemic with a high percentage of survivors. However, there are nonetheless quite a few trials showing a substantial epidemic with few survivors and long recovery times, noticeably different than the prediction of the deterministic model.

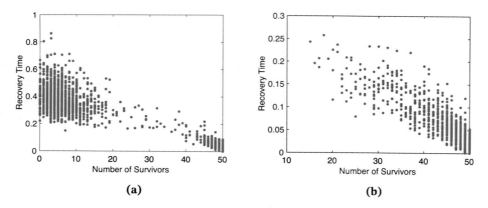

Figure 1.10. Scatter plot of recovery times vs. number of survivors for 2000 trials of the SIR stochastic process starting with $N = 50$ S individuals and one I (infected) initially, running the process until there are no I individuals, with parameters $\alpha = 1$, and (a) $\beta = 20$ ($R_0 = 2.5$), (b) $\beta = 55$ ($R_0 = 0.9$).

There is an important lesson to be learned here. In particular, the prediction of the deterministic model is not necessarily correct. For this problem, if $R_0 > 1$, it is not *necessarily* correct that there will be a substantial spread of the infection, and if $R_0 < 1$ it does not *necessarily* mean that there will no spread of the infection.

There are many other examples illustrating this kind of cautionary tale (for example, see Exercises 1.36–1.39). These are, however, important to help us understand the strengths, as well as the limitations, of mathematical models. And since forewarned is forearmed, let's embark on the task ahead, of modeling biological processes in both time and space.

Exercises

1.1. Calculate $\frac{\partial f}{\partial t}$ and $\frac{\partial^2 f}{\partial x^2}$ for $f = \frac{1}{\sqrt{t}} \exp(-\frac{x^2}{4t})$.

1.2. For the functions
   (i) $f = x^2 + y^2$,
   (ii) $f = xy$:
   (a) Find $\frac{\partial f}{\partial x}, \frac{\partial^2 f}{\partial x \partial y}, \nabla f$.
   (b) Determine if there are critical points. Which, if any, are local maxima?
   (c) Visualize the surface and the level curves for the function $z = f(x, y)$ using Matlab. Explore different Matlab functions for plotting: mesh, surf, contour, contour3, and see what they do. Type
      `help mesh`
      or similar to see the available options.

1.3. Determine which, if any, of the following vector fields are gradient fields. If it is a gradient field, find ϕ such that $\mathbf{F} = \nabla \phi$.
   (a) $\mathbf{F} = (x + y, x - y)$,

(b) $\mathbf{F} = (x^2 y, xy^2)$.

1.4. Suppose $u(x)$ is a smooth function. Use Taylor's theorem to verify that

$$u(x - \Delta x) - 2u(x) + u(x + \Delta x) = \frac{d^2 u(x)}{dx^2} \Delta x^2 + O(\Delta x^4).$$

1.5. Use Taylor's theorem and the fact that e^x satisfies $\frac{d}{dx}(e^x) = e^x$ and $e^0 = 1$ to find the power series representation of e^x.

1.6. Use graphical analysis to find the solution of the differential equation (often called the *logistic equation*)

$$\frac{du}{dt} = u(1 - u)$$

for all positive initial data.

1.7. Determine the type of the critical point at the origin and sketch phase portraits for the systems

$$\frac{d}{dt} \begin{pmatrix} u \\ v \end{pmatrix} = A \begin{pmatrix} u \\ v \end{pmatrix},$$

with
(a)

$$A = \begin{pmatrix} 0 & 1 \\ 1 & 0 \end{pmatrix},$$

(b)

$$A = \begin{pmatrix} 0.1 & 1 \\ -1 & 0.1 \end{pmatrix},$$

(c)

$$A = \begin{pmatrix} -0.1 & 1 \\ -1 & -0.1 \end{pmatrix},$$

(d)

$$A = \begin{pmatrix} -1 & 0.2 \\ 0.3 & -0.3 \end{pmatrix}.$$

1.8. Give a phase plane analysis for the equation $u_{xx} + f(u) = 0$ where $f(u) = u(1 - u)$.

1.9. What fraction of a population of susceptible individuals s_0 should be vaccinated in order to prevent the spread of an SIR epidemic with parameters α (rate of infection) and β (rate of recovery)?

1.10. Suppose the rate of susceptible infection is given by the enzymatic rate

$$\frac{ds}{dt} = -\frac{\alpha si}{1 + \frac{s}{K}}.$$

(a) Why is this likely to be more reasonable than the law of mass action reaction rate? (Think about what happens when s is very large.)
(b) Give a phase plane analysis of these SIR dynamics including recovery of infected individuals at rate β.
(c) What is the threshold for $s_0 = s(0)$ for there to be an epidemic? Is this larger or smaller than for a law of mass action (i.e., $K \to \infty$) epidemic?

(d) Find a relationship between $s(\infty)$ and $s(0)$ following an epidemic. Is $s(\infty)$ larger or smaller than that for a law of mass action (i.e., $K \to \infty$) epidemic?

1.11. Simulate the Hodgkin–Huxley equations

$$C_m \frac{dV}{dt} + I_{ion} = I_{stim},$$

where $I_{ion} = \bar{g}_{Na} m^3 h(V - V_{Na}) + \bar{g}_K n^4(V - V_K) + g_L(V - V_L)$, and m, n, and the h are solutions of the ordinary differential equation

$$\frac{dj}{dt} = \alpha_j(V)(1 - j) - \beta_j(V)j,$$

for $j = m, n, h$, and

$$\alpha_m = 0.1 \frac{-25 - V}{\exp\left(\frac{25-v}{10}\right) - 1}, \quad \beta_m = 4 \exp\left(\frac{-V}{18}\right),$$

$$\alpha_h = 0.07 \exp\left(\frac{-V}{20}\right), \quad \beta_h = \frac{1}{\exp\left(\frac{30-V}{10}\right) + 1},$$

$$\alpha_n = 0.01 \frac{10 - V}{\exp\left(\frac{10-V}{10}\right) - 1}, \quad \beta_n = 0.125 \exp\left(\frac{-V}{80}\right).$$

For these expressions, the potential V is measured in units of mV, current density is in units of $\mu A/cm^2$, conductances $\bar{g}$ are in units of mS/cm^2, and capacitance is in units of $\mu F/cm^2$. The remaining parameters are

$$\bar{g}_{Na} = 120, \qquad \bar{g}_K = 36, \qquad \bar{g}_L = 0.3, \qquad C_m = 1,$$

with Nernst potentials $V_{Na} = 115$ mV, $V_K = -12$ mV, $V_L = -10.6$ mV.
(a) Show that the solution goes to a steady state if $I_{stim} = 0$.
(b) Show that for a range of values of $I_{stim} > 0$, the solution is periodic.

1.12. Simulate and give a phase plane analysis for the reduced Hodgkin–Huxley equations

$$C_m \frac{dV}{dt} + I_{ion} = I_{stim},$$

where $I_{ion} = \bar{g}_{Na} m_\infty^3 h(V - V_{Na}) + \bar{g}_K n^4(V - V_K) + g_L(V - V_L)$, and n is the solution of the ordinary differential equation

$$\frac{dn}{dt} = \alpha_n(V)(1 - n) - \beta_n(V)n,$$

and

$$m_\infty(V) = \frac{\alpha_m(V)}{\alpha_m(V) + \beta_m(V)},$$

where

$$\alpha_m = 0.1 \frac{-25 - V}{\exp\left(\frac{25-v}{10}\right) - 1}, \quad \beta_m = 4 \exp\left(\frac{-V}{18}\right),$$

$$\alpha_n = 0.01 \frac{10 - V}{\exp\left(\frac{10-V}{10}\right) - 1}, \quad \beta_n = 0.125 \exp\left(\frac{-V}{80}\right),$$

and $n + h = n_0 = 0.8$.

For these expressions, the potential V is measured in units of mV, current density is in units of $\mu A/cm^2$, conductances $\bar{g}$ are in units of mS/cm^2, and capacitance is in units of $\mu F/cm^2$. The remaining parameters are

$$\bar{g}_{Na} = 120, \qquad \bar{g}_K = 36, \qquad \bar{g}_L = 0.3, \qquad C_m = 1,$$

with Nernst potentials $V_{Na} = 115$ mV, $V_K = -12$ mV, $V_L = -10.6$ mV.

(a) Show that the solution goes to a steady state if $I_{stim} = 0$.

(b) Show that for a range of values of $I_{stim} > 0$, the solution is periodic.

Hint. To determine the nullcline $\frac{dV}{dt} = 0$, use bisection to find the n value for each value of V.

As a reminder, the bisection method works as follows: Suppose you wish to find the zero of a function $f(u)$, and you know two values of u, say u_L and u_U, for which $f(u_L)f(u_U) < 0$. Set $u_c = \frac{1}{2}(u_L + u_U)$ and evaluate $f(u_c)$. If $f(u_L)f(u_c) > 0$, then replace u_L by u_c, whereas if $f(u_L)f(u_c) < 0$, then replace u_U by u_c. Repeat this until the difference between u_L and u_U is satisfactorily small. A Matlab code that does this and is readily adapted to work for your favorite function is found with the codes in Appendix A and is titled bisect_function.m.

1.13. (a) Suppose that y and z are independent random variables. Verify that $\mathrm{var}(y+z) = \mathrm{var}(y)+\mathrm{var}(z)$. *Remark.* Use that the joint probability function for y and z satisfies $p(\xi,\eta) = p_y(\xi)p_z(\eta)$.

   (b) Show that this may fail if y and z are not independent, for example with the random variable $x + x$.

1.14. Suppose $m_1, m_2, \ldots, m_N$ are independent, identically distributed, random variables, with mean $\mu = E(m_i)$ and variance $\sigma^2 = \mathrm{var}(m_i)$. Find the mean and the variance of the random variable

$$x_N = \sum_{j=1}^{N} m_j.$$

1.15. Suppose $m_1, m_2, \ldots,$ are independent, identically distributed, random variables, with mean $\mu = E(m_i)$ and variance $\sigma^2 = \mathrm{var}(m_i)$. Find the mean and variance of the random variable

$$x_N = \frac{1}{N}\sum_{j=1}^{N} m_j.$$

1.16. What are the mean and variance of the uniform distribution on the interval $[0, 1]$, $p(x) = 1$, for $0 \le x \le 1$?

1.17. What are the mean and variance of the discrete random variable $\{0,1\}$ with each occurring with equal probability?

1.18. What are the mean and variance of the roll of a die $\{1,2,3,4,5,6\}$ with equal probability?

1.19. Suppose you flip a coin N times, where N is a large even number.

   (a) Use the central limit theorem to estimate the probability that there will be exactly $\frac{N}{2}$ heads.

(b) Do a numerical experiment (using the Matlab function randi) to check the validity of this formula.

1.20. Use Matlab to explore the validity of the central limit theorem, as follows. Use the Matlab function randi to generate N random integers m_i, $i = 1, 2, \ldots, N$, and then find the average $x_N = \frac{1}{N} \sum_{j=1}^{N} m_j$. Collect many samples of x_N and plot the distribution (the normalized histogram) and compare it to the appropriate normal distribution as predicted by the central limit theorem.

1.21. Use Matlab to explore the validity of the central limit theorem, as follows. Use the Matlab function rand to generate N uniformly distributed random numbers m_i, $i = 1, 2, \ldots, N$, $0 \le m_i \le 1$, and then find the average $x_N = \frac{1}{N} \sum_{j=1}^{N} m_j$. Collect many samples of x_N and plot the distribution (the normalized histogram) and compare it to the appropriate normal distribution as predicted by the central limit theorem.

1.22. For the differential equation

$$\frac{dc}{dt} = -\frac{vc}{K + c},$$

(a) What are the units of the parameters v and K?
(b) Show that by introducing appropriately scaled variables for c and t, one can transform this equation into the equation with no free parameters

$$\frac{du}{d\tau} = -\frac{u}{1 + u}.$$

(c) Find and plot the solution of this equation for several different initial values including $u(0) \gg 1$ and $u(0) \ll 1$.
    Hint. Find τ as a function of u, but plot it as u as a function of τ.

1.23. Suppose a fisherman fishes for four hours at a lake with a fishing success rate of 1/hour. What is the probability that he gets skunked (no fish), and what is the probability that he catches eight or more fish?

1.24. Find the solution of the system of differential equations (1.86), subject to initial conditions $p_0(0) = 1$, $p_j(0) = 0$ for $j > 0$, as follows:
(a) Let $g(z, t) = \sum_{j=0}^{\infty} z^j p_j(t)$. Find a differential equation for g.
(b) Solve the differential equation subject to initial data $g(z, 0) = 1$.
(c) Expand $g(z, t)$ into its power series in z, thereby determining $p_j(t)$.

1.25. The decay rate of carbon-14 is 1.21×10^{-4} per year.
(a) Suppose you have one molecule of carbon-14 in a flask. What is the probability that it will decay within the next 30 seconds?
(b) The half-life of a radioactive particle is the time it takes for half of some initial quantity to decay. What is the half life of carbon-14?

1.26. (a) Suppose you go fishing with a friend who usually catches more fish than you do. (An experience I know all too well!) After much observation, you determine that, on average, he catches twice as many fish as you do. Suppose you both start fishing at the same time. What is the probability that you catch a fish before he does?

(b) More generally, suppose your friend catches fish at rate α_1 and you with rate α_2. What is the probability that you will catch a fish before he does?

Hint. The joint probability distribution function for two independent random variables t_1 and t_2 with probability density functions $f_1(\tau_1)$ and $f_2(\tau_2)$, respectively, is the product $f(\tau_1, \tau_2) = f_1(\tau_1)f_2(\tau_2)$. The probability that t_1, t_2 are in some domain Ω is $P((t_1, t_2) \in \Omega) = \int_\Omega f(\tau_1, \tau_2)d\tau_1 d\tau_2$. Suppose $f_1(\tau_1)$ and $f_2(\tau_2)$ represent the pdf's for catching a fish for fisherman 1 and 2, respectively, find the probability that $t_2 < t_1$, i.e., $P(t_2 < t_1)$.

1.27. An infection spreads in a neighborhood from person to person through nearest neighbor interaction only. Suppose the rate of spread is α meaning that if an individual is infected, her neighbor will become infected at rate α. However, recovery from infection is at rate β, so it might be that an infected individual recovers before her neighbor is infected. What is the probability that exactly n individuals will be infected after the neighbor at the end of the street becomes infected? What is the expected value and variance of n? *Hint.* Use the probability that passing the infection before recovery is $\frac{\alpha}{\alpha+\beta}$ and the probability of recovery before passing the infection is $\frac{\beta}{\alpha+\beta}$.

1.28. Suppose t is a random variable $0 < t < \infty$ with probability density function $f(\tau)$ with $\int_0^\infty f(\tau)d\tau = 1$. Show that the cumulative distribution function $r = \int_0^t f(\tau)d\tau$ is a uniformly distributed random variable on the interval $[0, 1]$. *Hint.* Calculate that the probability $P(r_0 < r < r_1) = r_1 - r_0$ for any $r_0 < r_1$ with $0 < r_0 < r_1 < 1$.

1.29. A finite birth-death process is identified by the reactions

$$S_1 \underset{\beta_2}{\overset{\alpha_1}{\rightleftharpoons}} S_2 \underset{\beta_3}{\overset{\alpha_2}{\rightleftharpoons}} \cdots S_{N-1} \underset{\beta_N}{\overset{\alpha_{N-1}}{\rightleftharpoons}} S_N.$$

(a) What is the matrix A defined by (1.85) for this process?

(b) Suppose all of the reaction rates α_j, β_{j+1}, $j = 1, 2, \ldots, N - 1$ are nonzero. Show that A, an $N \times N$ matrix, has rank $= N - 1$, i.e., has rank deficiency $= 1$. *Hint.* Use Gaussian elimination to row reduce the matrix to an upper diagonal matrix.

(c) Suppose $\alpha_1 = 0$ and all other reaction rates are nonzero. Show that the nullspace of A, i.e., the nontrivial solution of $A\mathbf{p_0} = 0$, is one dimensional and is spanned by the vector $\mathbf{p_0} = (1, 0, 0, \ldots, 0)^T$. *Remark.* The state S_1 is called an *absorbing state*.

(d) Realizing that A has $N-1$ eigenvalues with negative real part and one zero eigenvalue (you do not need to prove this) show that, for *any* initial data $\mathbf{p}(0)$ with $\mathbf{1}^T \cdot \mathbf{p}(0) = 1$, $\lim_{t\to\infty} \mathbf{p}(t) = \mathbf{p_0}$ where $\mathbf{p_0}$ is the unique element of the nullspace of A.

1.30. Use induction to verify that the solution of the equations (1.100) is given by

$$p_k(t) = \binom{N}{\kappa} \exp(-\alpha k t)(1 - \exp(-\alpha t))^{N-k}$$

so that the extinction probability is $p_0(t) = (1 - \exp(-\alpha t))^N$. How does this compare to the numerically computed solution found using the Matlab code exponential_decay_via_Gillespie.m?

1.31. Suppose the bimolecular decay process (1.109) has a rate constant β with units $(\text{time})^{-1}(\text{mM})^{-1}$. What is the conversion factor vol?

1.32. Suppose that some chemical species S is degraded by the bimolecular process

$$S + S \xrightarrow{\beta} S.$$

(a) What is the deterministic differential equation governing this decay process? What is the solution of this differential equation and what prediction does it make about the time course of decay for this process?

(b) There can never be less than one molecule of S. Do a stochastic simulation of this decay process and find the time distribution for arriving at one molecule for this process.

(c) What is the expected time for n molecules to decay into $n - 1$ molecules? What is the expected time for N molecules to decay to one molecule? *Hint.* Use that $\sum_{k=2}^{N} \frac{1}{k(k-1)} = 1 - \frac{1}{N}$.

(d) What are the equations governing $p_k(t)$, the probability of having k molecules at time t. Simulate these equations and compare $\frac{dp_1}{dt}$ with the arrival time distribution found from your stochastic simulation.

Hint. Use the Matlab code exponential_decay_via_Gillespie.m as a template for this solution.

1.33. Suppose that there is a chemical species S that is degraded into species I by the reaction

$$S + I \xrightarrow{\gamma} 2I.$$

(a) Supposing that $[S] + [I] = S_0$, determine the deterministic differential equation governing the decay of S and its solution.

(b) Do a stochastic simulation of this decay process and find the time distribution of extinction of S, starting from $1\ I$ and $N - 1\ S$ particles.

(c) What are the equations governing $p_k(t)$, the probability of having k molecules at time t. Simulate these equations and compare $\frac{dp_0}{dt}$ with the arrival time distribution found from your stochastic simulation.

Hint. Use the Matlab code exponential_decay_via_Gillespie.m as a template for this solution.

1.34. Suppose that some chemical species S degrades into another species I at some rate α, via the bimolecular reaction

$$S + S \xrightarrow{\alpha} S + I,$$

and that S can reproduce via the reaction

$$S \xrightarrow{\beta} 2S.$$

(a) What is the deterministic differential equation governing the dynamics of S, and what are its stable and unstable equilibria?

(b) Write the equations governing the probability $p_k(t)$ that there are k molecules of S at time t. Do a numerical simulation of these equations and show that the solution goes to an equilibrium. What is the relationship between this equilibrium solution and $\frac{\alpha}{\beta}$?

(c) Do a stochastic simulation of this process. The population cannot go extinct. What does the population do? Compare this to the equilibrium solution of $p_k(t)$. *Hint.* Use the Matlab code stochastic_birth_death.m as a template for this stochastic simulation.

1.35. An enzyme E converts a substrate S molecule into product P by the reactions

$$S + E \underset{\beta}{\overset{\alpha}{\rightleftharpoons}} C \overset{\gamma}{\longrightarrow} P + E.$$

(a) Do a stochastic simulation of this decay process, assuming there is a single enzyme molecule. How does the rate of this decay process compare with that of an exponential decay process? *Warning.* The simulation is slower as $\frac{\beta}{\gamma}$ gets larger. Why? *Hint.* Use the Matlab code stochastic_SIR.m as a template for this stochastic simulation.

(b) Calculate the extinction time distribution for this process, and compare it with a Gaussian distribution with mean and variance computed from the data.

(c) What are the equations governing $p_{k,1}(t)$ and $p_{k,0}(t)$, where $p_{k,1}$ is the probability of having k substrate molecules and one free enzyme molecule, and $p_{k,0}$ is the probability of having k substrate molecules and no free enzyme molecules. Solve these equations numerically and compare $\frac{dp_{0,1}}{dt}$ with the data for exit time distribution computed from your stochastic simulation.

1.36. Consider the chemical reactions

$$S + U \underset{k_{-1}}{\overset{k_1}{\rightleftharpoons}} 2U, \quad U \overset{k_2}{\longrightarrow} P.$$

Assume that $[S] = s$ is constant.

(a) Do a stochastic simulation of these reactions. Find the extinction time distribution starting with about $\frac{k_1 s - k_2}{k_{-1}}$ molecules of U. (Choose $\frac{k_1 s - k_2}{k_{-1}}$ to be of order 10. What happens to the simulation time if $\frac{k_1 s - k_2}{k_{-1}}$ is much larger than this?)

(b) Find the deterministic differential equation governing the concentration of species U. Give a complete analysis of the differential equation under the assumption that $k_1 s > k_{-1}$. What do you observe about the deterministic differential equation that is in contradiction with the stochastic simulation? *Remark.* This contradiction is referred to as *Keizer's paradox* [36],[10].

(c) Find the equation governing the probability $p_n(t)$ that there are n molecules of U at time t, and simulate this equation to find the probability of going extinct as a function of time. Observe that $p_0(t) \to 1$ as $t \to \infty$. How does $\frac{dp_0}{dt}$ compare with the extinction distribution found in your simulation?

1.37. Suppose that some chemical species S converts into another species I at some rate α, via the bimolecular reaction

(1.127) $$S + I \xrightarrow{\alpha} 2I,$$

and that I degrades back to S via the reaction

(1.128) $$I \xrightarrow{\beta} S.$$

Remark. If S represents susceptibles and I infectives, then this is called an *SIS* disease.

(a) What is the deterministic differential equation describing the dynamics of S? Notice that $[S] + [I] = S_0$ is a constant. Under what conditions on parameters is there an endemic stable steady state for which $I > 0$?

(b) Do a stochastic simulation of this reaction. Show that I *always* goes extinct, even when the deterministic model predicts a stable endemic state. Explain this apparently paradoxical behavior. (See Exercise 1.29.)

(c) Find the equation governing the probability $p_n(t)$ that there are n individuals of I at time t, and simulate this equation to find the probability of going extinct as a function of time. Observe that $p_0(t) \to 1$ as $t \to \infty$. How does $\frac{dp_0}{dt}$ compare with the extinction distribution found in your simulation?

1.38. An *SIRS* disease is a disease for which recovery and immunity is only temporary, and is described by the reaction scheme

(1.129) $$S + I \xrightarrow{\alpha} 2I, \quad I \xrightarrow{\beta} R, \quad R \xrightarrow{\gamma} S.$$

(a) Write the deterministic differential equations for these reactions. Give a phase plane analysis of this system and show that if $\frac{\beta}{\alpha s_0} < 1$, where $s + i + r = s_0$, then there is an endemic state, i.e., a nontrivial, stable steady state solution with $i > 0$. Show also that the steady state solution $s = s_0$, $i = 0$ is unstable.

(b) Do a stochastic simulation of this system and show that the infection *always* goes extinct. *Hint.* Assume that a concentration of one corresponds to 100 individuals. Choose parameter values for which the steady state of I is not too large. Why is this helpful?

(c) Explain this paradoxical result.

1.39. Consider the chemical reactions

$$U + V \xrightarrow{\alpha} 2V, \quad U \xrightarrow{\beta} 2U, \quad V \xrightarrow{\gamma} \emptyset.$$

(a) Find the deterministic differential equations governing the concentrations of species U and V. Give a complete phase plane analysis of this system, including plotting some typical trajectories. Find a first integral of the motion. (These equations are known as the Lotka–Volterra equations.)

(b) Do a stochastic simulation of these reactions with the same parameter values. Assume that a concentration of one corresponds to 100 individuals. Make a plot of typical stochastic trajectories in $u - v$ concentration space to compare with the deterministic phase portrait. Notice that one of the populations always goes extinct; explain why this is in contradiction to the deterministic solution. Find the distribution of extinction times.

Hint. Without loss of generality, $\alpha = \beta = 1$, so the only free parameter is γ. Choose "easy" values of γ for this exercise.

Chapter 2

Conservation— Learning How to Count

2.1. The Conservation Law

The purpose of this text can be summarized as learning how to count biological objects as they change over time. Demographers do this by taking a census of their population of interest from time to time and then making a plot of the pointwise values and connecting the points with lines. This approach is of limited value because it gives no explanation, or mechanism, for the observed changes, and it has no predictive value. Even if data points are fit to a regression curve, there is no confidence that the fit curve can be extrapolated to values outside the range of times for which data was collected.

The approach taken here is to recognize that for any quantity of some material with density u (i.e., number per unit volume) which is changing in time, it *must* be that the total amount of the material in some region of space can change only because of flux (i.e., movement) across the boundary or production/destruction in the interior of the region. In mathematical language, this can be stated as

$$(2.1) \qquad \frac{d}{dt} \int_\Omega u \, dV = - \int_{\partial\Omega} \mathbf{J} \cdot \mathbf{n} \, dS + \int_\Omega f \, dV,$$

where Ω is a closed region in space, $\partial\Omega$ is its boundary surface, and $\mathbf{n}$ is the outward unit normal to the boundary of Ω. Here, f is the rate of production (or destruction, if f is negative) of u. Since the units of the terms on the left and right hand side of this equation must match, f must have units of u/time. Since dV has units of volume, and dS has units of area, the flux $\mathbf{J}$ is the vector-valued quantity with units of u times length/time, i.e., units of u times velocity, which is the same as number per unit area per time.[1] The minus sign here is to recognize that if $\mathbf{J} \cdot \mathbf{n}$ is positive, then the flux of

---

[1]More generally, in a d dimensional space, where $d = 1, 2$ or 3, u has units of number/(length)^d, dV has units of (length)^d, and dS has units of (length)$^{d-1}$, so that the flux must have units of u times velocity = units of number per (length)$^{d-1}$ per time.

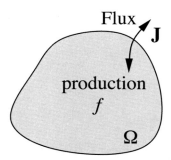

material is outward across the boundary, hence decreasing the amount of material in the domain.

As a side note, notice that the number of biological objects is always an integer, so treating the density u as a real number that can vary continuously is an approximation, albeit a very useful one (see Exercise 2.1).

The integral equation (2.1), while correct, accounting for the behavior of quantities in the aggregate, is not very useful in helping us understand the behavior of u at specific points in the interior of Ω. However, if we apply the divergence theorem to the first term on the right hand side of (2.1),

$$(2.2) \qquad \int_{\partial\Omega} \mathbf{J} \cdot \mathbf{n} dS = \int_{\Omega} \nabla \cdot \mathbf{J} dV,$$

we can combine the terms on the right hand side of (2.1) into a single integral. Then, we pass the time derivative through the integral on the left side to get the single integral

$$(2.3) \qquad 0 = \int_{\Omega} \left(\frac{\partial u}{\partial t} + \nabla \cdot \mathbf{J} - f \right) dV.$$

Since the region Ω is arbitrary, it must be that the integrand is zero, that is,

$$(2.4) \qquad \frac{\partial u}{\partial t} = -\nabla \cdot \mathbf{J} + f.$$

We argue this as follows: Suppose the integrand is not zero at some point in space. If the integrand is a continuous function of space, then there is some open neighborhood of the point where the integrand remains nonzero. If we then choose Ω to be this neighborhood, the integral over Ω is nonzero, a contradiction.

It is impossible to overstate the importance of the equation (2.4), as it underlies **everything** discussed in this book. The equation (2.4) is called a *conservation equation*, and it is inviolable.

What allows us to pass the time derivative through the integral in (2.1)? The argument is as follows: Let $Q(t) = \int_\Omega u(x,t)dV$. It is certainly correct that

(2.5) $$\frac{1}{\Delta t}(Q(t + \Delta t) - Q(t)) = \int_\Omega \frac{1}{\Delta t}(u(x, t + \Delta t) - u(x,t))dV,$$

so the question is if we can take the limit $\Delta t \to 0$ on both the inside and outside of the integral and get the same answer. This question is answered in the affirmative by Arzelà's theorem, or the dominated convergence theorem. This theorem states that for any sequence of functions f_n for which $|f_n|$ are uniformly bounded and $\lim_{n\to\infty} f_n = f$, then

(2.6) $$\lim_{n\to\infty} \int_\Omega f_n dV = \int_\Omega \lim_{n\to\infty} f_n dV = \int_\Omega f dV.$$

For all the calculations in this text, this assumption is valid.

However, there is still a lot of work to be done. Specifically, to study biological systems and phenomena, we need to see how the empirical evidence or known laws of physics and chemistry suggest forms for $\mathbf{J}$ and f, and then determine if those forms lead to behavior that is consistent with experimental observations. In this way, we are able to make, check, or improve hypotheses about how things work and in so doing deepen our understanding of these biological systems.

So let's get started with an exploration of flux $\mathbf{J}$, i.e., how things move.

2.2. Examples of Flux—How Things Move

There are several examples of flux that are important in biology.

Advection. Suppose particles with concentration u are dissolved in water and the water is moving with velocity $\mathbf{v}$ and that the dissolved particles are moving with the same velocity. The flux of concentration at any point is the velocity of the water times the concentration

(2.7) $$\mathbf{J} = \mathbf{v}u.$$

This flux is a pointwise object having units of concentration times velocity. If this is constant in a tube like a vein or artery, with crossectional area A, then the flow in the tube is given by

(2.8) $$Q = A\mathbf{J} = A\mathbf{v}u,$$

which has units of volume times concentration per unit time = number of particles per unit time. This formula will be useful for Exercise 2.3.

Fick's law. If individual particles have a velocity that is different than that of the water in which they are dissolved, for example, a random motion, then we might reasonably expect that they would tend to spread out, by moving, on average, *down* their concentration gradient. This is certainly what happens in our ordinary experience. For example, if you put a drop of ink into water, it will very quickly disperse, or diffuse, away, and eventually the ink will be uniformly distributed throughout the water, with no regions with higher or lower concentration. In math language, this is stated as

$$(2.9) \qquad\qquad \mathbf{J} = -D\nabla u,$$

and is called *Fick's law*, and D is called the *diffusion coefficient*. Notice that D must have units of (length)^2/time, since the flux must have units of velocity times units of u.

Fick's law is not truly a law, but a model, hence appropriate in certain contexts. For example, it applies if the particles are diffuse with no self-interactions, but not so few that u cannot be viewed as a continuous variable.

A derivation of Fick's law can be given using ideas from statistical mechanics. For a dilute chemical species the Gibbs free energy is approximately $G = k_B T u \ln u$ and the chemical potential is $\mu = \frac{\partial G}{\partial u} = k_B T(\ln u + 1)$, where k_B is Boltzmann's constant and T is temperature in degrees Kelvin. (In the chemical literature, the chemical potential is taken to be $\mu = k_B T \ln u$, ignoring the additive constant, since only the shape of a potential matters and not its absolute height.) Now, as is known from physics, force is the negative gradient of potential, $F = -\nabla\mu = -k_B T \frac{\nabla u}{u}$, and in a highly viscous environment where inertia is negligible, velocity is proportional to force, $\eta v = F$, with proportionality factor η known as the drag. Since flux is velocity times concentration, it follows that

$$(2.10) \qquad\qquad \mathbf{J} = -\frac{k_B T}{\eta}\nabla u,$$

which is Fick's law, and the diffusion coefficient is $D = \frac{k_B T}{\eta}$.

In his theory of Brownian motion, Einstein gave a quantitative understanding of diffusion by showing that if a spherical solute molecule is large compared to the solvent molecules in which it is dissolved, the diffusion coefficient of the solute is

$$(2.11) \qquad\qquad D = \frac{k_B T}{6\pi\eta r},$$

where η is the coefficient of viscosity for the solute, r is the radius of the solute molecule, k_B is Boltzmann's constant, and T is the temperature in degrees Kelvin. Equation (2.11) implies that molecules diffuse faster when the solvent temperature is high rather than low, and large molecules diffuse slower than small molecules. You can check the validity of this first statement at home by adding a small droplet of milk or cream into both a cup of cold and hot coffee and then checking to see if there is a difference in the rate of spread of the droplet between the two cups. To check the validity of the second statement, see Exercise 2.4.

Fick's law shows up in other contexts, and is known as *Newton's law of cooling* if u is heat, while it is known as *Ohm's law* if u is voltage and $\mathbf{J}$ is current. In the last case, the units of D are different, to account for the conversion of voltage to current, but the interpretation of the relationship remains the same: flux of heat is down the temperature gradient, and flux of (positive) ions is down the gradient of a voltage potential.

Darcy's law is of exactly the same form as Fick's law, but it describes the flow velocity of a fluid through a porous medium (think of water moving through a sandstone

Table 2.1. Molecular weight and diffusion coefficients of some biochemical substances in dilute aqueous solution.

Substance	Molecular Weight	$D(cm^2/s)$
hydrogen	1	4.5×10^{-5}
oxygen	32	2.1×10^{-5}
carbon dioxide	48	1.92×10^{-5}
glucose	192	6.60×10^{-6}
insulin	5,734	2.10×10^{-6}
Cytochrome c	13,370	1.14×10^{-6}
Myoglobin	16,900	5.1×10^{-7}
Serum albumin	66,500	6.03×10^{-7}
hemoglobin	64,500	6.9×10^{-7}
Catalase	247,500	4.1×10^{-7}
Urease	482,700	3.46×10^{-7}
Fibrinogen	330,000	1.97×10^{-7}
Myosin	524,800	1.05×10^{-7}
Tobacco mosaic virus	40,590,000	5.3×10^{-8}

aquifer). It is typically expressed as

$$(2.12) \qquad q = -\frac{k}{\eta}\nabla p,$$

where q is the fluid flux (with units of velocity), p is the pressure, η is the fluid viscosity, and k is the permeability of the medium. Darcy's law gives quantitative expression to the fact that flow in a porous medium is down its pressure gradient.

Taxis. It is often the case that objects respond to the gradient of some other quantity, say ψ, so that

$$(2.13) \qquad \mathbf{J} = \chi u \nabla \psi.$$

When ψ is a chemical concentration and u is cellular concentration, this is called *chemotaxis*, and can either be up the gradient if $\chi > 0$ (a chemoattractant) or down the gradient if $\chi < 0$ (a chemorepellant). When ψ is the voltage potential and u is the concentration of charged ions, this describes the response of ions to an electric field.

Since ions both diffuse and move along voltage potential gradients, their movement is described by a combination of diffusion and taxis terms,

$$(2.14) \qquad \mathbf{J} = -D(\nabla u + \frac{zF}{RT}u\nabla\psi),$$

which is called the *Poisson–Nernst law*. Here, z is the (integer) charge of the ion, F is Faraday's constant, $R = k_B N_A$ is the universal gas constant, and N_A is Avogadro's number.

Other kinds of taxis include aerotaxis (stimulation by oxygen), barotaxis (by pressure), gravitaxis or geotaxis (by gravity), hydrotaxis (by moisture), magnetotaxis (by a magnetic field), phototaxis (by light), and thermotaxis (by changes in temperature).

Momentum Flux. According to Newton's second law, the rate of change of momentum (which, recall, is mass times velocity) of an object is equal to the net force on the object. Consequently, to develop a theory of motion of material objects it is necessary to understand conservation of momentum, and to do this, one must know about momentum flux.

Suppose some material, such as a fluid, is moving with vector velocity field $\mathbf{v}(x, t)$. If its local density is ρ, then the flux of material is given by $\rho\mathbf{v}(x, t)$ which is also its local momentum density. The total material inside some region of space Ω is the integral $\int_\Omega \rho dV$ and the total momentum inside that region of space is $\int_\Omega \rho\mathbf{v}dV$. Since flux of any quantity is that quantity times the velocity with which it is moving, the flux of momentum is the outer product

$$(2.15) \qquad \mathbf{J} = \rho\mathbf{v}\mathbf{v}^T,$$

a tensor quantity.

If there are no sources or sinks of material, then conservation of mass (equation (2.4)) implies that

$$(2.16) \qquad \frac{\partial\rho}{\partial t} = -\nabla \cdot (\rho\mathbf{v}),$$

and conservation of momentum (i.e., Newton's law) implies that

$$(2.17) \qquad \frac{\partial}{\partial t}(\rho\mathbf{v}) = -\nabla \cdot (\rho\mathbf{v}\mathbf{v}^T) + F,$$

where F are local forces, i.e., rates of production or destruction of momentum. While it is beyond the scope of this text to give further discussion of the nature of F, suffice it to say that this is the beginning of the derivation of the famous *Navier–Stokes equation*.

Exercises

2.1. This exercise is to illustrate the usefulness/validity of approximating concentration as a continuously varying real number.[2] The potassium concentration of a mammalian heart cell is about 100mM, and the intracellular volume is on the order of $10^4 \mu m^3$. Suppose a single molecule of potassium escapes from the cell. What is the resulting fractional change in the potassium concentration?

2.2. A stream that is about 10 ft. wide and 2 ft. deep has a constant flow rate of 200 ft^3 per min. What is the average velocity of the water?

2.3. Suppose that a drug in solution with concentration 1mM is delivered intravenously into the vein of a patient at the rate of 200 mL per hour.
    (a) Suppose the IV syringe is a 20 gauge needle (0.603 mm diameter). What is the flow velocity in the syringe?
    (b) What is the concentration flux in the syringe?
    (c) What is the flux of drug molecules in units of number of molecules per unit time?

---

[2]For a refresher on units, see Appendix B.

(d) The syringe is inserted into a vein with diameter 0.5 cm with a blood flow velocity of 20 cm/s. What is the concentration flux of drug in the vein after it has been well mixed?

2.4. A rule of thumb that follows from equation (2.11) is that the diffusion coefficient for a globular molecule satisfies $D \sim M^{-1/3}$ where M is the molecular weight. Determine how well this relationship holds for the substances listed in Table 2.1 by plotting D and M on a log-log plot.

2.5. Molecules such as carbon dioxide (CO_2) and oxygen (O_2) diffuse freely across the membrane wall of cells. Suppose the concentration of a diffusible molecule is c_e on the outside and c_i on the inside of a cell with total surface area A, and that the flux J across the cell wall of thickness L is constant. Use Fick's law to find the total molecular flux out of the cell in terms of c_e, c_i, L and A, in units of number of molecules per unit time.

2.6. Many bacteria such as *e. coli* and *salmonella* have flagellar motors with long hollow filaments through which they secrete various molecules. Molecules are inserted into the basal end of the flagellum by a proton-driven pump and then they diffuse by Fickian diffusion through the filament until they reach the distal end of the filament. Suppose that $u(x, t)$ represents the density of secreted molecules along the filament, with units of number of molecules per unit length, and that the maximum possible value of u is $1/l$, where l is the length of a single secreted molecule when it is in the flagellum. The rate at which the proton-driven pump is able to insert molecules is given by the condition

$$J = -Du_x(0, t) = k_{on}(1 - lu(0, t)).$$

Suppose the flux of molecules in a flagellum is a constant independent of x and t, and that the concentration of molecules at the distal end $u(L, t)$ is zero.
(a) Find an expression in terms of the parameters of the problem for the flux of molecules as a function of filament length L.
(b) Assuming parameter values for diffusion coefficient $D = 5 \times 10^{-9}$ cm² s⁻¹, secreted molecule length $l = 75$nm, and $k_{on} = 200$/min [61], how many molecules are secreted per minute when the flagellar length is $L = 1\mu m$?

2.7. Suppose a large number of proteins are each attached by an extensible tether (i.e., a spring) to a fixed position. Let $u(x, t)$ denote the density of proteins whose tether length is x, and suppose that a particle at tether length x moves with velocity $\frac{dx}{dt}$ where $\mu \frac{dx}{dt} = -kx$, where k is the spring constant, and μ is the drag coefficient for the particle. What is the density flux?

2.8. Ions (like calcium Ca^{++}, sodium Na^+, and potassium K^+) move across cell membranes through small ion-selective pores called ion channels, at a rate governed by the Poisson–Nernst equation (2.14). Suppose that the voltage potential on the inside of a cell is V_i and the voltage potential on the outside of the cell is V_e, so that the voltage difference across the cell wall is $V = V_i - V_e$. Suppose also that the voltage gradient across the cell wall is constant, and that the cell wall thickness is L. Finally, suppose that the external and internal ion concentrations are C_e and C_i, respectively. Find an expression for the flux of ions through the channel in terms of V, C_e and C_i.

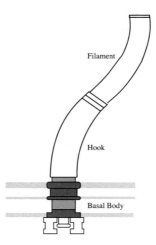

Figure 2.1. Diagram of a rotary flagellar motor, consisting of three basic parts, the basal body spanning the cell inner and outer membrane, which contains the secretion machinery and the rotary motor, the hook which is a flexible "U-joint" approximately 55 nm long, connecting to the filament which can be the order of 10 μm long.

2.9. Suppose that $u(a, t)$ represents the density of individuals whose age is a. Using that age and time change at the same rate (i.e., $\frac{da}{dt} = 1$), find an expression for the flux of this density through age.

2.10. A simple theory for traffic is that the speed of automobiles on a single lane highway is a decreasing function of the vehicle density. Suppose the velocity v is related to the density u by

$$v = v_{max}(1 - \frac{u}{u_{max}}).$$

(a) What is the partial differential equation that describes the evolution of traffic density?

(b) Find a change of variables that converts this equation into the dimensionless, parameter-free, Burgers' equation

$$\frac{\partial U}{\partial \tau} + U \frac{\partial U}{\partial \xi} = 0.$$

2.11. A one-dimensional fluid material (or a fluid whose velocity depends on only the single spatial variable x) has velocity $u(x, t)$ and density $\rho(x, t)$.

(a) Use the conservation law for amount of material (i.e., density) to derive a partial differential equation describing the evolution of ρ.

(b) Suppose that momentum is neither created nor destroyed (i.e., there are no external or internal forces on the fluid). Use the conservation law for momentum to derive a partial differential equation describing the evolution of $u(x, t)$. Use the conservation equation for ρ to eliminate ρ and find an equation for u independent of ρ.

Chapter 3

The Diffusion Equation— Derivations

We start our exploration of partial differential equations with the *diffusion equation*. The diffusion equation results from the conservation equation (2.4) for some species with concentration u when we assume that Fick's law holds, and there is no production or destruction, so that

$$(3.1) \qquad \frac{\partial u}{\partial t} = \nabla \cdot (D\nabla u),$$

or, in one spatial dimension

$$(3.2) \qquad \frac{\partial u}{\partial t} = D\frac{\partial^2 u}{\partial x^2},$$

provided D is homogeneous in space. In this chapter, we give three different derivations, and corresponding interpretations, of this equation.

3.1. Discrete Boxes

Suppose there are a number of boxes connected side-by-side along a one-dimensional line, with concentration of some chemical species u_j in box j, $-\infty < j < \infty$. Now suppose that the chemical leaves box j at rate 2λ, so that the concentration in box j is governed by

$$(3.3) \qquad \frac{du_j}{dt} = -2\lambda u_j,$$

provided there is no inflow. This is exactly the decay process described in Section 1.3.1. However, here we assume that the particles that flow out of box j are evenly split to go into the neighboring boxes $j - 1$ and $j + 1$. Consequently, half of the particles that leave boxes $j - 1$ and $j + 1$ enter box j, so that

$$(3.4) \qquad \frac{du_j}{dt} = \lambda u_{j-1} - 2\lambda u_j + \lambda u_{j+1}.$$

It is a straightforward matter to simulate this system of ordinary differential equations. The Matlab file to do so is titled diffusion_via_MOL.m, and you are encouraged to run this code to see if what happens matches with your intuition.

Now suppose that u_j is a sample of a smooth function $u(x,t)$ at points $x = j\Delta x$, i.e., $u_j = u(j\Delta x, t)$. Using Taylor's theorem,

$$
\begin{aligned}
u_{j\pm 1} &\equiv u(x_j \pm \Delta x, t) \\
&= u(x_j, t) \pm \Delta x \frac{\partial}{\partial x} u(x_j, t) + \frac{1}{2}\Delta x^2 \frac{\partial^2}{\partial x^2} u(x_j, t) \\
&\pm \frac{1}{6}\Delta x^3 \frac{\partial^3}{\partial x^3} u(x_j, t) + O(\Delta x^4).
\end{aligned}
$$

(3.5)

Substituting this Taylor series into (3.4), It follows that

(3.6)
$$
\frac{\partial u}{\partial t} = \lambda \Delta x^2 \frac{\partial^2 u}{\partial x^2} + O(\Delta x^4),
$$

which, keeping only the largest terms in Δx, is the diffusion equation with diffusion constant $D = \lambda \Delta x^2$.

3.2. A Random Walk

Consider the problem where we take a number of random steps at discrete times, and for each step we make a decision to take a step of length $m\Delta x$ where $m = -1, 0$, or 1, with probability α, $1 - 2\alpha$, and α, respectively. Let x_n be the position after n steps, $x_n = \Delta x \sum_{j=1}^{n} m_j$.

The first thing to do here is to simulate this process. This is easy to do, and the Matlab code for this is entitled discrete_random_walk.m. (Or, with a group of friends or classmates, perform this experiment for yourselves, taking steps on a sidewalk to the left when a coin flip gives heads and a step to the right when a coin flip gives tails.) Examples of sample paths for this process are shown in Figure 3.1(a) and the mean squared displacement $\langle x_n^2 \rangle$, defined as $\langle x_n^2 \rangle = \frac{1}{N} \sum_{N \; trials} x_n^2$, as a function of time step n, averaged over $N = 1000$ particle trajectories, is shown in Figure 3.1(b).

Let's now calculate the probability that x_n has the value $k\Delta x$, denoted $p_{k,n} = P(x_n = k\Delta x)$,

(3.7)
$$
p_{k,n} = \alpha p_{k-1,n-1} + (1 - 2\alpha) p_{k,n-1} + \alpha p_{k+1,n-1}.
$$

In words, the probability that x_n is $k\Delta x$ is the sum of three terms, α times the probability that x_{n-1} is $(k-1)\Delta x$, α times the probability that x_{n-1} is $(k+1)\Delta x$, and $1 - 2\alpha$ times the probability that x_{n-1} is $k\Delta x$. Now, suppose that $p_{k,n} = P(x_n = k\Delta x)$ is the sampling of a smooth function $p(x,t)$, where $p_{k,n} = P(x_n = k\Delta x) = p(k\Delta x, n\Delta t)$. Again, using Taylor series, it follows that, to leading order in Δt and Δx (i.e., keeping only the largest terms in Δt and Δx),

(3.8)
$$
\frac{\partial p}{\partial t} = \alpha \frac{\Delta x^2}{\Delta t} \frac{\partial^2 p}{\partial x^2},
$$

which is, once again, the diffusion equation, with diffusion coefficient $D = \alpha \frac{\Delta x^2}{\Delta t}$. This is the same diffusion coefficient as above if we make the identification $\lambda = \frac{\alpha}{\Delta t}$.

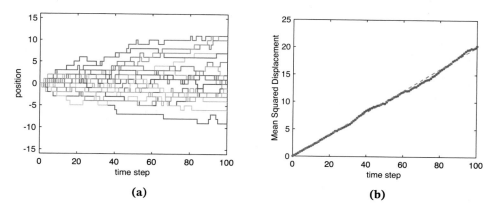

Figure 3.1. (a) Twenty examples of sample paths for 100 steps of a discrete random walk for which $\alpha = 0.1$. (b) Mean squared displacement as a function of time step n for 1000 trajectories, with the line $2\alpha n$ shown dashed.

The variables m and x_n are *random variables*. Clearly, since m can take the three values -1, 0, and 1, with probability α, $1 - 2\alpha$, and α, respectively, the expected value of m is

$$(3.9) \qquad E(m) = -1 \cdot \alpha + 0 \cdot (1 - 2\alpha) + 1 \cdot \alpha = 0.$$

Furthermore, the expected value of x_n is

$$(3.10) \qquad E(x_n) = E(\sum_{i=1}^{n} \Delta x m_i) = \Delta x \sum_{i=1}^{n} E(m_i) = 0.$$

The variance of m is

$$(3.11) \qquad \text{var}(m) = E(m^2) = (-1)^2 \alpha + 0^2(1 - 2\alpha) + (1)^2 \alpha = 2\alpha.$$

The variance of x_n is a little more complicated to calculate. It is

$$(3.12) \qquad \text{var}(x_n) = E(x_n^2) = E((\sum_{i=1}^{n} \Delta x m_i)^2) = \Delta x^2 \sum_{i=1}^{n} \sum_{j=1}^{n} E(m_i m_j).$$

Now, we need to calculate $E(m_i m_j)$ for $i \neq j$. Since there are three values that m_i and m_j can each take on, there are nine ways that $m_i m_j$ can be arranged, but that ends up with three different possible values, namely 1, 0, and -1. It is 1 if m_i and m_j are the same and nonzero, with probability $2\alpha^2$, and similarly it is -1 if m_i and m_j are different and nonzero, also with probability $2\alpha^2$. It is zero if either of m_i or m_j are zero. Consequently,

$$(3.13) \qquad E(m_i m_j) = -1 \cdot 2\alpha^2 + 0 \cdot (1 - 4\alpha^2) + 1 \cdot 2\alpha^2 = 0.$$

It follows directly that

$$(3.14) \qquad \text{var}(x_n) = \Delta x^2 \sum_{i=1}^{n} E(m_i^2) = 2\alpha n \Delta x^2.$$

It is interesting to compare the statistics of the random variable x_n with those of the probability density function described by the diffusion equation (3.8). Suppose x is a random variable whose probability density is given by $p(x, t)$ satisfying the diffusion equation (3.2). For $p(x, t)$ to be a probability density means that at time t, the probability of finding the random variable in the interval between x and $x + dx$ is $p(x, t)dx$. Consequently, since at any time t, the random variable x resides somewhere on the real line, $-\infty < x < \infty$,

$$(3.15) \qquad \int_{-\infty}^{\infty} p(x, t)dx = 1.$$

This is actually a consequence of the diffusion equation, since, if we integrate both sides of the equation with respect to x, we find

$$(3.16) \qquad \frac{d}{dt} \int_{-\infty}^{\infty} p(x, t)dx = D \int_{-\infty}^{\infty} \frac{\partial^2 p}{\partial x^2} dx = D \frac{\partial p}{\partial x}\Big|_{-\infty}^{\infty} = 0$$

(here we assume that $\frac{\partial}{\partial x} p(x, t)$ decays to zero as $|x| \to 0$) so that $\int_{-\infty}^{\infty} p(x, t)dx$ is constant in time.

Now, let's determine $E(x)$ by multiplying both sides of the diffusion equation (3.2) by x and integrating, to find

$$\frac{d}{dt} E(x) = \frac{d}{dt} \int_{-\infty}^{\infty} xp(x, t)dx = D \int_{-\infty}^{\infty} x \frac{\partial^2 p}{\partial x^2} dx$$

(now integrate by parts)

$$= Dx \frac{\partial p}{\partial x}\Big|_{-\infty}^{\infty} - D \int_{-\infty}^{\infty} \frac{\partial p}{\partial x} dx$$

$$(3.17) \qquad = Dp\Big|_{-\infty}^{\infty} = 0,$$

assuming $p(x, t)$ and $\frac{\partial}{\partial x} p(x, t)$ decay at $\pm\infty$ sufficiently fast (which they do). In other words, $E(x)$ is a constant independent of time.

The variance can be calculated in similar fashion

$$\frac{d}{dt} E(x^2) = \frac{d}{dt} \int_{-\infty}^{\infty} x^2 p(x, t)dx = D \int_{-\infty}^{\infty} x^2 \frac{\partial^2 p}{\partial x^2} dx$$

(now integrate by parts)

$$= Dx^2 \frac{\partial p}{\partial x}\Big|_{-\infty}^{\infty} - 2D \int_{-\infty}^{\infty} x \frac{\partial p}{\partial x} dx$$

(now integrate by parts again)

$$(3.18) \qquad = -2Dxp\Big|_{-\infty}^{\infty} + 2D \int_{-\infty}^{\infty} p(x, t)dx = 2D,$$

so that $E(x^2)$ grows linearly in time at rate $2D$. If we start this process with a particle located exactly at the origin $x = 0$, then $E(x) = 0$ for all time and $\text{var}(x) = 2Dt$. $E(x^2)$ is the *mean squared displacement* for this process.

"What might this distribution $p(x, t)$ be?", you ask. We get a clue from the central limit theorem.

Central Limit Theorem. Suppose $m_1, m_2, \ldots,$ are independent, identically distributed, random variables, with mean $\mu = E(m_i)$ and variance $\sigma^2 = \text{var}(m_i)$. Then, for n large, the random variable

(3.19)
$$s_n = \sum_{j=1}^{n} m_j$$

is approximately normally distributed with mean $\mu_n = n\mu$ and variance $\sigma_n^2 = n\sigma^2$.

In other words, the distribution for s_n is well approximated by

(3.20)
$$f_n(s) = \frac{1}{\sqrt{2\pi n}\sigma} \exp\left(-\frac{(s - n\mu)^2}{2n\sigma^2}\right),$$

for n sufficiently large.

For the random walk here for which $x_n = \Delta x s_n$, this means that the probability $P(x_n = k\Delta x)$ is approximately (substitute $\mu = 0$ and $\sigma^2 = 2\alpha \Delta x^2$)

$$P(x_n = k\Delta x) = \frac{1}{\sqrt{4\pi n \alpha}\Delta x} \exp(-\frac{x^2}{4\alpha n \Delta x^2}).$$

Now, if we set $n = \frac{t}{\Delta t}$ and $k\Delta x = x$, this becomes

$$P(x_n = x) = \sqrt{\frac{\Delta t}{4\pi t \alpha \Delta x^2}} \exp(-\frac{x^2 \Delta t}{4\alpha t \Delta x^2}),$$

(3.21)
$$= \frac{1}{\sqrt{4\pi Dt}} \exp(-\frac{x^2}{4Dt}),$$

where $D = \alpha \frac{\Delta x^2}{\Delta t}$. This suggests, but does not prove, that the function

(3.22)
$$p(x, t) = \frac{1}{\sqrt{4\pi Dt}} \exp(-\frac{x^2}{4Dt})$$

(a Gaussian distribution) is a solution of the diffusion equation (3.2).

To see if this is correct, we try a solution of the form

(3.23)
$$p(x, t) = a(t) \exp(b(t)x^2),$$

substituting this into the diffusion equation. After factoring out $\exp(bx^2)$, one is left with the requirement

(3.24)
$$\frac{da}{dt} - 2Dab + (a\frac{db}{dt} - 4Dab^2)x^2 = 0.$$

This is a quadratic polynomial in x which is identically zero if and only if the individual coefficients of powers of x are zero, i.e., if and only if

(3.25)
$$\frac{da}{dt} = 2Dab, \qquad a\frac{db}{dt} = 4Dab^2.$$

Since this is nontrivial only if $a \neq 0$, we find

(3.26)
$$b(t) = -\frac{1}{4Dt}$$

(taking $\frac{1}{b(0)} = 0$), and then we can solve $\frac{da}{dt} = 2Dab$ for a to find

(3.27)
$$\frac{da}{a} = -\frac{1}{2}\frac{dt}{t}$$

or

(3.28)
$$a(t) = \frac{a(0)}{\sqrt{t}}.$$

Note that $a(0)$ should be chosen so that $\int_{-\infty}^{\infty} p(x,t)dx = 1$, in which case this is exactly the same as (3.22).

3.3. The Cable Equation

The third derivation of the diffusion equation comes from a completely different, and perhaps surprising, consideration.

The membrane of a cell is a phospholipid bilayer that acts as a barrier to the movement of ions between the intracellular (inside) and extracellular (outside) spaces. As a barrier, it can store charge much like a capacitor. Further, the movement of ions across a membrane is carefully regulated and they flow through a variety of ion channels. This is true for many electrically active cells, including neurons, cardiac cells, and smooth muscle cells. For example, the neurons studied by Hodgkin and Huxley (see Exercise 1.11) have three different ion species that flow through ion channels. These are depicted in Figure 3.2 as I_{Na}, I_K, and I_l, for sodium, potassium, and leak, respectively. Consequently, the electrical nature of these cells can be described by a capacitor (the membrane) and resistors (the ion channels) in parallel, as shown in the circuit diagram in Figure 3.2. For this diagram there are two transmembrane currents, the ionic currents I_{ion}, and the capacitive current. The fundamental law of capacitance states that the total charge on the capacitor is capacitance times voltage, $Q = C_m V$, where C_m is the membrane capacitance, and $V = V_i - V_e$ is the transmembrane voltage potential, V_i and V_e are the intracellular and extracellular voltage potentials, respectively. This implies that the capacitive current is $I_c = \frac{dQ}{dt} = C_m\frac{dV}{dt}$. Thus, the total transmembrane current, I_t, is the sum of capacitive and ionic currents, i.e.,

(3.29)
$$C_m\frac{dV}{dt} + I_{\text{ion}} = I_t.$$

This model applies only for a small homogeneous patch of membrane. However, nerve cells, or neurons, have axons, that are long slender cylindrical projections that extend away from the neuron's cell body, or soma, and can be quite long (cf. Figure 3.3). For example, the human sciatic nerve originates in the lower back and extends down the back of the thigh and leg, ending in the foot.

To incorporate the effects of an elongated membrane, we view the axon as a long cylindrical piece of membrane surrounding an interior of cytoplasm (called a cable), and suppose that everywhere along its length, the potential depends only on the length variable and not on radial or angular variables. We divide the cable into a number of short pieces of isopotential membrane each of length dx, two sections of which are depicted in Figure 3.4.

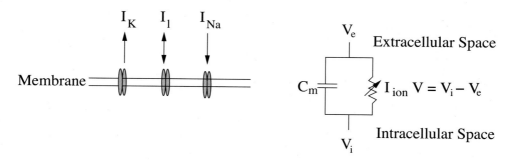

Figure 3.2. Electrical circuit diagram for a cell.

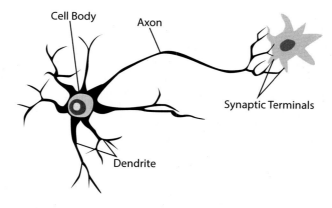

Figure 3.3. Schematic diagram of a nerve cell, with dendritic inputs, the cell body, the axon, ending in synaptic terminals. Image credit: Johanna Bossart

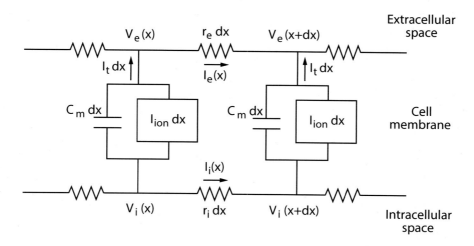

Figure 3.4. Electrical circuit diagram for two cell membrane patches of length dx.

In this era of cell phones and laptop computers, there is a reasonable chance that you have never seen an electrical circuit or felt the need to write a mathematical model of one. However, in the biological realm, there are (at least) two places where knowledge of electrical circuit theory can be beneficial, and these are membrane electrical activity and fluid (blood) circulation. An electrical circuit typically comprises different elements which are connected by wires at nodes. There are two fundamental principals governing the behavior of a circuit. Kirchhoff's current law is a conservation law saying that current is conserved so that the total current into any node is zero, or said another way, the flow in must equal the flow out. The same is true for water flow in a river: at the confluence of two rivers, the flow in (flux) from the upstream rivers must be exactly equal to the flow out downstream. In the circulatory system, at a branching of an artery, the flow out of the branches must exactly equal the flow in from the larger artery. The second of Kirchhoff's laws is that the total change in voltage when going around a closed loop must be zero. This also makes sense when you think of voltage potential as a height or elevation of a trail in the mountains: If you go around a closed loop, the amount of descent must exactly equal the amount of ascent. These two laws, when combined with appropriate constitutive relationships between current and voltage, enable one to write equations governing the currents and voltage in a circuit. In classical circuit theory, there are three useful elements: the resistor, the capacitor, and the inductor. Only the capacitor and resistor are relevant to biological applications. The constitutive current-voltage ($I - V$) relationship for a resistor is the well-known Ohm's law, $RI = V$, where R is resistance, I is current, and V is voltage drop across the resistor, and the current flows in the direction of voltage decrease (down the gradient). For a capacitor the constitutive relationship between voltage and charge is $Q = CV$, where Q is total charge, C is capacitance, and V is voltage drop. Since $I = \frac{dQ}{dt}$, we have $I = C\frac{dV}{dt}$.

For a model of the circulatory system, pressure takes the place of voltage and fluid flow takes the place of current, with resistive vessels (such as capillaries) and compliance vessels (such as arteries and veins) playing the role of resistors and capacitors.

According to Kirchhoff's current law, the sum of all currents into a node must exactly balance the currents out of a node. In any cable section, there are three types of current, namely, transmembrane currents and the intracellular and extracellular axial currents. The axial currents are assumed to be ohmic, i.e., linear functions of the voltage. Hence,

(3.30) $$V_i(x + dx) - V_i(x) = -I_i(x)r_i dx,$$
(3.31) $$V_e(x + dx) - V_e(x) = -I_e(x)r_e dx,$$

where I_i and I_e are the intracellular and extracellular axial currents respectively. The minus sign on the right hand side appears because of the convention that positive current is a flow of positive charges from left to right (i.e., in the direction of increasing x). If $V_i(x + dx) > V_i(x)$, then positive charges flow in the direction of decreasing x, giving a negative current. In the limit $dx \to 0$,

$$(3.32) \qquad I_i = -\frac{1}{r_i}\frac{\partial V_i}{\partial x},$$

$$(3.33) \qquad I_e = -\frac{1}{r_e}\frac{\partial V_e}{\partial x}.$$

The numbers r_i and r_e are the resistances per unit length of the intracellular and extracellular media, respectively. In general,

$$(3.34) \qquad r_i = \frac{R_c}{A_i},$$

where R_c is the *cytoplasmic resistivity*, measured in units of Ohms-length, and A_i is the cross-sectional area of the cylindrical cable. A similar expression holds for the extracellular space.

Next, again from Kirchhoff's laws, any change in extracellular or intracellular axial current must be due to a transmembrane current, and thus

$$(3.35) \qquad I_i(x) - I_i(x + dx) = I_t dx = I_e(x + dx) - I_e(x),$$

where I_t is the total transmembrane current (positive outward) per unit length of membrane. In the limit as $dx \to 0$, this becomes

$$(3.36) \qquad I_t = -\frac{\partial I_i}{\partial x} = \frac{\partial I_e}{\partial x}.$$

In a cable with no additional current sources, the total axial current is $I_{\text{tot}} = I_i + I_e$, so using that $V = V_i - V_e$, we find

$$(3.37) \qquad -I_{\text{tot}} = \frac{r_i + r_e}{r_i r_e}\frac{\partial V_i}{\partial x} - \frac{1}{r_e}\frac{\partial V}{\partial x},$$

from which it follows that

$$(3.38) \qquad \frac{1}{r_i}\frac{\partial V_i}{\partial x} = \frac{1}{r_i + r_e}\frac{\partial V}{\partial x} - \frac{r_e}{r_i + r_e}I_{\text{tot}}.$$

On substituting (3.38) into (3.36), we obtain

$$(3.39) \qquad I_t = \frac{\partial}{\partial x}\left(\frac{1}{r_i + r_e}\frac{\partial V}{\partial x}\right),$$

where we have used (3.32) and the fact that I_{tot} is constant. Finally, recall that the transmembrane current I_t is a sum of the capacitive and ionic currents, and thus

$$(3.40) \qquad I_t = p\left(C_m\frac{\partial V}{\partial t} + I_{\text{ion}}\right) = \frac{\partial}{\partial x}\left(\frac{1}{r_i + r_e}\frac{\partial V}{\partial x}\right),$$

where p is the perimeter of the axon and C_m is the membrane capacitance per unit area. Equation (3.40) is usually referred to as the *cable equation*. Note that C_m has units of capacitance per unit area of membrane, and I_{ion} has units of current per unit area of membrane. If a current I_{applied}, with units of current per unit area, is applied across the membrane (as before, taken positive in the outward direction), then the cable equation becomes

$$(3.41) \qquad p\left(C_m\frac{\partial V}{\partial t}\right) = \frac{\partial}{\partial x}\left(\frac{1}{r_i + r_e}\frac{\partial V}{\partial x}\right) - pI_{\text{ion}} - pI_{\text{applied}}.$$

Here we have written the equation in the form of equation (2.4) in order to point out that the flux of current is

(3.42)
$$\mathbf{J} = -\frac{1}{r_i + r_e}\frac{\partial V}{\partial x},$$

which is known as *Ohm's law*, relating current flux to the voltage gradient. This has the same form as Fick's law, which relates the flux of a chemical species to its concentration gradient. When pI_{ion} and pI_{applied} are zero, equation (3.41) reduces to the diffusion equation, with diffusion coefficient

(3.43)
$$D = \frac{1}{pC_m(r_e + r_i)},$$

which (you, the reader should check this) has units of (length)^2 per unit time, as required. Of course, real nerve axons have ionic currents, the nature of which are described in Chapter 7.

Table 3.1. Physical parameters for axons

C_m	membrane capacitance	$1\mu F\ cm^{-2}$
R_c	cytoplasmic resistivity	$100\Omega\ cm$

Table 3.2. Diameters of nerve axons

sciatic nerve	16-20 mm
squid giant axon	1 mm
human brain	0.16-9 μm

Exercises

3.1. Using that $\int_{-\infty}^{\infty} \exp(-x^2)dx = \sqrt{\pi}$, verify that $\int_{-\infty}^{\infty} p(x,t)dx = 1$ for all time, where $p(x,t)$ is given by equation (3.22).

3.2. Use the code discrete_random_walk.m to numerically simulate a discrete random walk with $\alpha = 0.1, 0.2, 0.3$. Estimate the variance for this process from the data generated as a function of time and compare this estimate with the theoretically derived variance for this process.

3.3. Suppose a particle moves to the right with probability α, to the left with probability β, and stays put with probability $1-\alpha-\beta$. Following the above arguments, formulate this as a discrete random walk process and determine the following.
   (a) The limiting partial differential equation.
   (b) The mean and the variance for the process using the limiting partial differential equation.

(c) Modify the code discrete_random_walk.m to numerically simulate this random walk with $\alpha = 0.1$, $\beta = 0.2$. Estimate the mean and variance for this process as a function of time and compare these with the mean and the variance derived directly from the partial differential equation.

(d) Write the limiting differential equation in conservation form, and identify the flux terms.

3.4. Suppose a random walker moves a distance Δx at times determined by a Poisson process with rate α. Consequently the probability of being at position j at time t is governed by the equation (1.86). Let $p_j(t) = p(j\Delta x, t)$, use Taylor's theorem, and retain only terms of order $O(\Delta x^2)$ to derive a partial differential equation governing the evolution of $p(x, t)$. What is the diffusion coefficient for this process?

3.5. Suppose that particles in discrete boxes of size Δx leave box j to box $j \pm 1$ at the rate $\frac{\lambda_j}{\Delta x^2}$, where $\lambda_j = \lambda(j\Delta x)$ for some smooth function $\lambda(x)$. Derive the limiting diffusion equation.

3.6. Suppose that particles in discrete boxes of size Δx leave box j to box $j \pm 1$ at the rate $\frac{\lambda_{j\pm1}}{\Delta x^2}$, where $\lambda_j = \lambda(j\Delta x)$ for some smooth function $\lambda(x)$. Derive the limiting diffusion equation, written in conservation form. Identify the different flux terms.

3.7. Suppose that particles in discrete boxes of size Δx leave box j to box $j \pm 1$ at the rate $\frac{\lambda_{j\pm\frac{1}{2}}}{\Delta x^2}$, where $\lambda_j = \lambda(j\Delta x)$ for some smooth function $\lambda(x)$. Derive the limiting diffusion equation, written in conservation form. Identify the different flux terms.

3.8. Suppose that particles in discrete boxes of size Δx leave the box at a rate that is dependent on the particle density of the adjacent boxes, that is, the rate of leaving box j to box $j \pm 1$ is $\frac{\lambda(u_{j\pm1})}{\Delta x^2}$, where u_j is the particle density of the jth box. Derive the limiting diffusion equation. Identify the flux terms.

3.9. A population of cells of two types, say type A and type B, is required to have a fixed total population size N. With each time step of time Δt exactly one cell reproduces and one cell dies, so that the total population size stays the same. A population is said to be fixed (reached fixation) when one of the types has become extinct leaving only the other type in the entire population. (This random walk is known in population genetics as the *Moran process.*) Suppose at some time there are i cells of type A, and $j = N - i$ cells of type B. Then, in the next time step, the probability of going from state i to $i - 1$ is $k_{i-1,i} = \frac{ij}{N^2}$, because one of the i cells will die and one of the j cells will reproduce. For the similar reason, the probability of going from state i to $i + 1$ is $k_{i+1,i} = \frac{ij}{N^2}$. Necessarily, the probability of staying the same is $k_{i,i} = 1 - 2\frac{ij}{N^2}$.

(a) Simulate the process and estimate the time to fixation as a function of N, starting with an equal number of cells of the two types. Estimate the expected fixation time $E(T)$ as a function of N. *Remark.* The Matlab code discrete_random_walk.m can serve as a template to get started for this problem.

(b) Let $p_i(t)$ be the probability that there are i type A cells at time t. Write an equation for $p_i(t + \Delta t)$ in terms of $p_i(t)$.

(c) Suppose N is large. Let $\Delta x = \frac{1}{N}$ and let $p_i(t) = u(x, t)$ with $x = \frac{i}{N}$. Supposing Δt and Δx are both small, find a partial differential equation for $u(x, t)$ of the form $\frac{\partial u}{\partial t} = \frac{\partial^2}{\partial x^2}(D(x)u)$. What is $D(x)$?

3.10. Determine the voltage diffusion coefficient for squid giant axons and for sciatic nerves. Assume $r_e = 0$.

Chapter 4

Realizations
of a Diffusion Process

What we have seen so far is that the diffusion equation can be viewed as describing the movement of a large number of molecules, or the probability of finding a single particle at a particular position and time. But, of course, these are the same. Because, if we follow a large number of molecules once, or follow a single particle many times (many repeated experiments), the answer will be the same, as long as the many particles are noninteracting, i.e., independent. This is a reasonable assumption if the particles are dilute, but if they are not dilute, then there are likely to be interactions so that the diffusion equation is no longer valid. But this is a topic for another time and place.

The question to be addressed here is how to follow (i.e., simulate) a diffusion process. The answer to this question depends on the context.

4.1. Following Individual Particles

It may be that one is interested in following a single diffusing object. To do this, we make use of a fact about Brownian motion (which is the name for this process). Suppose one were able to precisely follow a particle and collect large amounts of data on its change of position, denoted dx, in a fixed time increment dt. Recall from above that the solution of the diffusion equation has the feature that the expected value of position of a particle is unchanging in time while the variance of position grows linearly in time with rate $2D$. What this means for a fixed (small) time increment dt is that dx is random but distributed according to

(4.1) $$dx = \sqrt{2Ddt}\mathcal{N}(0,1).$$

In other words, dx is a continuous random variable that is normally distributed with mean zero and variance $2Ddt$. The equation (4.1) is is called a *stochastic differential equation* as it specifies the change of position of the particle as a stochastic process, not as a deterministic process.

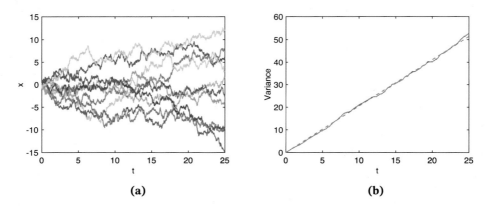

Figure 4.1. (a) Ten examples of sample paths for Brownian motion. (b) Variance for 1000 particles as a function of time compared with the straight line $\sigma^2 = 2Dt$ (dashed), both for $D = 1$.

This, then, gives a formula for how to simulate a diffusion process. Specifically, let the position of the particle after n time steps be denoted by x_n. Then, x_n is updated by the formula

$$(4.2) \qquad x_{n+1} = x_n + dx_n,$$

where dx_n is a random number chosen according to (4.1). The Matlab code that carries this out is entitled single_particle_diffusion.m, and ten examples of sample paths for a diffusing particle are shown in Figure 4.1.

Question: How fast does a molecule of oxygen move, on average?
The answer is found by understanding the Boltzman equation

$$(4.3) \qquad \frac{1}{2}mv^2 = k_B T,$$

which, in words, says that the kinetic energy of a particle in an ideal gas is $k_B T$. Now, you can look up in any book on chemical physics (or Wikipedia) that oxygen (O_2) has a molecular weight of 32 g/mole or about 5.3×10^{-23} g/molecule and diffusion coefficient in air of 0.18 cm^2/s (roughly 1000 times larger than in water). It follows that, at room temperature (about 300 degrees Kelvin = 27 degrees centigrade), the velocity is

$$(4.4) \qquad v = \sqrt{\frac{2k_B T}{m}} \approx 4 \times 10^4 \text{cm/s.}$$

Now, since $v = \frac{dx}{dt}$ and $D = \frac{dx^2}{2dt}$,

$$(4.5) \qquad dx = \frac{2D}{v} = 1 \times 10^{-5}\text{cm}, \qquad dt = \frac{dx}{v} = 2.5 \times 10^{-10}\text{s.}$$

In other words, on average, an oxygen molecule in air has a velocity of 40 m/s, but runs into something else (like another molecule) and changes direction every 2.5×10^{-10} seconds, and between collisions moves about 10^{-5}cm.

4.2. Other Features of Brownian Particle Motion

Now that we know a little bit about how a diffusing particle moves, we can ask several other interesting questions. The first is to determine escape times. The question is as follows: How long, on average, does it take for a diffusing particle to escape from some region? In biological terms, how long does it take, on average, for a molecule that is made in the nucleus of a cell to diffuse to the boundary of the cell? Or, how long does it take a signaling molecule that is produced at the boundary of a cell to diffuse to the nucleus? A second question is, if there are two different places that a particle can escape from a region, what are the probabilities of escape through each exit? (This is called the *splitting probability*.)

Let's begin by simulating this. First, for the exit time problem, simulate (using Matlab code first_exit_times.m) the motion of a Brownian particle on a one-dimensional line that starts at some position $0 < x < L$, and let the simulation run until the particle hits $x = L$, with the additional restriction that the particle reflects off the boundary at $x = 0$, i.e., the particle position is never allowed to be negative. For obvious reasons, the boundary at $x = 0$ is called a *reflecting boundary* and the boundary at $x = L$ is called an *absorbing boundary*.

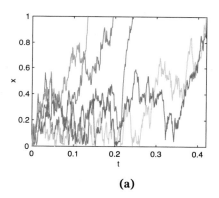
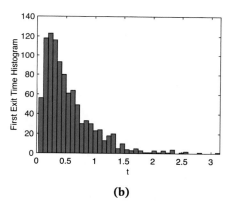

(a) (b)

Figure 4.2. (a) Five sample paths of particles starting at $x = 0$ and terminating at the first arrival at $x = 1$. (b) Histogram of first exit times for 1,000 particles all starting from $x = 0$, both with $D = 1$.

An example of a simulation result is shown in Figure 4.2, where several sample particle trajectories (a) and a histogram of first exit times for a simulation with 1,000 particles (b) are shown, with $D = 1$ and $L = 1$. In Figure 4.3 are shown the simulated mean first exit times plotted as a function of initial position.

To simulate the splitting probability, start the particle at some position between $x = 0$ and $x = L$ and allow the simulation to run until either $x \geq L$ or $x \leq 0$ and record the fraction of time the simulation terminates with $x \geq L$, call this π_L. A plot of the result from a simulation using Matlab code splitting_probability.m is shown in Figure 4.4.

The data from simulation shown in Figure 4.4 are strongly suggestive of a straight line with slope $\frac{1}{L}$. To see that this is indeed the case, we argue as follows: Suppose that a

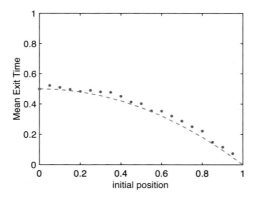

Figure 4.3. Simulated mean first exit times plotted as a function of starting position on an interval of length $L = 1$ with $D = 1$ compared with the first exit time formula in equation (4.13) (dashed line).

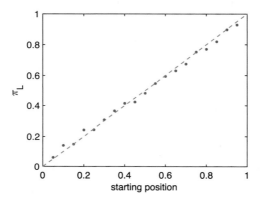

Figure 4.4. Simulated splitting probability π_L plotted as a function of starting position on an interval of length $L = 1$, with $D = 1$, compared with the splitting probability formula in equation (4.8) (dashed line).

particle diffuses on a one dimensional line of length L. Let $\pi_L(x)$ denote the probability that the particle starting at point x will hit point $x = L$ before it hits the point $x = 0$, and (vice versa) let $\pi_0(x)$ denote the probability that the particle starting at point x will hit point $x = 0$ before it hits the point $x = L$. Obviously, $\pi_0(x) + \pi_L(x) = 1$ for all starting positions x, and $\pi_L(0) = 0$ and $\pi_L(L) = 1$, since if the particle starts at $x = 0$ it will certainly exit there, while if it starts at $x = L$ it will exit there.

To derive the relevant equation, consider a line that is discretized into boxes of size Δx. For unbiased diffusion, the probability of moving left or right is equal and so

$$(4.6) \qquad \pi_L(x) = \frac{1}{2}\pi_L(x + \Delta x) + \frac{1}{2}\pi_L(x - \Delta x).$$

In words, the probability of escaping at $x = L$ from x is half the probability of escaping from $x + \Delta x$ plus half the probability of escaping from $x - \Delta x$ since, starting at position x, after one step the particle is at position $x + \Delta x$ with probability $\frac{1}{2}$ and at position

$x - \Delta x$ with probability $\frac{1}{2}$. Now, we make our usual assumption that $\pi_L(x)$ is a smooth function with a Taylor series expansion, and find that equation (4.6) approaches

$$(4.7) \qquad \frac{d^2 \pi_L}{dx^2} = 0$$

in the limit $\Delta x \to 0$.

The solution of this problem is easy to find and as we anticipated is

$$(4.8) \qquad \pi_L(x) = \frac{x}{L}.$$

Now, let $T(x)$ denote the expected time to hit either L or $-L$ starting from position x. Clearly $T(-L) = T(L) = 0$. Also, since steps to the left or right are with equal probability,

$$(4.9) \qquad T(x) = \frac{1}{2}T(x + \Delta x) + \frac{1}{2}T(x - \Delta x) + \Delta t,$$

where Δt is the time, on average, it takes to move distance Δx. Again, we use Taylor series for $T(x)$ and find, to leading order in Δx and Δt,

$$(4.10) \qquad \frac{\Delta x^2}{2}\frac{d^2 T}{dx^2} = -\Delta t.$$

However, we know that for a diffusion process, the mean of Δx^2 is $2D\Delta t$, so that

$$(4.11) \qquad D\frac{d^2 T}{dx^2} = -1.$$

To find the first exit time at $x = L$ with reflection at $x = 0$, notice that $T(x)$ above is an even function of x around $x = 0$. This implies that $T'(0) = 0$ is the reflecting boundary condition at $x = 0$.

We do not prove the statement here, but it can be shown that for any region Ω with boundary $\partial\Omega$, where the boundary is divided into two subboundaries $\partial\Omega_a$ and $\partial\Omega_r$ which are absorbing and reflecting, respectively, the expected escape time $T(x)$ for a particle starting at position x satisfies the boundary value problem

$$(4.12) \qquad D\nabla^2 T = -1, x \in \Omega, \qquad T\big|_{\partial\Omega_a} = 0, \qquad \mathbf{n} \cdot \nabla T\big|_{\partial\Omega_r} = 0.$$

The solution of this problem is interestingly different for different spatial dimensions. For example, in one dimension, suppose the boundary at $x = 0$ is *reflecting* (particles bounce off and cannot escape). Then, we must solve $D\frac{d^2 T}{dx^2} = -1$, subject to boundary conditions $T'(0) = 0$, $T(L) = 0$. The solution is

$$(4.13) \qquad T(x) = \frac{L^2}{2D}(1 - \frac{x^2}{L^2}).$$

This curve is shown dashed in Figure 4.3, and the simulated data agree reasonably well with this curve (but see Exercise 4.5).

Compare this to the situation for escape from a circle of radius R, for which the escape time T satisfies

$$(4.14) \qquad \frac{D}{r}\frac{d}{dr}(r\frac{dT}{dr}) = -1,$$

with $T(R) = 0$. The solution of this problem is

(4.15)
$$T(r) = \frac{R^2}{4D}(1 - \frac{r^2}{R^2}).$$

For escape from a sphere of radius R, T satisfies

(4.16)
$$\frac{D}{r^2}\frac{d}{dr}(r^2\frac{dT}{dr}) = -1,$$

with $T(R) = 0$. The solution is

(4.17)
$$T(r) = \frac{R^2}{6D}(1 - \frac{r^2}{R^2}).$$

The obvious conclusion of this is that escape from the interior of a circle (or a sphere) is two times (or three times) faster than along a line.

4.2.1. Higher Dimensions. The above simulations model the diffusion of a particle in one dimension. However, extensions to two or three dimensional domains are relatively straightforward, since motion in different coordinate directions is independent. So, to simulate a Brownian particle motion in two dimensions, simply update the positions x and y by changes dx and dy, where each of dx, and dy are normally distributed with zero mean and variance $2Ddt$.

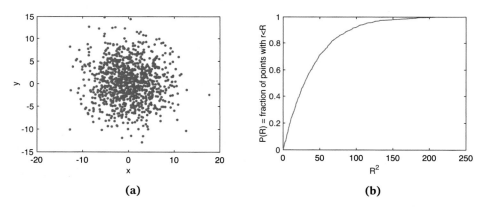

(a)   (b)

Figure 4.5. (a) Location of $N = 1000$ points at $t = 10$ following diffusion from the origin with $D = 1$. (b) Plot of the fraction of points inside a circle of radius R plotted as a function of R^2.

This calculation is carried out by the Matlab code two_d_diffusion.m and the location of 1000 points following ten time units with $D = 1$, each starting at the origin is shown in Figure 4.5(a). A plot of the percentage of these points that are at radius $r < R$, call it $P(R)$, is shown in Figure 4.5(b), plotted as a function of R^2. This curve looks suspiciously like an exponential function of the form $P(R) = 1 - \exp(-\frac{R^2}{\alpha})$, so to see if it is, in Figure 4.6(a) we plot $\ln(1 - P(R))$ as a function of R^2. This is close to the straight line $-\frac{R^2}{40}$ (shown dashed), and gives strong evidence (but does not prove) that $P(R) = 1 - \exp(\frac{-R^2}{4t})$. In Figure 4.6(b) is shown the mean squared displacement as a function of time, which is close to a straight line with slope 4, suggesting that

$E(x^2 + y^2) = 4t$. (Question to think about: How should this answer depend on D when $D \neq 1$? See Exercise 4.9.) A theoretical explanation for why these curves are as they are (and where the number 40 came from) is given in the Chapter 5.

An example of a two dimensional sample path is shown in Figure 4.7(a), and a histogram of exit times for 2,000 sample paths is shown in Figure 4.7(b). These figures were generated using Matlab code two_d_mean_first_exit_time.m.

A practical word of advice (which will be useful for the exercises): Suppose one wishes to simulate Brownian motion on a circular domain with a reflecting boundary condition at the outer radius R. A simple way to do this, if a simulation step ends up outside the circle, is to reflect it back into the circle along the radial, or normal, direction. In math language, suppose $\mathbf{x}$ is the vector position of the particle after a simulation step, outside the circle. To reflect it back into the circle, replace $\mathbf{x}$ by

(4.18)
$$\mathbf{x}\Big(2\min(\frac{R}{|\mathbf{x}|}, 1) - 1\Big).$$

4.3. Following Several Particles

It is possible to follow a small number of particles using the above simulation method. However, it is definitely not possible if the particle numbers are large, say a mole. To follow the diffusion of a medium number (whatever that means) of particles, we adopt the model (3.4) and do a stochastic simulation of it.

The direct stochastic simulation of (3.4) can be done using the Gillespie algorithm. To describe this algorithm, we start with the simple example of exponential decay, modeled by the equation

(4.19)
$$\frac{du}{dt} = -\alpha u.$$

Since we already know how to track the number of particles in a single compartment, we can think about multiple compartments. Suppose there are a total of M particles

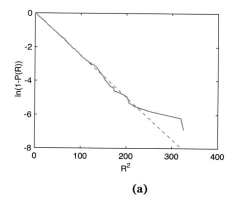

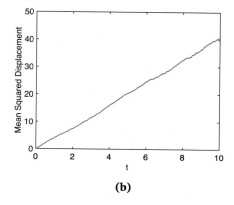

(a) (b)

Figure 4.6. (a) Plot of $\ln(1 - P(R))$ as a function of R^2 (solid) at $t = 10$, and the straight line $-\frac{R^2}{40}$ (dashed line). (b) The mean squared displacement as a function of t for this simulation.

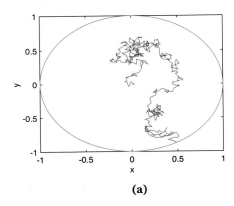
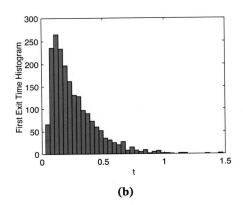

(a)   **(b)**

Figure 4.7. (a) Sample path for a diffusing particle in a circular domain of radius $R = 1$. (b) Histogram of exit times for a circular domain for 2000 particles starting at the center of the circle.

that are distributed among N boxes, arranged in a row. Let u_j, $j = 1, \ldots, N$, represent the integer number of particles in box j. We assume that each particle can leave its box and move to one of its nearest neighbors by an exponential process with rate 2α if it is an interior box, and rate α if it is a boundary box. Consequently, the *rate of reaction*, where by reaction we mean leaving its box, is $r_j = 2\alpha u_j$ for $j = 2, \ldots, N-1$, and $r_j = \alpha u_j$ for $j = 1, N$. Now, pick three uniformly distributed random numbers between 0 and 1; the first, R_1, we use to determine when the next reaction occurs, and the second two, R_2 and R_3, we use to determine which of the possible reactions it is. As described in Chapter 1, the time increment to the nth reaction, δt_n, is taken to be

(4.20)
$$\delta t_n = \frac{-1}{R_\Sigma} \ln R_1,$$

where $R_\Sigma = \sum_{j=1}^{K} r_j$. Then, take j to be the smallest integer for which $R_2 < \rho_j = \frac{1}{R_\Sigma} \sum_{i=1}^{j} r_i$, and if $2 \leq j \leq N - 1$, take the particle in the jth box to move to the right if $R_3 > \frac{1}{2}$ and to the left if $R_3 \leq \frac{1}{2}$. If $j = 1$, the particle moves to the right, and if $j = N$ it moves to the left.

Matlab code to simulate this process is titled discrete_diffusion_via_Gillespie.m. One thing worth noting is that the process becomes less and less noisy, and much slower to simulate, as more particles are included in the system, suggesting that for a sufficiently large number of particles we need not (and should not) use a Gillespie algorithm, but rather a direct simulation of the diffusion equation.

4.4. Effective Diffusion

Diffusion by Brownian motion gives a very good description of the motion of small molecules. However, for many objects, like flying insects or swimming bacteria, motion may look like diffusion, but on closer examination it is not exactly diffusion, and in fact, it may not be obvious how to represent the motion of the object by a partial differential equation. In Chapter 3, we used a discrete random walk as an example of a random process for which a diffusion equation approximation could be derived. However, real life is not always so straightforward. An interesting example of this is the run and tumble motion of swimming bacteria, such as *Salmonella* (*Salmonella enterica*) or *E. coli* (*Escherichia coli*). These bacteria are in one of two states, a running state and a tumbling state. In the running state they swim in some direction with constant velocity v, and in the tumbling state they do not move but they change their orientation by what looks like rotational diffusion (see Figure 4.8). *Question*: Is this overall process a diffusion process, at least approximately, and if so, what is the (effective) diffusion coefficient?

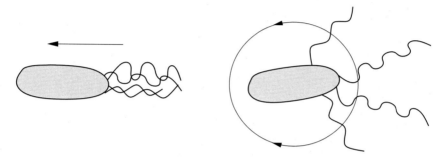

Figure 4.8. Depiction of bacterium in the running state, with flagella rotating as a bundle in the counterclockwise direction (left), and in the tumbling state, with flagella unbundled rotating in the clockwise direction (right).

Let's think about this question with a simpler example. Suppose that a swimming organism on a one dimensional line moves with constant velocity v but randomly switches direction by an exponential process with rate constant k. Is this a diffusion process?

The most direct way to approach this question is by a simulation and to calculate the mean squared displacement as a function of time for the motion. Recall that a characteristic feature of a diffusion process is that its mean squared displacement is a linear function of time. In fact, this is how to identify a diffusion process—if its mean squared displacement is a linear function of time.

How can we simulate this? We start at time $t = 0$ with the swimmer in one of the two states at position $x = 0$, say moving to the right. Pick a time to switch to the leftward moving state that is exponentially distributed, i.e., t_1, where $t_1 = t_0 + \delta t_1$, $\delta t_1 = -\frac{1}{k} \ln R_1$, where R_1 is a uniformly distributed random number, $0 < R_1 < 1$. Increment x by the amount $\delta x_1 = -v \delta t_1$. Then, pick the next exponentially distributed transition time, say $t_2 = t_1 + \delta t_2$ where $\delta t_2 = -\frac{1}{k} \ln R_2$, and R_2 is a uniformly distributed random number, $0 < R_2 < 1$, and increment x by the amount $\delta x_2 = v \delta t_2$, and one full cycle is complete. Repeat this cycle many times for many particles, and plot the mean squared displacement as a function of time for these trajectories. As already stated, if this is a diffusion process, the mean squared displacement will be a linearly increasing function of time, and the slope will be twice the effective diffusion coefficient $2D_{\text{eff}}$.

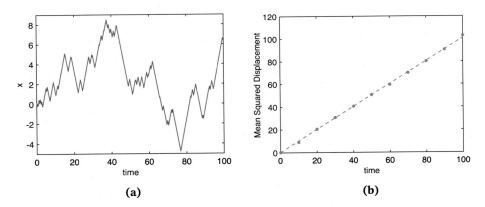

Figure 4.9. (a) Sample path for a particle that moves with constant velocity $v = 1$ and switches direction with rate $k = 1$. (b) Mean squared displacement as a function of time for $N = 1,000$ particles, with line of slope 1 shown dashed.

This algorithm is implemented in the Matlab code one_d_direction_switcher.m, and results of the simulation are shown in Figure 4.9. As hoped, the mean squared displacement is linearly increasing as a function of time, with slope 1.007 for this simulation.

So, what is the effective diffusion coefficient for this process? We know that the diffusion coefficient has units of (length)^2/time, and for this problem there are only two parameters, v with units of velocity = length/time, and the switching rate k with units of 1/time. The only possible combination of these two parameters with units of a diffusion coefficient is $\frac{v^2}{k}$. So, the effective diffusion coefficient for this process must be $D_{\text{eff}} = \alpha \frac{v^2}{k}$, for some scalar α. From our simulation we learned that the slope of the mean squared displacement was $2D_{\text{eff}} \approx 1$ when $v = 1$, $k = 1$, so we conclude that $\alpha = \frac{1}{2}$, i.e., $D_{\text{eff}} = \frac{v^2}{2k}$.

Let's try this again for a slightly more complicated example. Suppose the organism is in one of three states, moving on a one dimensional line to the left with velocity v, moving to the right with velocity v, or paused. It switches out of the paused state into one of the moving states with rate k_{on} and switches into the paused state from the moving state with rate k_{off}. It seems reasonable that this is approximately a diffusion process, but how might we know, and if so, what is the effective diffusion coefficient? The answer to this is again found by determining the mean squared displacement as a function of time.

How can we simulate this process? Start at time $t_0 = 0$ in one of the three states, say the paused state, and pick an exponentially distributed time to switch into the moving state, say t_1, where $t_1 = t_0 + \delta t_1$, $\delta t_1 = -\frac{1}{k_{\text{on}}} \ln R_1$, where R_1 is a uniformly distributed random number, $0 < R_1 < 1$. Then, decide if the moving state is leftward or rightward moving by picking a second uniformly distributed random number R_2, $0 < R_2 < 1$, and setting $\sigma = -1$ if $R_2 < \frac{1}{2}$ and $\sigma = 1$ if $R_2 \geq \frac{1}{2}$. Continuing, determine the next exponentially distributed switching time, say $t_2 = t_1 + \delta t_2$ where $\delta t_2 = -\frac{1}{k_{\text{off}}} \ln R_3$, and

R_3 is a uniformly distributed random number, $0 < R_3 < 1$. Then, move the particle the distance $\delta x = \sigma v \delta t_2$, and one cycle is complete. Repeat this cycle many times for many particles and plot the mean squared displacement as a function of time for these trajectories. If this is a diffusion process, the mean squared displacement will be a linear increasing function of time with slope $2D_{\text{eff}}$.

The Matlab code for this simulation is titled one_d_run_and_pause.m, and results from a simulation are shown in Figure 4.10. For this simulation the parameters were $v = 1$, $k_{\text{on}} = 1$, $k_{\text{off}} = 1$, and the slope of the mean squared displacement using $N = 1000$ particles was 0.992.

Clearly the mean squared displacement is a linearly increasing function of time, so our conjecture that this is a diffusion process is verified. To determine the effective diffusion coefficient, however, is more subtle than the last example. For this problem, there are three parameters, v, k_{on} and k_{off}. Because of our experience with the last problem, we suspect that the effective diffusion coefficient should be proportional to $\frac{v^2}{k_{\text{off}}}$. However, this is clearly not the whole story as a simulation with $v = 1$, $k_{\text{off}} = 1$, $k_{\text{on}} = 2$ gives a slope for the mean squared displacement of 1.333, while a simulation with $v = 1$, $k_{\text{off}} = 2$, $k_{\text{on}} = 1$ gives a slope for the mean squared displacement of 0.333. With $v = 1$, $k_{\text{off}} = 2$, $k_{\text{on}} = 2$ the mean squared displacement has a slope of 0.500. A summary of these simulation results is shown in Table 4.1.

What else might be involved? The fact that the organism spends part of its time paused and part of its time moving should be significant. In fact, on average, it spends $\frac{\frac{1}{k_{\text{on}}}}{\frac{1}{k_{\text{on}}}+\frac{1}{k_{\text{off}}}} = \frac{k_{\text{off}}}{k_{\text{on}}+k_{\text{off}}}$ fraction of time in the paused state and $\frac{k_{\text{on}}}{k_{\text{on}}+k_{\text{off}}}$ fraction of time in the moving state. This suggests that D_{eff} should be proportional to $D_{guess} = \frac{v^2}{k_{\text{off}}}\frac{k_{\text{on}}}{k_{\text{on}}+k_{\text{off}}}$. A simple check reveals that (see Table 4.1) $2D_{guess} = 1$ when $v = 1$, $k_{\text{off}} = 2$, $k_{\text{on}} = 1$, $2D_{guess} = \frac{4}{3}$ when $v = 1$, $k_{\text{off}} = 1$, $k_{\text{on}} = 2$, $2D_{guess} = \frac{1}{3}$ when $v = 1$, $k_{\text{off}} = 2$, $k_{\text{on}} = 1$, and $2D_{guess} = \frac{1}{2}$ when $v = 1$, $k_{\text{off}} = 2$, $k_{\text{on}} = 2$, all of which match the simulation data beautifully. We conclude, based on this simulation evidence, that $D_{\text{eff}} = \frac{v^2}{k_{\text{off}}}\frac{k_{\text{on}}}{k_{\text{on}}+k_{\text{off}}}$ for this process.

Table 4.1. Calculated mean squared displacement (MSD) slope for different parameter values from Matlab code one_d_run_and_pause.m.

v	k_{off}	k_{on}	MSD slope	$2D_{guess}$
1	1	1	0.992	1
1	1	2	1.333	$\frac{4}{3}$
1	2	1	0.333	$\frac{1}{3}$
1	2	2	0.500	$\frac{1}{2}$

4.5. An Agent-Based Approach

A popular way to simulate a population of particles is with an agent-based (or individual-based) approach, in which particles are tracked separately, but simultaneously.

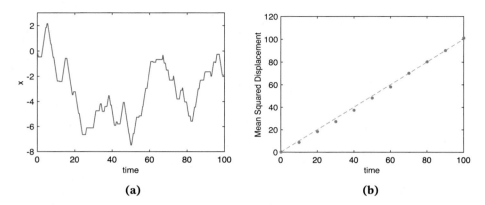

Figure 4.10. (a) Sample path for a particle that switches between a paused state and a state moving with constant velocity $v = 1$ to the left or right, with rates $k_{on} = 1$, and $k_{off} = 1$. (b) Mean squared displacement as a function of time for $N = 1,000$ particles, with line of slope one shown dashed.

Suppose, for example, we want to simulate a population (say, several hundred) of one dimensional run and tumble organisms. In the last section, we followed the motion of individuals one at a time, using a next reaction time algorithm to determine changes of state and position. This will not work for following several particles at once, since the transitions and movement are not synchronous.

So how does an agent-based approach work? We suppose that there are N particles with position x_n, $n = 1, 2, \ldots, N$, each in state s_n, $n = 1, 2, \ldots, N$, where s_j is one of the K possible states $1, 2, \ldots, K$. Now, there are rules for how a particle in state k moves, say, with velocity $v(k) = v_k$, and there are rates for transitioning between states, say λ_{jk} is the rate of transitioning from state k to state j. We discretize time with a fixed time step Δt, and with each time step, let $\lambda_{jk}\Delta t$ be the probability of changing from the state k to state j. The algorithm proceeds by first moving each particle by the amount $v(s_n)\Delta t$ and then modifying the states based on the probabilities $\lambda_{jk}\Delta t$ and N uniformly distributed random numbers R_n.

To be specific, for the one dimensional run and tumble model, there are three states, say, $s = \{1, 2, 3\}$ corresponding to leftward, resting, and rightward motion. The velocities in these three states are $-v, 0, v$, respectively. The rates of transition are $\lambda_{21} = \lambda_{23} = k_{off}$ and $\lambda_{12} = \lambda_{32} = \frac{k_{on}}{2}$.

The Matlab code that simulates this agent-based particle movement for run and tumble particles in one dimension is titled agent_based_run_and_tumble.m.

A reason that agent-based modeling is both useful and popular is that the rules for movement and change of state can be diverse and can be easily simulated, even though a partial differential equation description of the dynamics may not be known. We use agent-based modeling throughout this book, especially in Chapter 14 on Collective Behavior, where we discuss swarming behaviors of things like flying birds.

Exercises

4.1. Do a numerical experiment using the code single_particle_diffusion.m and make a plot of the slope of the variance as a function of time, as a function of the input parameter D. Verify that the variance has slope $2D$.

4.2. (a) Determine the time it takes for oxygen and hemoglobin to escape from the center of circular or spherical domains with radii 10^{-4}, 10^{-2}, and 10 cm using the formulas in (4.15) or (4.17). (The diffusion coefficient for oxygen in water is 2.1×10^{-5}cm^2/s and for hemoglobin is 6.9×10^{-7} cm^2/s.)

   (b) Perform a stochastic simulation experiment to find the first exit time for a diffusing particle in a circular or spherical domain, starting at the origin. (Start with a particle at the origin and allow it to diffuse until it hits a boundary at distance R from the origin, and record the time of the first hit. Do this for many such particles, plot the distribution of times, and check to see if the mean of this distribution agrees with what you calculated in the previous exercise.) Do this experiment for hemoglobin and oxygen for circular and spherical domains with radii 10^{-4}, 10^{-2}cm. Why is simulation a bad idea for a domain of radius 10 cm?

4.3. (a) Determine the time it takes for a diffusing particle in a circle or sphere of radius R starting at the outer boundary to find a small circle/sphere of radius $\rho < R$, assuming the particle reflects at the outer boundary.
   Hint. Find $T(R)$ where $T(r)$ satisfies $D\nabla^2 T = -1$ with $T(\rho) = 0$ and $\frac{\partial T}{\partial r} = 0$ at $r = R$.

   (b) Suppose that a molecule enters a spherical cell of radius 5 μm at its outer boundary. How long will it take, on average, for the molecule to move by diffusion to find a binding target of radius 0.5 nm located at the center of the cell? Use a diffusion coefficient of 10^{-6}cm^2/s.

   (c) Simulate this process for a circle with $R = 1, D = 1$ as a function of the inner radius ρ and compare your simulated answer with the analytical result.

4.4. Figure 4.3 was made with $D = 1$. Compute the mean first exit time for the one dimensional region $0 < x < 1$ with reflection at $x = 0$ for several values of D. For each value of D, fit the data to a curve $T(L) = a(1 - x^2)$, and then make a plot of a as a function of D. Compare the computed curve to the theoretical answer.

4.5. There appears to be a consistent error between the data shown in Figure 4.3 and the theoretical curve for mean first exit times given by (4.13). Figure 4.3 was made using a discrete time step of $dt = 0.001$. Determine how the error in the data changes as a function of dt as follows: Simulate this process for several values of dt (using Matlab code first_exit_times.m). For each value of dt, fit the data to a curve $T(L) = a(1 - \frac{x^2}{L^2})$, and then make a plot of a as a function of dt. How does a depend on dt? (*Remark.* We expect that $a \approx -0.5 + \alpha(dt)^p$, for some power p. Estimate p by examining the curve $\ln(-a - 0.5)$ vs. $\ln(dt)$.)

4.6. For the two dimensional diffusion equation with diffusion coefficient D on a doubly infinite domain, verify that

$$\frac{d}{dt}E(x^2 + y^2) = \frac{d}{dt}\int_{-\infty}^{\infty}\int_{-\infty}^{\infty}(x^2 + y^2)p(x, y, t)dxdy = 4D.$$

4.7. For the three dimensional diffusion equation with diffusion coefficient D on a triply infinite domain, verify that

$$\frac{d}{dt}E(x^2 + y^2 + z^2) = \frac{d}{dt}\int_{-\infty}^{\infty}\int_{-\infty}^{\infty}\int_{-\infty}^{\infty}(x^2 + y^2 + z^2)p(x, y, z, t)dxdydz = 6D.$$

4.8. Do a numerical simulation of diffusion in three dimensions with particles starting at the origin and verify that $\frac{d}{dt}E(x^2 + y^2 + z^2) = 6D$.

4.9. Figures 4.5 and 4.6 were made using the Matlab code two_d_diffusion.m with $D = 1$. How should those curves change as a function of D? Verify your prediction by doing the simulation.

4.10. **Flight of a Bumblebee.** Suppose that an insect (say, a bumblebee) flies with constant velocity v in the direction θ, i.e., $\frac{dx}{dt} = v\cos\theta$, $\frac{dy}{dt} = v\sin\theta$, and that θ changes by angular diffusion with diffusion coefficient D_θ. Simulate this process starting with N particles at $x = y = 0$ with random initial angle. Show, by plotting the mean squared displacement as a function of time, that for large enough time, this process behaves like a two dimensional diffusion process with effective diffusion coefficient $\frac{v^2}{2D_\theta}$. *Hint.* Start with $v = 1$, $D_\theta = 1$ to find the rate of growth of the mean squared displacement, and then vary v and D_θ to determine the rate of change of the mean squared displacement. (*Warning.* If D_θ is small it takes longer for the diffusive character of the motion to become apparent. Why?)

4.11. Suppose that a flying insect can be in one of two states, bound (e.g., landed on a flower) or unbound. It transitions between the two states with rates k_{on} to bind and k_{off} to unbind. In the bound state it is motionless and in the unbound state it moves by diffusion in one dimension with diffusion coefficient D. Simulate this process and use the data from the simulation (i.e., the rate of change of the mean squared displacement) to estimate the effective diffusion coefficient for the process as a function of the parameters D, k_{on} and k_{off}.

4.12. **Run and Tumble.** Suppose that a particle (a swimming bacterium) is in one of two states, swimming (in two dimensions) or tumbling. It changes state with rates k_{on} and k_{off} to swim or tumble, respectively. In the swimming state it moves with constant velocity v in the direction θ, i.e., $\frac{dx}{dt} = v\cos\theta$, $\frac{dy}{dt} = v\sin\theta$. In the tumbling state, it does not change its position, but θ changes to a new angle with uniform probability. Simulate this process (using the Gillespie algorithm) and show, by plotting the mean squared displacement as a function of time, that this process behaves like a two dimensional diffusion process. Estimate the effective diffusion coefficient as a function of parameters v, k_{on} and k_{off}.

4.13. **Run and Tumble, Part 2.** Suppose that a particle (a swimming bacterium) is in one of two states, swimming (in two dimensions) or tumbling. It changes state with rates k_{on} and k_{off} to swim or tumble, respectively. In the swimming state it moves with constant velocity v in the direction θ, i.e., $\frac{dx}{dt} = v\cos\theta$, $\frac{dy}{dt} = v\sin\theta$. In the tumbling state, it does not change its position, but θ changes to a new angle by a diffusion process with angular diffusion coefficient D_θ. Simulate this process (using the Gillespie algorithm) and show, by plotting the mean squared displacement as a function of time, that this process behaves like a two dimensional diffusion process. Estimate the effective diffusion coefficient as a function of parameters v, k_{on} and k_{off} and D_θ. *Hint.* To determine the new angle after tumbling for a time Δt, set $\theta_{new} = \text{mod}(\theta_{old} + \sqrt{2D_\theta \Delta t}\mathcal{N}(0,1), 2\pi)$.

4.14. Molecular motors, such as kinesin and dynein, attach and detach from (one dimensional) microtubules. When attached they "walk" with constant velocity v in one direction, and when unattached they diffuse with diffusion coefficient D. Suppose that they attach and detach at rates k_{on} and k_{off}, respectively. Simulate this process and determine the mean and variance of this process as a function of time.

    (a) What is the mean velocity of this process in terms of v, k_{on} and k_{off}?

    (b) Verify that the effective diffusion coefficient for this process is

$$D_{eff} = v^2 \frac{k_{on}k_{off}}{(k_{on} + k_{off})^3} + D\frac{k_{off}}{k_{on} + k_{off}}.$$

4.15. Suppose that a particle can be in one of two states, unattached or attached to a one dimensional line. It changes state with rates k_{on} and k_{off} to attach or detach, respectively. When it is in the unattached state it diffuses with diffusion coefficient D. When it attaches it does so with a random direction, walking at constant velocity v in the forward or backward direction. It can change direction only by detaching and reattaching.

    Simulate this process and determine the effective diffusion coefficient by calculating the mean squared displacement as a function of time for the process.

4.16. **Run and Tumble revisited.** Suppose that a particle (a swimming bacterium) is in one of two states, swimming in two dimensions or tumbling. It changes state with rates k_{on} and k_{off} to swim or tumble, respectively. In the swimming state it moves with constant velocity v in the direction θ, i.e., $\frac{dx}{dt} = v\cos\theta$, $\frac{dy}{dt} = v\sin\theta$. In the tumbling state, it does not change its position, but θ changes to a new angle with uniform probability. Do an agent-based simulation of this process. Estimate the effective diffusion coefficient. Compare the results of this agent-based approach to that of Exercise 4.12. Which is faster? Which is more accurate?

4.17. A random walker takes steps of size dx along a one dimensional line at times that are determined by a Poisson process, i.e., exponentially distributed with a time constant τ.

    (a) Simulate this process to estimate its mean and variance.

    (b) Use equations (1.92) and (1.93) to determine the mean and the variance for the position of this random walker.

4.18. A random walker takes steps at times that are determined by a Poisson process, i.e., exponentially distributed with a time constant τ, and step size that is also random with the symmetric exponential distribution $\frac{1}{2\lambda} \exp(-\frac{|x|}{\lambda})$. Is this effectively a diffusion process, and if so, what is the effective diffusion coefficient? *Remark.* Simulate this process.

Chapter 5

Solutions of the Diffusion Equation

Now we attack the question of how to find solutions of the diffusion equation. We start with analytical solutions because they give important insights as to what is happening. However, analytical solutions are too limited in their usefulness for most biological applications, so we also describe how to find solutions numerically.

5.1. On an Infinite Domain

If the domain is the infinite line, and the initial data are concentrated at the origin, a solution is the normal distribution $\mathcal{N}(0, 2Dt)$, found in Chapter 3 and given by

$$(5.1) \qquad u(x, t) = \frac{1}{\sqrt{4\pi Dt}} \exp(-\frac{x^2}{4Dt}),$$

If the domain is the two dimensional plane, we look for radially symmetric solutions, and therefore need a solution of the equation

$$(5.2) \qquad \frac{\partial u}{\partial t} = \frac{D}{r} \frac{\partial}{\partial r}(r \frac{\partial u}{\partial r}),$$

where r is the radius. We guess a solution of the form

$$(5.3) \qquad u(r, t) = \frac{1}{a(t)} \exp(\frac{-r^2}{b(t)}),$$

and find it must be that

$$(5.4) \qquad a(\frac{db}{dt} - 4D)r^2 + 4abD - b^2 \frac{da}{dt} = 0$$

for all r. This is a quadratic polynomial in r which can be identically zero for all r only if the individual coefficients of powers of r are zero, or, that

$$(5.5) \qquad \frac{db}{dt} = 4D, \qquad \frac{da}{dt} = 4D\frac{a}{b},$$

so that $b(t) = 4Dt$, $a(t) = a_0 t$. Consequently, the solution is

$$(5.6) \qquad\qquad u(r, t) = \frac{1}{4\pi Dt} \exp\left(\frac{-r^2}{4Dt}\right),$$

and this solution has the property

$$(5.7) \qquad\qquad 2\pi \int_0^\infty u(r, t) r \, dr = 1$$

for all time. Furthermore, the percentage of the population contained within a circle of radius R is given by

$$(5.8) \qquad 2\pi \int_0^R u(r, t) r \, dr = \int_0^R \frac{1}{2Dt} \exp\left(\frac{-r^2}{4Dt}\right) r \, dr = 1 - \exp\left(\frac{-R^2}{4Dt}\right),$$

confirming what we observed in the particle diffusion simulation in the last chapter. (See Figures 4.5 and 4.6.)

For a three-dimensional infinite domain, a spherically symmetric solution must satisfy

$$(5.9) \qquad\qquad \frac{\partial u}{\partial t} = \frac{D}{r^2} \frac{\partial}{\partial r}\left(r^2 \frac{\partial u}{\partial r}\right).$$

Again, we try a solution of the form (5.3), and the solution is similar, requiring the quadratic polynomial in r

$$(5.10) \qquad\qquad -a\left(4D - \frac{db}{dt}\right)r^2 - \frac{da}{dt}b^2 + 6baD = 0.$$

This leads to the two differential equations

$$(5.11) \qquad\qquad \frac{db}{dt} = 4D, \quad \frac{da}{dt} = 6D\frac{a}{b},$$

from which we learn that $b(t) = 4Dt$, and $a(t) = a_0 t^{\frac{3}{2}}$. So,

$$(5.12) \qquad\qquad u(r, t) = \frac{1}{(2\pi Dt)^{\frac{3}{2}}} \exp\left(\frac{-r^2}{4Dt}\right),$$

and this solution has the feature that

$$(5.13) \qquad\qquad 4\pi \int_0^\infty u(r, t) r^2 \, dr = 1$$

for all time (see Exercise 5.1).

The differences between these three solutions are interesting. Notice that the spatial profile of these three solutions is the same; it is their amplitudes that are different. Specifically, the amplitude of the d-dimensional solution is proportional to $t^{-\frac{d}{2}}$, so that the amplitude decays faster for larger d.

5.2. On the Semi-infinite Line

Suppose that a long capillary, open at one end, with uniform cross-sectional area A and filled with water, is inserted into a solution of known chemical concentration u_0, and the chemical species is free to diffuse into the capillary through the open end. Since the concentration of the chemical species depends only on the distance along the tube and time, it is governed by the diffusion equation (3.2), and for convenience we assume that the capillary is infinitely long, so that $0 < x < \infty$. Because the solute bath in which the capillary sits is large, it is reasonable to assume that the chemical concentration at the tip is fixed at $u(0, t) = u_0$, and since the tube is initially filled with pure water, $u(x, 0) = 0$ for all x, $0 < x < \infty$.

There are (at least) two ways to find the solution of this problem. One is to use the Fourier–Sine transform, a technique which is beyond the scope of this text (but you can learn about it in [**34**]). The second is to make a lucky (or semi-informed) guess. Here, we make the guess that the solution should be of the form $u(x, t) = f(\xi)$, where $\xi = \frac{x}{\sqrt{2Dt}}$. Substitute this guess into the diffusion equation and find

$$(5.14) \qquad f'\xi + f'' = 0.$$

This is a separable equation for f' and can be written as

$$(5.15) \qquad \frac{df'}{f'} = -\xi d\xi,$$

so that

$$(5.16) \qquad \frac{df}{d\xi} = a\exp(-\frac{\xi^2}{2}),$$

where a is a yet to be determined constant. From this we determine that a solution of the diffusion equation is given by

$$(5.17) \qquad u(x, t) = b + a\int_0^z \exp\left(-\frac{s^2}{2}\right)ds, \qquad z = \frac{x}{\sqrt{2Dt}},$$

with constants a and b determined from boundary and initial data. Setting $x = z = 0$, and requiring $u(0, t) = u_0$ determines that $b = u_0$. Setting $t = 0$, i.e., $z = \infty$, and requiring $u(x, 0) = 0$ implies that $a = -u_0\sqrt{\frac{2}{\pi}}$, and consequently,

$$(5.18) \qquad u(x, t) = u_0\left(1 - \sqrt{\frac{2}{\pi}}\int_0^z \exp\left(-\frac{s^2}{2}\right)ds\right), \qquad z = \frac{x}{\sqrt{2Dt}}.$$

Plots of this solution plotted as a function of z (a surrogate for x), and as a function of $z^{-\frac{1}{2}}$ (a surrogate for t) are shown in Figure 5.1 and were made using Matlab code tube_diffusion.m.

From this solution, one can readily calculate that the total number of molecules that enter the capillary in a fixed time T is (using integration by parts)

$$(5.19) \qquad N = A\int_0^\infty u(x, T)dx = 2u_0 A\sqrt{\frac{TD}{\pi}}.$$

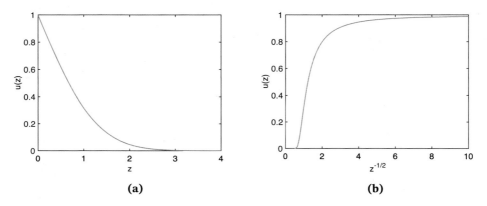

(a)   (b)

Figure 5.1. Plots of the solution (5.18) plotted as a function of z in (a), and as a function of $z^{-\frac{1}{2}}$ in (b) with $u_0 = 1$.

From this equation, it is also possible to determine the diffusion coefficient by solving (5.19) for D, yielding

$$(5.20) \qquad\qquad D = \frac{\pi N^2}{4u_0^2 A^2 T}.$$

A second useful piece of information is found from (5.18) by observing that $u(x, t)/u_0$ is constant on any curve for which z is constant. Thus, the curve $t = x^2/D$ is a level curve for the concentration, and gives a measure of how fast the substance is moving into the capillary. The time $t = x^2/D$ is called the *diffusion time* for the process. To give some idea of the effectiveness of diffusion in various cellular contexts, in Table 5.1 we show typical diffusion times for a variety of cellular structures. Clearly, diffusion is effective for transport when distances are short, but totally inadequate for longer distances, such as along a long nerve axon. Obviously, biological systems must employ other mechanisms in these situations in order to survive.

Table 5.1. Estimates of diffusion times for cellular structures of typical dimensions, computed from the relation $t = x^2/D$ using $D = 10^{-5} \text{cm}^2/\text{s}$ (typical for molecules the size of oxygen or carbon dioxide in water).

x	t	Example
10 nm	100 ns	Thickness of cell membrane
1 μm	1 ms	size of mitochondrion
10 μm	100 ms	Radius of small mammalian cell
100 μm	10s	Diameter of a large muscle fiber
250 μm	60 s	Radius of squid giant axon
1 mm	16.7 min	Half-thickness of frog sartorius muscle
2 mm	1.1 h	Half-thickness of lens in the eye
5 mm	6.9 h	Radius of mature ovarian follicle
2 cm	2.6 d	Thickness of ventricular myocardium
1 m	31.7 yrs	Length of a (long, e.g., sciatic) nerve axon

5.3. With Boundary Conditions

Up to this point we have not discussed much about boundary conditions, but these can be avoided no longer. As the name implies, a boundary condition is a condition on the solution at the boundary of the domain of interest. In general, one needs one condition for every derivative that appears in the equation. Thus, for example, for a differential equation that describes the time evolution of some object with an equation of the form $u_t = f(u, t)$, one needs one initial condition to specify $u(t_0)$, where t_0 is the start time. On the other hand for a differential equation that can be written as $u_{xx} = g(u, u_x, x)$, one needs two conditions at the boundaries in order to specify u completely. Thus, for the diffusion equation on a finite domain, one needs to specify an initial condition at $t = 0$ for all values of x in the domain, and two boundary conditions at the ends of the spatial domain. For a one dimensional spatial domain there are four possibilities:

- *Dirichlet condition* is when the value of the unknown u is specified at the boundary. If u is a probability, the condition $u = 0$ is said to be an *absorbing* boundary condition, because a particle that crosses the boundary disappears and cannot re-enter the domain.

- *Neumann condition* is when the flux of the unknown u across the boundary is specified. In a biological context, the flux across a boundary is zero if the boundary is impermeable to the particles, and is often called a *no-flux* condition. If u is a probability, $\nabla u \cdot \mathbf{n} = 0$ is called a *reflecting* boundary condition.

- *Robin condition* is a weighted combination of Dirichlet and Neumann boundary conditions, typically of the form $D\nabla u \cdot \mathbf{n} + au = b$ and is often appropriate when the diffusing species can undergo a chemical reaction at the boundary, or, as we see below, when the species can diffuse across a porous boundary.

- *Periodic conditions* apply when the one dimensional domain is actually a closed loop of length L, with the point at $x = 0$ the same as the point at $x = L$. In this case, one requires that the function u and its derivative be continuous at the "boundary".

5.3.1. At Steady State. Before we move on to solve the diffusion equation with different boundary conditions, it is worthwhile to gain some exposure to these by examining what happens when a diffusion process is at steady state. Steady state means that u is not changing in time, i.e., $\frac{\partial u}{\partial t} = 0$, so that the process is in equilibrium, but it does not mean that nothing is happening.

To illustrate, suppose u is held fixed at $u = u_0$ at $x = 0$ and $u = u_L$ at $x = L$. Then, the steady state solution satisfies $u_{xx} = 0$, which implies that u is a linear function satisfying the boundary conditions, i.e.,

$$(5.21) \qquad u(x) = u_L \frac{x}{L} + u_0 \left(1 - \frac{x}{L}\right).$$

To verify that something is happening, notice that the flux is

$$(5.22) \qquad J = -Du_x = \frac{D}{L}(u_0 - u_L),$$

which is not zero, unless $u_L = u_0$.

Suppose, instead, that the boundaries at $x = 0$ and $x = L$ are porous membranes, with $u = u_0$ and $u = u_L$ just outside the domain, and the species u can diffuse through the boundaries and therefore must satisfy the Robin boundary conditions

(5.23) $Du_x|_{x=0} = \delta(u(0) - u_0),\quad -Du_x|_{x=L} = \delta(u(L) - u_L).$

where $\delta > 0$ represents the porosity of the boundary membrane, and $u(0)$, $u(L)$ are the values of u at the membrane just inside the domain. Notice what these conditions mean in words: the term $\delta(u(0) - u_0)$ is the diffusive flux of u across the membrane to the outside, and $Du_x|_{x=0}$ is the flux of u out of the domain at $x = 0$. Clearly these must match. Notice also the difference in the sign for these two conditions. This is because if $u(0) > u_0$, the flux will be out of the domain to the left, i.e., negative (and because flux is the negative spatial derivative of u, u must therefore have positive slope). If $u(L) > u_L$, the flux will be out of the domain to the right, i.e., positive (hence u must have a negative slope). As before, u is a linear function in the interior of the domain, and the requirement that it satisfy the two Robin boundary conditions yields that

(5.24) $u(x) = \dfrac{1}{1 + 2\Delta}(u_L - u_0)\dfrac{x}{L} + \dfrac{\Delta(u_0 + u_L) + u_0}{1 + 2\Delta},$

where $\Delta = \frac{D}{\delta L}$. Once again, the flux is nontrivial, being

(5.25) $J = -Du_x = \dfrac{D}{1 + 2\Delta}\dfrac{u_0 - u_L}{L}.$

The quantity $D_{\text{eff}} = \frac{D}{1+2\Delta}$ is the effective diffusion coefficient for this membrane bound medium, since the species must diffuse across both membranes and well as through the interior of the medium. Notice also the identity

(5.26) $\dfrac{L}{D_{\text{eff}}} = \dfrac{1}{\delta} + \dfrac{L}{D} + \dfrac{1}{\delta}.$

(What do you suspect the answer is if the two porosities are different? Can you verify this suspicion? See Exercise 5.5.) Clearly, in the limit that the porosity of the membrane $\delta \to \infty$, the problem reduces to the Dirichlet boundary condition with solution (5.22) (see Figure 5.2).

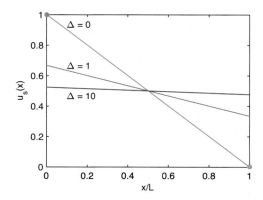

Figure 5.2. Steady state solutions for the diffusion equation with Robin boundary conditions with $\Delta = 0, 1, 10$, where $\Delta = \frac{D}{\delta L}$, with $u_0 = 1$, $u_L = 0$.

How do we know that this steady solution is ever attained? Let $u = u_s + v$, where u_s is the steady solution just computed. Then v satisfies the diffusion equation with homogeneous boundary conditions. Now, let $\mathcal{L}(t) = \int_0^L v^2 dx$, and compute that

$$
\begin{aligned}
\frac{d\mathcal{L}}{dt} &= \int_0^L vv_t dx = D\int_0^L vv_{xx}dx = Dvv_x|_0^L - D\int_0^L v_x^2 dx \\
&= Dv(L)v_x(L) - Dv(0)v_x(0) - D\int_0^L v_x^2 dx \\
&= -\delta(v^2(L) + v^2(0)) - D\int_0^L v_x^2 dx,
\end{aligned}
$$

which is strictly negative unless v is identically zero. In other words, if $\mathcal{L}(t)$, which is always nonnegative, is positive, then it is decreasing. This shows that differences from the steady state solution decay to zero, i.e., $\lim_{t\to\infty} v(t) = 0$. The function $\mathcal{L}(t)$ is called a *Lyapunov function*.

This argument is fine for Dirichlet and Robin boundary conditions, however it fails when both boundary conditions are no-flux (Neumann) conditions. For this case, we use a different function $\mathcal{L}_N(t) = \int_0^L v_x^2 dx$ and compute

$$
\begin{aligned}
\frac{d\mathcal{L}_N}{dt} &= \int_0^L v_x v_{xt} dx = D\int_0^L v_x v_{xxx} dx = Dv_x v_{xx}|_0^L - D\int_0^L v_{xx}^2 dx \\
&= -D\int_0^L v_{xx}^2 dx.
\end{aligned}
$$

Clearly, unless v is a linear function ($v_{xx} = 0$), $\mathcal{L}_N$ is a decreasing function. However, the only linear function that also satisfies the boundary conditions is a constant function. So, unless v is a constant function, $\mathcal{L}_N$ is decreasing. Thus, in the limit $t \to \infty$, $\mathcal{L}_N \to 0$ implying that v approaches a constant function.

Which constant function does v approach? Since $\int_0^L v dx$ is a conserved quantity (check that $\frac{d}{dt}\int_0^L v dx = 0$),

(5.27)
$$
\lim_{t\to\infty} v(x,t) = \frac{1}{L}\int_0^L v(x, t = 0)dx.
$$

5.4. Separation of Variables

In biological applications, the most common boundary condition is the no-flux (homogeneous Neumann) condition, when particles are trapped inside a bounded domain, and this is where we begin our study of time dependent solutions of the diffusion equation on a bounded domain.

An important feature of the no-flux boundary condition is that the total amount of the quantity u is conserved; this follows immediately from the conservation law as stated in (2.1). When solving *any* differential equation (in time) with constant coefficients, it is reasonable to try a solution that is exponential in time. For the diffusion equation, we try a solution of the form

(5.28) $$u(x,t) = U(x)\exp(\lambda t),$$

and upon substituting into the diffusion equation (3.2), we find

(5.29) $$D\frac{d^2 U}{dx^2} - \lambda U = 0.$$

This equation must be solved subject to the no-flux boundary condition $U'(0) = U'(L) = 0$.

There are an infinite number of possible solutions, but they are all of the same form, namely

(5.30) $$U_n(x) = a_n \cos(\frac{n\pi x}{L}),$$

with the important restriction that

(5.31) $$\lambda = \lambda_n \equiv -\frac{n^2 \pi^2 D}{L^2},$$

with $n = 0, 1, 2, \ldots$.

Since there are an infinite number of possible solutions, and the diffusion equation is linear, the fully general solution is an arbitrary linear combination of the possible solutions, namely

(5.32) $$u(x,t) = \sum_{n=0}^{\infty} a_n \exp(-\frac{Dn^2\pi^2 t}{L^2}) \cos(\frac{n\pi x}{L}).$$

At time $t = 0$, $u(x,0)$ is specified to be some function $U_0(x)$, so for consistency it must be that

(5.33) $$U_0(x) = \sum_{n=0}^{\infty} a_n \cos(\frac{n\pi x}{L}).$$

Now, use the fact that

(5.34) $$\int_0^L \cos(\frac{n\pi x}{L}) \cos(\frac{m\pi x}{L}) dx = \delta_{mn} \frac{L}{2},$$

provided n and m are not both zero.[1] Multiply the equation (5.33) by $\cos(\frac{m\pi x}{L})$ and integrate from zero to L, to determine that

(5.35) $$a_0 = \frac{1}{L}\int_0^L U_0(x)dx, \qquad a_n = \frac{2}{L}\int_0^L U_0(x)\cos(\frac{n\pi x}{L})dx, \qquad n \neq 0.$$

One of the important consequences of expressing the solution in this form is that it shows how different *modes* behave. Clearly the average value of u, expressed as a_0, does not change, since $\lambda_0 = 0$. Other components of the solution decay, and their rate of decay is proportional to the square of the mode number, n. In other words, the solution smooths out its ripples very rapidly while variations that are more gradual (i.e., smaller n) smooth out less rapidly. To illustrate this point, in Figure 5.3 are shown the solutions of the diffusion equation with homogeneous Neumann boundary conditions on

---

[1]The Kronecker delta, δ_{mn}, is defined to be $\delta_{mm} = 1$ and $\delta_{mn} = 0$ if $m \neq n$.

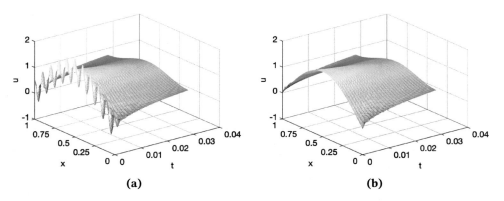

Figure 5.3. Plots of the solution of the diffusion equation on the interval $[0, 1]$ with $D = 1$ and with initial data $u(x, 0) = 1.5 \cos(\pi(x - \frac{1}{2}) + C \cos(20\pi x)$ with (a) $C = 0.5$ and (b) $C = 0$.

the interval $[0, 1]$ and $D = 1$, with initial data $u(x, 0) = 1.5 \cos(\pi(x - \frac{1}{2})) + C \cos(20\pi x)$ with $C = 0.5$ in Figure 5.3(a) and $C = 0$ in Figure 5.3(b). Notice that the initial high frequency ripples dissappear very quickly so that after a very short time, the two solutions are almost identical.

Separation of variables is a very important classical technique for solving many linear partial differential equations. However, in this book, this technique is not given a lot of attention, for several reasons. First, even though it is an exact solution, understanding it requires summing an infinite series, which is not necessarily easy to do. Indeed, one would typically evaluate partial sums numerically to plot the solution. However, if one is going to use numerical evaluation to make plots of the solution, why not do a direct numerical simulation of the equation?

There is, however, useful information contained in one or two terms of the infinite series solution. That is, taking only two terms one finds

$$(5.36) \qquad u(x, t) \approx a_0 + a_1 \exp(-\frac{D\pi^2 t}{L^2}) \cos(\frac{\pi x}{L}).$$

Realizing that the terms ignored in this approximation are of the order of $\exp(-\frac{4D\pi^2 t}{L^2})$, which decays much faster than the term $\exp(-\frac{D\pi^2 t}{L^2})$ means that the approximate solution becomes increasingly accurate as time progresses. Consequently, an understanding of the long-time behavior of the solution is readily available from the two term approximation.

Another important point to be made here is that separation of variables and this modal analysis work only for problems with homogeneous boundary conditions. To solve a problem with inhomogeneous boundary conditions, one must first subtract off the steady state solution and then the remainder problem will have homogeneous boundary conditions, a problem for which separation of variables can be used.

Problems with other boundary conditions are given in the Exercises.

5.5. Numerical Methods

As discussed above, the method of separation of variables is important from a classical perspective, but is of limited modern usefulness. With the advent of readily available computers, the method of choice to find solutions is numerical simulation.

5.5.1. Method of Lines. The first method to numerically simulate the diffusion equation is one that we have already used, namely the *method of lines*. With this method, we discretize the spatial region into a grid with points at $x_j = j\Delta x$, $j = 0, 1, \ldots, N$, and then write the diffusion equation approximately as the system of ordinary differential equations

$$(5.37) \qquad \frac{du_j}{dt} = \frac{D}{\Delta x^2}(u_{j+1} - 2u_j + u_{j-1}).$$

At the endpoints, take the equations to be

$$(5.38) \qquad \frac{du_0}{dt} = \frac{2D}{\Delta x^2}(u_1 - u_0), \qquad \frac{du_N}{dt} = \frac{2D}{\Delta x^2}(u_{j-1} - u_N).$$

This choice follows from the approximation to the derivative of u, $\frac{\partial u}{\partial x}|_{x=j\Delta x} \approx \frac{u_{j+1}-u_{j-1}}{2\Delta x}$, so at the boundaries the zero derivative (Neumann) boundary condition implies that $u_{-1} = u_1$, and $u_{N+1} = u_{N-1}$. (The points at $j = -1$ and $j = N+1$ are called ghost points and are useful for this calculation, but are never actually computed.)

This system of equations is then simulated using a numerical ordinary differential equation solver. The Matlab code for this for Neumann or Robin boundary conditions is titled Diffusion_NR_via_MOL.m and for Dirichlet boundary conditions is titled Diffusion_Dirichlet_via_MOL.m.

It is convenient for future discussions to represent $u(j\Delta x, t)$ as a vector $\mathbf{u}(t) = (u_j)$, and then to rewrite (5.37) using vector/matrix notation as

$$(5.39) \qquad \frac{d\mathbf{u}}{dt} = \frac{D}{\Delta x^2}A\mathbf{u},$$

where the matrix A has diagonal elements -2, and first upper and lower off-diagonal elements 1, except the first element of the upper diagonal and last element of the lower diagonal are both 2, i.e.,

$$(5.40) \qquad A = \begin{pmatrix} -2 & 2 & 0 & \cdots & 0 \\ 1 & -2 & 1 & 0 & \cdots \\ & & \vdots & & \\ 0 & \cdots & 1 & -2 & 1 \\ 0 & \cdots & 0 & 2 & -2 \end{pmatrix}.$$

5.5.2. Forward Euler Method. Suppose that to solve the diffusion equation by the method of lines, we wish to use a simple numerical time step integrator, rather than one of the black box integrators provided by Matlab. To do so requires discretization of the time step, as well.

The *forward Euler method* numerically solves equation (5.37) by doing a forward time step discretization. If the time step is Δt, and we set $\mathbf{u}^n$ to be the vector $\mathbf{u}(n\Delta t)$, we have

(5.41)
$$\frac{1}{\Delta t}(\mathbf{u}^{n+1} - \mathbf{u}^n) = \frac{D}{\Delta x^2} A \mathbf{u}^n.$$

We can rewrite this in matrix notation to show its iterative nature, as

(5.42)
$$\mathbf{u}^{n+1} = (I + \frac{D\Delta t}{\Delta x^2} A)\mathbf{u}^n,$$

where I is the identity matrix, and it is easy to write code that carries this out. However, one drawback of this method quickly becomes apparent.

The forward Euler method is an example of a matrix iteration of the form

(5.43)
$$\mathbf{u}^{n+1} = B\mathbf{u}^n,$$

which is known to be stable[2] only if all the eigenvalues of the matrix B lie between -1 and 1.

Notice that since A is diagonally semidominant, its eigenvalues are all nonpositive. It is easy to verify that the eigenvalues of A all lie between -4 and 0 (see Exercise 5.7). In fact, using the trigonometric identity,

(5.44)
$$\cos(x + y) + \cos(x - y) = 2\cos(y)\cos(x),$$

one can verify directly that the vector with components $\phi_j = \cos(\frac{(j-1)k\pi}{N})$, $j = 1, 2, \ldots,$ $N+1$, is an eigenvector of the matrix A corresponding to eigenvalue $\lambda_k = 2(\cos(\frac{k\pi}{N})-1)$, $k = 0, 1, 2, \ldots, N$.

With this information in hand, it is apparent that the eigenvalues of the matrix $I + \frac{D\Delta t}{\Delta x^2}A$ are $1 + \frac{D\Delta t}{\Delta x^2}\lambda_k$. Consequently, if $\frac{D\Delta t}{\Delta x^2}$ is bigger than $\frac{1}{2}$, the matrix $I + \frac{D\Delta t}{\Delta x^2}A$ has eigenvalues which are negative with magnitude larger than 1, so that the iterations of (5.42) oscillate with growing amplitude, hence they are unstable.

From a practical point of view, this means that to have a stable simulation using the Euler method, it is necessary to keep $\frac{D\Delta t}{\Delta x^2} < \frac{1}{2}$, and if one wants a high spatial resolution solution (with Δx small), Δt must be even smaller, meaning simulations will take a long time to calculate. For example, to halve Δx one must decrease Δt by a factor of 4.

The Matlab code to simulate the diffusion equation with Neumann or Robin boundary conditions using the forward Euler method is titled FEuler_diffusion_NR.m.

5.5.3. Backward Euler Method. To get around this severe time step restriction, we try a different time step algorithm, called the *backward Euler method*. For this method, we approximate the time derivative using values of the function at the forward time step to estimate the spatial derivative,

(5.45)
$$\frac{1}{\Delta t}(\mathbf{u}^{n+1} - \mathbf{u}^n) = \frac{D}{\Delta x^2} A \mathbf{u}^{n+1}.$$

Since, $\mathbf{u}^n$ is known and we wish to determine $\mathbf{u}^{n+1}$, this is an implicit method, rather than explicit, as was the forward Euler method. This can be written in matrix form as

(5.46)
$$(I - \frac{D\Delta t}{\Delta x^2}A)\mathbf{u}^{n+1} = \mathbf{u}^n,$$

---

[2]The equilibrium of a differential or difference equation is said to be *stable* if any solution that starts close to the equilibrium remains close to the equilibrium for all time. It is *asymptotically stable* if any solution that starts close to the equilibrium converges to the equilibrium as $t \to \infty$. An equilibrium for which neither of these hold is *unstable*.

and we see that to find $\mathbf{u}^{n+1}$ from $\mathbf{u}^n$, we must solve a system of equations. In fact, since the iteration can be written as

$$(5.47) \qquad \mathbf{u}^{n+1} = (I - \frac{D\Delta t}{\Delta x^2}A)^{-1}\mathbf{u}^n,$$

and the eigenvalues of A are all negative, it is apparent that this iteration is always stable, since $0 < \frac{1}{1 - \frac{D\Delta t}{\Delta x^2}\lambda_k} < 1$ for all the eigenvalues λ_k.

The Matlab code to simulate the diffusion equation with Neumann or Robin boundary conditions using the backward Euler method is titled BEuler_diffusion_NR.m.

5.5.4. Crank–Nicolson Method.

While the backward Euler method is always stable, it is not very accurate, as you will find when you do Exercise 5.9. A better method is with a scheme called the *Crank–Nicolson* algorithm.[3] The idea of this is to split the spatial difference between time steps, as

$$(5.48) \qquad \frac{\mathbf{u}^{n+1} - \mathbf{u}^n}{\Delta t} = \frac{D}{\Delta x^2}A\frac{\mathbf{u}^{n+1} + \mathbf{u}^n}{2},$$

which leads to the iteration

$$(5.49) \qquad (I - \frac{D\Delta t}{2\Delta x^2}A)\mathbf{u}^{n+1} = (I + \frac{D\Delta t}{2\Delta x^2}A)\mathbf{u}^n.$$

The stability of this iteration is determined by the eigenvalues of the matrix

$$(5.50) \qquad B = (I - \frac{D\Delta t}{2\Delta x^2}A)^{-1}(I + \frac{D\Delta t}{2\Delta x^2}A).$$

Notice that the eigenvectors of A are also eigenvectors of B. So, if λ_k is an eigenvalue of A, then the corresponding eigenvalue of B is

$$(5.51) \qquad \frac{1 + \frac{D\Delta t}{2\Delta x^2}\lambda_k}{1 - \frac{D\Delta t}{2\Delta x^2}\lambda_k},$$

but since $-4 \le \lambda_k \le 0$, this quantity is always between -1 and 1. Hence, this iteration is stable for all choices of Δx and Δt, a significant improvement over the forward Euler time step.

Since this method is stable and more accurate than both the Euler methods, it is the preferred method for the numerical calculations in this book.

The Matlab code to solve the diffusion equation using the Crank–Nicolson method for Neumann and Robin conditions is titled CN_diffusion_NR.m.

---

[3]Stability of a numerical scheme refers to the specific conditions under which the algorithm produces a bounded solution. Accuracy of a numerical scheme describes the error of the numerical solution compared to the exact solution of the underlying equation. If the error of a numerical scheme is $O(\Delta t)$, then halving the time step will in general reduce the error by a factor of 2, whereas if the error is $O(\Delta t^2)$ then halving Δt will reduce the error by a factor of 4. Both the forward and backward Euler methods are $O(\Delta t)$ schemes, while the Crank–Nicolson method is an $O(\Delta t^2)$ scheme. It is beyond the scope of this text to verify these statements.

5.5.5. Other Boundary Conditions. Everything discussed in the previous section was for Neumann boundary conditions. However, the only difference for the numerical methods with different boundary conditions is with the definition of the corner entries of the matrix A. For homogeneous Robin boundary conditions (5.23), we write the approximations

$$(5.52) \qquad D\left(\frac{u_1 - u_{-1}}{2\Delta x}\right) = \delta u_0, \quad -D\left(\frac{u_{N+1} - u_{N-1}}{2\Delta x}\right) = \delta u_N,$$

which when substituted into the finite difference approximation of the diffusion equation (5.37) yields

$$(5.53) \qquad \frac{du_0}{dt} = \frac{D}{\Delta x^2}\left(2u_1 - 2(1 + \frac{\delta \Delta x}{D})u_0\right),$$

$$(5.54) \qquad \frac{du_N}{dt} = \frac{D}{\Delta x^2}\left(2(-1 - \frac{\delta \Delta x}{D})u_N + 2u_{N-1}\right).$$

This implies that the matrix A in (5.40) needs to be modified slightly to have first and last diagonal elements

$$(5.55) \qquad A_{1,1} = -2 - 2\frac{\delta \Delta x}{D}, \quad A_{N+1,N+1} = -2 - 2\frac{\delta \Delta x}{D}.$$

For homogeneous Dirichlet boundary conditions, the unknown variables are u_j, $j = 1, 2, \ldots, u_{N-1}$, (two less than for Neumann and Robin conditions) and the finite difference approximation (5.37) for u_1 and u_{N-1} reduces to

$$(5.56) \qquad \frac{du_1}{dt} = \frac{D}{\Delta x^2}(u_2 - 2u_1), \quad \frac{du_{N-1}}{dt} = \frac{D}{\Delta x^2}(-2u_{N-1} + u_{N-2})$$

(since $u_0 = u_N = 0$) and consequently, the matrix A (which is now an $N - 1 \times N - 1$ matrix) is

$$(5.57) \qquad A = \begin{pmatrix} -2 & 1 & 0 & \cdots & 0 \\ 1 & -2 & 1 & 0 & \cdots \\ & & \vdots & & \\ 0 & \cdots & 1 & -2 & 1 \\ 0 & \cdots & 0 & 1 & -2 \end{pmatrix}.$$

For Dirichlet boundary conditions, the Matlab codes are FEuler_diffusion_dirichlet.m, BEuler_diffusion_Dirichlet.m, and CN_diffusion_Dirichlet.m for forward Euler, backward Euler, and Crank–Nicolson methods, respectively.

5.6. Comparison Theorems

Perhaps you noticed that all of the solutions of the diffusion equation that have been calculated so far are nonnegative. This is good for physical reasons if the solution $u(x, t)$ represents a population density or a probability density, since these objects make sense only if they are nonnegative. However, there is a mathematical reason for this nonnegativity as well.

Theorem. *Suppose $u(x, y, z, t)$ is a smooth function (at least twice continuously differentiable in x, y, z and continuously differentiable in t) with $u(x, y, z, 0) \geq 0$ and satisfying*

(5.58)
$$\frac{\partial u}{\partial t} \geq \nabla^2 u + k(x, y, z, t)u$$

for some bounded function $k(x, y, z, t)$. Then $u(x, y, z, t) \geq 0$ for all $t \geq 0$.

The proof of this result is as follows. Since $u(x, y, z, 0) \geq 0$, the only way that u can become negative is if there is a point at which it changes sign. The only way it can change sign is if u crosses 0 and the only way to cross 0 is if $\frac{\partial u}{\partial t} < 0$ at a point where $u = 0$. So, suppose that $u(x_0, y_0, z_0, t_0) = 0$ and that $u(x, y, z, t) \geq 0$ for $t \leq t_0$ and for (x, y, z) in a neighborhood of (x_0, y_0, z_0). Then, at $(x, y, z) = (x_0, y_0, z_0)$, u is a local minimum. At a local minimum $\nabla^2 u \geq 0$ so that $\frac{\partial u}{\partial t} \geq 0$. In other words, u does not change sign.

The above statement applies to the interior of a domain but does not preclude the possibility that solutions change sign at the boundary of a domain. Of course, if the function u satisfies homogeneous Dirichlet boundary conditions at the domain boundary, it is obviously true that it cannot change sign there. If the function u satisfies homogeneous Neumann or Robin boundary conditions, or if the boundary is not smooth (has corners, for example), the arguments are more subtle and beyond the scope of this text, but the statement is nonetheless true. If you want to see the details of these arguments, consult the book by Protter and Weinberger [**60**], for example.

The important consequence of this theorem that we often make use of is the following.

Corollary. *Two solutions of the diffusion equation that are initially ordered remain ordered for all time.*

If u_1 and u_2 are both solutions of the diffusion equation, and $u_1 \geq u_2$ at time $t = 0$, then their difference $v = u_1 - u_2$ is initially nonnegative and so is nonnegative for all time.

5.7. FRAP

FRAP (fluorescence recovery after photobleaching) is an important experimental technique by which the diffusion coefficient of molecules can be measured. One starts with a thin layer solution of fluorescently labeled molecules and, at time $t = 0$, exposes a circular region of the solution to a laser beam, which bleaches the fluorescence there. Then, as the remaining fluorescent molecules diffuse back into the bleached region, the fluorescence at the center of the circle gradually recovers. From the measured time course of this recovery, the diffusion coefficient of the molecules can be estimated, *if* one knows how to solve the diffusion equation in two dimensions; see Figure 5.4.

What are some ways we can approach this problem? The first might be a numerical simulation. That is, we numerically solve the diffusion equation on a circular domain (5.2) subject to boundary conditions $u(R, t) = U_0$, and initial data $u(r, 0) = 0$ for $0 < r < R$. A direct way to do this is using the method of lines. That is, we set up

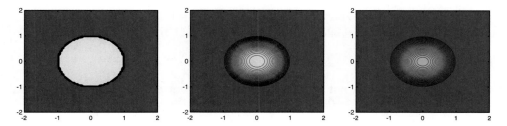

Figure 5.4. Illustration of FRAP with three snapshots of fluorescence following photobleaching, at times $t = 0, 0.01$, and 0.02.

a grid of points $r_j = \frac{jR}{N} = j\Delta r$, $j = 0, 1, \ldots, N$, and then discretize the radial spatial operator $\frac{1}{r}\frac{\partial}{\partial r}(r\frac{\partial u}{\partial r})$ to find a set of ordinary differential equations for $u_j = u(r_j)$,

$$(5.59) \qquad \frac{du_j}{dt} = \frac{D}{\Delta r^2}\frac{1}{r_j}\Big((u_{j+1} - u_j)r_{j+\frac{1}{2}} - (u_j - u_{j-1})r_{j-\frac{1}{2}}\Big),$$

with conditions $u_0 = u_1$ and $u_N = U_0$.

The solution of this system of differential equations is found using the Matlab code Diffusion_2D_via_MOL.m with $U_0 = 1$, $D = 1$, and $R = 1$, and the solution at the origin $u(0, t)$ is shown plotted in Figure 5.5(a). A quick look at this figure suggests that this curve is an exponential, and in fact a plot of $\ln(1 - u(0, t))$ shown in Figure 5.5(b) verifies this intuition. A fit of this curve beyond an initial transient to a straight line yields a slope of -5.77. By a simple rescaling of space and time, this implies that the return of the solution $u(0, t)$ to its original level should be an exponential of the form $\exp(\frac{-5.77Dt}{R^2})$. This suffices to estimate D from the collected data. That is, if the return of the solution $u(0, t)$ to its original level is approximately exponential with rate λ, $\exp(-\lambda t)$, then $D = \frac{\lambda R^2}{5.77}$.

For those of you who would like a more theoretical understanding of where the number -5.77 comes from, let's try the separation of variables technique. We look for a

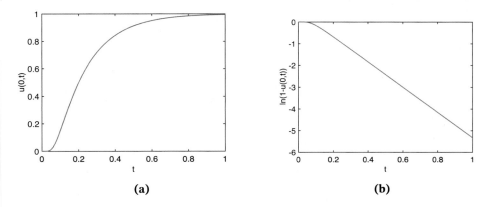

(a)   (b)

Figure 5.5. (a) $u(0, t)$ plotted as a function of t, and (b) $\ln(1 - u(0, t))$ plotted as a function of t. Both are determined numerically as the solution of (5.59) with boundary condition $u(R, t) = 1$, initial data $u(r, 0) = 0$, and parameters $D = 1$ and $R = 1$.

solution of (5.2) subject to boundary conditions $u(R, t) = 0$ and initial data $u(r, 0) = U_0$ of the form $u(r, t) = \exp(-\lambda t)U(r)$, and find quickly that $U(r)$ must satisfy the equation

$$(5.60) \qquad r^2 U'' + rU' + r^2 \frac{\lambda}{D} U = 0.$$

This equation is probably not familiar to most readers, but all you need to know is that this is an example of *Bessel's equation*,

$$(5.61) \qquad r^2 U'' + rU' + (r^2 - n^2)U = 0,$$

and solutions of this equation are known as Bessel functions of the first kind, denoted $J_n(r)$. Most of what you need to know about Bessel functions can be learned by plotting them in Matlab, using the command besselj(n,r). What you will find (see Figure 5.6) is that $J_0(x)$ is a decaying oscillatory function with an infinite number of zeros, denoted by $j_{0,k}$. The first few zeros of J_0 are 2.4048, 5.5201, 8.6537.

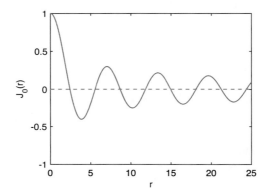

Figure 5.6. Plot of the Bessel function $J_0(r)$.

Now back to our problem. What we see is that $U(r)$ is a Bessel function $U = J_0(\sqrt{\frac{\lambda}{D}}r)$ and to satisfy the boundary condition at $r = R$, it must be that $\sqrt{\frac{\lambda}{D}}R = j_{0,k}$ for some value of k. This means that the general solution of the original problem can be written in the form

$$(5.62) \qquad u(r, t) = \sum_{k=1}^{\infty} a_k \exp\left(-\frac{D j_{0,k}^2}{R^2}t\right)J_0\left(\frac{j_{0,k}}{R}r\right).$$

But, of course, the slowest decaying of these infinite number of terms is the first, so that after a brief initial time the solution at the origin is

$$(5.63) \qquad u(0, t) \approx a_1 \exp\left(-\frac{D j_{0,1}^2}{R^2}t\right),$$

and $j_{0,1}^2 = 5.78$. The numerical solution and analytical solution agree quite nicely.

Exercises

5.1. Show that for the solution of the spherically symmetric diffusion equation

$$\frac{\partial u}{\partial t} = D\frac{1}{r^2}\frac{\partial}{\partial r}(r^2\frac{\partial u}{\partial r})$$

in a three-dimensional infinite domain, $4\pi\int_0^\infty u(r,t)r^2dr$ is a constant indepen-dent of time.

5.2. A particle is placed at the origin of a one-, two-, or three-dimensional infinite domain and allowed to diffuse. For which of these domains is diffusion away from the origin fastest? Explain this.

5.3. Many species of ant use pheromones as a danger signal. Consider an experiment in which ants are released into a long tube and one ant is stimulated until it releases a quantity of pheromone. Use the one-dimensional diffusion equation as a model for the spread of the pheromones in the tube. Assume that at time $t = 0$ a bolus of pheromone with total amount α is released, and that other ants react to the stimulus if the level of pheromone reaches 0.1α. For this exercise assume that $D = 1$.
   (a) Plot the time course of the pheromone level at several different values of position $x > 0$.
   (b) Find the region in the tube $0 \le x \le X(t)$ where the other ants react to the stimulus (i.e., the region of influence).
   (c) Sketch the time evolution of the boundary $X(t)$.
   (d) Find the region of space that is outside the domain of influence for all time.

5.4. Segel, Chet, and Henis [64] used (5.20) to estimate the diffusion coefficient D for bacteria. With the external concentration c_0 at $7\times 10^7\text{ml}^{-1}$, at times $t = 2, 5,$ 10, 12.5, 15, and 20 minutes, they counted N of 1,800, 3,700, 4,800, 5,500, 6,700, and 8,000 bacteria, respectively, in a capillary of length 32 mm with 1 μl total capacity. In addition, with external concentrations c_0 of 2.5, 4.6, 5.0, and 12.0 $\times 10^7$ bacteria per milliliter, counts of 1,350, 2,300, 3,400, and 6,200 were found at $t = 10$ minutes. Estimate D.

5.5. Find the steady state solution to the diffusion equation subject to Robin condi-tions with porosity δ_0 at $x = 0$ and δ_1 at $x = L$. Verify that the effective diffusion coefficient for this medium satisfies the identity

$$\frac{L}{D_{\text{eff}}} = \frac{1}{\delta_0} + \frac{L}{D} + \frac{1}{\delta_1}.$$

5.6. Find the steady state solution to the diffusion equation subject to the Robin con-dition $Du_x|_{x=0} = \delta(u(0) - u_0)$ at $x = 0$ and a no-flux (homogeneous Neumann) condition at $x = L$.

5.7. Find the eigenvalues of the $(N + 1) \times (N + 1)$ matrix

$$A = \begin{pmatrix} -2 & 2 & 0 & \cdots & & 0 \\ 1 & -2 & 1 & 0 & & \cdots \\ & & \vdots & & & \\ 0 & \cdots & 1 & -2 & 1 \\ 0 & \cdots & 0 & 2 & -2 \end{pmatrix}.$$

Hint. The eigenvectors are vectors ϕ whose jth component is $\phi_j = \cos(\frac{(j-1)k\pi}{N})$, $j = 1, 2, \ldots, N + 1$.

5.8. Find the eigenvalues of the $(N - 1) \times (N - 1)$ matrix

$$A = \begin{pmatrix} -2 & 1 & 0 & \cdots & & 0 \\ 1 & -2 & 1 & 0 & & \cdots \\ & & \vdots & & & \\ 0 & \cdots & 1 & -2 & 1 \\ 0 & \cdots & 0 & 1 & -2 \end{pmatrix}.$$

Hint. The eigenvectors are vectors ϕ whose jth component is $\phi_j = \sin(\frac{jk\pi}{N})$, $j = 1, 2, \ldots, N - 1$.

5.9. (a) Solve the diffusion equation analytically using separation of variables, with initial data $u_0(x) = 1 - \cos(2\pi x)$ on the interval $0 \le x \le 1$ with diffusion coefficient $D = 1$ and subject to no-flux boundary conditions at $x = 0$ and $x = 1$.

(b) Solve the diffusion equation numerically using the two algorithms (backward Euler and Crank–Nicolson) with initial data $u_0(x) = 1 - \cos(2\pi x)$ on the interval $0 \le x \le 1$ with diffusion coefficient $D = 1$ and subject to no-flux boundary conditions at $x = 0$, and $x = 1$, using exactly the same discretization parameters Δt and Δx.

(c) Compare your numerically computed solutions $u_n(x, t)$ with the exact solution $u(x, t)$ by examining the maximal relative error

$$E_n(t) = \max_x \left(\frac{u_n(x, t)}{u(x, t)} - 1 \right).$$

Which of the two methods is the most accurate?

5.10. (a) Solve the diffusion equation analytically using separation of variables, with initial data $u_0(x) = 2 \sin(\pi x)$ on the interval $0 \le x \le 1$ with diffusion coefficient $D = 1$ and subject to homogeneous Dirichlet conditions $u = 0$ at $x = 0$ and $x = 1$.

(b) Solve the diffusion equation numerically using the two algorithms (backward Euler and Crank–Nicolson) with initial data $u_0(x) = 2 \sin(\pi x)$ on the interval $0 \le x \le 1$ with diffusion coefficient $D = 1$ and subject to homogeneous Dirichlet boundary conditions $u = 0$ at $x = 0$ and $x = 1$, using exactly the same discretization parameters Δt and Δx.

(c) Compare your numerically computed solutions $u_n(x, t)$ with the exact solution $u(x, t)$ by examining the maximal relative error

$$E_n(t) = \max_x \left(\frac{u_n(x, t)}{u(x, t)} - 1 \right).$$

Which of the two methods is the most accurate?

5.11. Use separation of variables to find the slowest rate of decay for the diffusion equation with a Dirichlet condition $u = 0$ at $x = 0$ and a Robin condition $u' + au = 0$ at $x = L$, with $0 < a < \infty$, $L = 1$. Compare this rate of decay with the slowest rate of decay with $a = 0$ (a homogeneous Neumann condition) and $a = \infty$ (a homogeneous Dirichlet condition). Is this rate of decay a monotone increasing, monotone decreasing, or neither, function of a?

5.12. (a) Find the steady state solution of the diffusion equation $u_t = Du_{xx}$ subject to boundary conditions $u_x(0) = 0$, $u(L) = U_L$.
   (b) Find the smallest rate of decay of the solution to the steady state.
   (c) Solve this equation numerically for $D = 1$, $L = 1$, and verify that the solution converges to the steady state solution found above. Estimate the rate of decay of the solution to steady state and compare this estimate with the rate computed above.

5.13. (a) Find the steady state solution of the diffusion equation $u_t = Du_{xx}$ subject to boundary conditions $u_x(0) = 0$, $u_x(L) + au(L) = 1$.
   (b) Find a transcendental equation for the smallest rate of decay of the solution to steady state.
   (c) Solve this equation numerically for $D = 1$, $a = 1$, $L = 1$, and verify that the solution converges to the steady state solution found above. Estimate the rate of decay of the solution to steady state and compare this estimate with the rate computed above.

5.14. Many bacteria execute a run and tumble motion, and during their tumbling motion they rotate by a diffusive process. To analyze this process, use separation of variables to solve the diffusion equation $\frac{\partial u}{\partial t} = D_\theta \frac{\partial^2 u}{\partial \theta^2}$ on the periodic domain $-\pi \le \theta < \pi$ subject to the initial condition $u(\theta, 0) = \delta(\theta)$. Find the slowest rate of decay of the solution. What is the limiting behavior of the solution as $t \to \infty$? What is the meaning of the solution $u(\theta, t)$.

5.15. Suppose u satisfies the diffusion equation $u_t = D\nabla^2 u$ on a domain Ω subject to Robin boundary condition $D\nabla u \cdot \mathbf{n} + au = 0$ with $a \ge 0$ on the boundary $\partial\Omega$. Verify that the function $\mathcal{L}(t) = \int_\Omega u^2 dV$ is strictly decreasing unless $u = 0$. *Hint.* Make use of the identity (1.16).

5.16. Suppose u satisfies the diffusion equation $u_t = D\nabla^2 u$ on a domain Ω subject to the homogeneous Neumann condition $D\nabla u \cdot \mathbf{n} = 0$ on the boundary $\partial\Omega$. Verify that the function $\mathcal{L}_N(t) = \int_\Omega (\nabla u)^2 dx$ is strictly decreasing unless $\nabla^2 u = 0$. *Hint.* Make use of the identity (1.16).

5.17. Suppose that a FRAP experiment could be done on a one dimensional domain of length L. Determine the exponential rate of recovery of fluorescence at the center of the domain $x = \frac{L}{2}$. How does this compare to the rate of recovery for a circle of radius $R = \frac{L}{2}$?

5.18. Find the solution of the diffusion equation inside a sphere of radius R, with Dirichlet boundary condition $u(R, t) = 0$. How does the slowest rate of decay at the center of the sphere compare to those for one and two dimensional domains with the same radius?

Hint. Let $u = \frac{v}{r}$ and solve the equation for v using separation of variables.

Chapter 6

Diffusion and Reaction

As we have seen, diffusion acts to spread things out. For living organisms, this is, generally speaking, not a good thing; in fact, much of what living organisms do is work to reverse the natural tendency of things to break down and spread apart. However, as we shall see, this tendency of things to spread out can be exploited by incorporating appropriate chemical reactions. The goal of this chapter is to begin the exploration of how diffusion coupled with reactions can do things that are not possible with either process acting in isolation.

6.1. Birth-Death with Diffusion

Suppose that there is some population or chemical species U that diffuses on an infinite domain and experiences either decay, as in

$$(6.1) \qquad U \xrightarrow{\alpha} \emptyset,$$

or birth via asexual duplication as in

$$(6.2) \qquad U \xrightarrow{\alpha} 2U.$$

Setting $u = [U]$, the equation describing the evolution of this population is

$$(6.3) \qquad \frac{\partial u}{\partial t} = D \frac{\partial^2 u}{\partial x^2} + \sigma \alpha u,$$

where $\alpha > 0$, $\sigma = -1$ for decay, and $\sigma = 1$ for growth.

As an example, suppose that signaling molecules are produced at some point, and that the target of the signal is some distance away. Specifically, many copies of a transcription factor may be made when only one is needed to activate transcription of a gene. What percentage, if any, of the signaling molecules reach the target before they degrade? Roughly 10^8 sperm cells are initially released to reach the oocyte in human fertilization when only one is required. What are the consequences of releasing fewer sperm cells? This could also be a model to determine the distribution of seeds falling

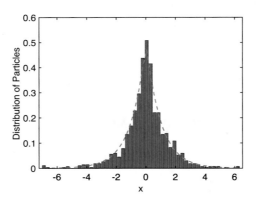

Figure 6.1. Distribution of decay position for diffusing particles, with $D = 1$, $\alpha = 1$, $\sigma = -1$, for $N = 1,000$ particles.

to the ground after release from a seed pod into the air. This seed dispersal problem is discussed more in Chapter 13.

Let's begin our study of this problem of diffusion with decay with a stochastic simulation. To do this, we modify the algorithm from Chapter 4 that simulates diffusing particles to account for the possibility of degradation. At each time step, the particle can move or degrade, and if it degrades, its motion is terminated. The Matlab code to implement this is titled decay_probability.m, and the result of a simulation is shown in Figure 6.1. What we see in this figure may be a bit surprising; the distribution of decay position is clearly *not* a Gaussian distribution. But what is it?

To get some ideas, we start our analysis by simulating equation (6.3) numerically. A reasonable numerical scheme is to use the Crank–Nicolson method for the diffusion part and the Euler method (explicit forward time step) for the reaction term. After appropriately modifying (5.48) using (1.52), we obtain

$$(6.4) \qquad \frac{\mathbf{u}^{n+1} - \mathbf{u}^n}{\Delta t} = \frac{D}{2\Delta x^2} A(\mathbf{u}^{n+1} + A\mathbf{u}^n) + \sigma\alpha\mathbf{u}^n,$$

which leads to the time step algorithm

$$(6.5) \qquad (I - \frac{D\Delta t}{2\Delta x^2} A)\mathbf{u}^{n+1} = (I + \frac{D\Delta t}{2\Delta x^2} A + \sigma\alpha\Delta t)\mathbf{u}^n.$$

This algorithm is implemented by the Matlab code CN_diffusion_w_growth.m.

Figure 6.2 shows snapshots of the solution for several times for the two cases with $\sigma = -1$ and $\sigma = 1$. In Figure 6.3, the natural logarithm of the ratios of the solution to the solution of the diffusion equation (i.e., set $\alpha = 0$) are shown. An interesting feature of these solutions is that their ratios are functions of time, independent of space. This observation gives a clue as to how to solve the equation (6.3) analytically. That is, we try a solution of the form $u(x, t) = f(t)v(x, t)$ where $v(x, t)$ satisfies the diffusion equation. Obviously,

$$(6.6) \qquad \frac{\partial u}{\partial t} = \frac{df}{dt} v + f \frac{\partial v}{\partial t}, \qquad \frac{\partial^2 u}{\partial x^2} = f \frac{\partial^2 v}{\partial x^2},$$

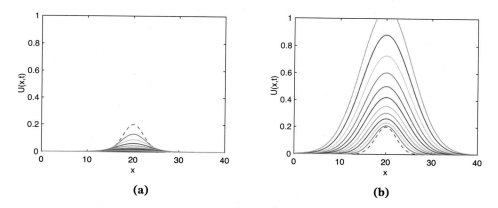

Figure 6.2. Solution of the equation (6.3), with (a) $\sigma\alpha = -0.2$ and (b) $\sigma\alpha = 0.2$, and $D = 1$, shown for equal time steps of $\Delta t = 1.2$. Initial data profile is shown as a dashed curve, and is the same for both plots.

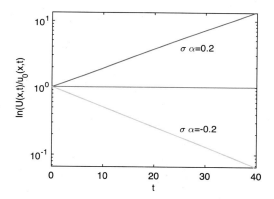

Figure 6.3. Natural logarithm of the ratio $\frac{u_k(x,t)}{u_0(x,t)}$ plotted as a function of time, with $\sigma\alpha = -0.2$ and $\sigma\alpha = 0.2$ and with $u_0(x,t)$ the solution of (6.3) with $\alpha = 0$.

and equation (6.3) is satisfied provided

$$(6.7) \qquad \frac{df}{dt} = \sigma\alpha f,$$

and the solution is

$$(6.8) \qquad f(t) = \exp(\sigma\alpha t),$$

which is not surprising, given the plots in Figure 6.3. In words, the effect of the linear reaction term is to scale the solution of the diffusion equation by an exponential factor, corresponding to the exponential growth or decay.

Now, we can answer the original question, to determine where particles are when they decay. We can keep track of the concentration of decayed particles by

$$(6.9) \qquad \frac{\partial v}{\partial t} = \alpha u$$

(assuming $\sigma = -1$). If u_0 particles are released from the origin $x = 0$ at time $t = 0$, then $u(x,t)$, the distribution of particles at time t (using (3.22)) is

$$(6.10) \qquad u(x,t) = \frac{u_0}{\sqrt{4\pi Dt}} \exp(-\frac{x^2}{4Dt} - \alpha t),$$

and when the process has run its course (all the particles have decayed), their distribution is given by

$$(6.11) \qquad v(x) = \alpha \int_0^\infty u(x,t)dt = \alpha \int_0^\infty \frac{u_0}{\sqrt{4\pi Dt}} \exp(-\frac{x^2}{4Dt} - \alpha t)dt.$$

Now, we use the fact that[1]

$$(6.13) \qquad \int_0^\infty \frac{1}{\sqrt{t}} \exp(-\frac{a^2}{t} - t)dt = \sqrt{\pi} \exp(-2|a|),$$

to conclude that

$$(6.14) \qquad v(x) = \frac{u_0}{2}\sqrt{\frac{\alpha}{D}} \exp(-\sqrt{\frac{\alpha}{D}}|x|).$$

It is easy to check that

$$(6.15) \qquad \int_{-\infty}^\infty v(x)dx = u_0,$$

as it must, since all of the u_0 particles initially released must eventually decay. It is also easy to check, using the code decay_probability.m, that (6.14) matches the data from the stochastic simulation very well. In fact, the dashed curve in Figure 6.1 is exactly the curve (6.14).

---

[1] Don't be alarmed if this formula is not immediately obvious to you. Fortunately, Maple and Mathematica know how to do this integral. But for those of you who still enjoy doing integrals by hand, the calculation is as follows: Assuming $a > 0$ (split the integral into two equal parts),

$$\int_0^\infty \frac{1}{\sqrt{t}} \exp(-\frac{a^2}{t} - t)dt = \frac{1}{2}\int_0^\infty \frac{1}{\sqrt{t}} \exp(-\frac{a^2}{t} - t)dt + \frac{1}{2}\int_0^\infty \frac{1}{\sqrt{t}} \exp(-\frac{a^2}{t} - t)dt$$

(add and subtract a term with $at^{-\frac{3}{2}}$)

$$= \int_0^\infty \left[\frac{1}{2}(\frac{1}{t^{\frac{1}{2}}} - \frac{a}{t^{\frac{3}{2}}})\exp(-\frac{a^2}{t} - t) + \frac{1}{2}(\frac{1}{t^{\frac{1}{2}}} + \frac{a}{t^{\frac{3}{2}}})\exp(-\frac{a^2}{t} - t)\right]dt$$

(complete the square in the exponential)

$$= \int_0^\infty \frac{1}{2}(\frac{1}{t^{\frac{1}{2}}} - \frac{a}{t^{\frac{3}{2}}})\exp\left(-(\frac{a}{t^{\frac{1}{2}}} + t^{\frac{1}{2}})^2 + 2a\right)dt$$

$$+ \int_0^\infty \frac{1}{2}(\frac{1}{t^{\frac{1}{2}}} + \frac{a}{t^{\frac{3}{2}}})\exp\left(-(\frac{a}{t^{\frac{1}{2}}} - t^{\frac{1}{2}})^2 - 2a\right)dt$$

(make the change of variables $s = at^{-\frac{1}{2}} \pm t^{\frac{1}{2}}$)

$$(6.12) \qquad = \exp(-2a)\int_{-\infty}^\infty \exp(-s^2)ds = \sqrt{\pi}\exp(-2a).$$

6.1.1. Growth on a Finite Domain. Suppose we have a population that can grow but is confined to a finite domain with homogeneous Dirichlet boundary conditions. Homogeneous Dirichlet boundary conditions correspond to a harsh external environment in which the organism is killed immediately upon leaving the confined region (with traps, for example). Apparently, then, there is a competition between favorable growth conditions on the interior and harsh conditions on the outside. The question is to determine the effect of the harsh outside world on the growth inside the domain.

To study this problem we wish to solve equation (6.3) with $\sigma = 1$ on the domain $0 < x < L$, subject to boundary conditions $u(0, t) = u(L, t) = 0$.

6.1.2. Interlude: Units, Scaling, and Dimensional Analysis. Before going any further in our study of this problem, it is important to describe a technique to simplify model equations, called *dimensional analysis* or *nondimensionalization*.

You may have already noticed that in earlier chapters, many of the simulations were done with diffusion coefficient $D = 1$ on a domain of length or radius $L = 1$. This choice completely ignores units and, while it may have been computationally convenient, without knowing the physical units, it is impossible to draw physical conclusions or compare with data. Units matter! Diffusion coefficients are always in units of (length)^2/time, and the diffusion coefficient of oxygen molecules in water (about 1.2×10^{-5}cm^2/s) is vastly different than that of mosquitoes (about 500 m^2/day, see Exercise 8.8).

If units matter so much, how could we get away with such simple choices of D and L? The answer is scaling. Let's think for a moment about the diffusion equation (3.2) on a one dimensional domain of length L, $0 < x < L$. Notice that the units associated with the time derivative $\frac{\partial u}{\partial t}$ are units of u/time, say concentration/time, and the units of $\frac{\partial^2 u}{\partial x^2}$ are concentration/(length)^2. The units of D are necessary to make the units of the left and right side of the equation match. Now, if we introduce the change of variables $x = L\xi$, use the chain rule

$$(6.16) \qquad \frac{\partial^2 u}{\partial x^2} = \frac{1}{L^2} \frac{\partial^2 u}{\partial \xi^2},$$

and ξ does not have units, it is dimensionless. But now we notice that $\frac{D}{L^2}$ has units of 1/time, which suggests a natural unit of time. That is, we set $t = \frac{L^2}{D}\tau$ so that τ is dimensionless, and then, from the chain rule

$$(6.17) \qquad \frac{\partial u}{\partial t} = \frac{D}{L^2} \frac{\partial u}{\partial \tau},$$

and in terms of the new unitless variables, the diffusion equation is

$$(6.18) \qquad \frac{\partial u}{\partial \tau} = \frac{\partial^2 u}{\partial \xi^2}$$

on the unit interval $0 < \xi < 1$, a problem for which there are no free parameters. Said another way, if $U(\xi, \tau)$ is the solution of the diffusion equation (6.18) on the interval

$0 < \xi < 1$, then the solution $u(x,t)$ of the diffusion equation (3.2) on the interval $0 < x < L$, is given by

$$(6.19) \qquad\qquad u(x,t) = U(\frac{x}{L}, \frac{Dt}{L^2}).$$

Take a moment to go back and look at all of the solutions of the diffusion equation that have been found so far, and you will see that that they are *always* expressed in terms of nondimensional variables. For example, expressions like $\exp(-\frac{x^2}{4Dt})$, $\exp(-\sqrt{\frac{\alpha}{D}}|x|)$, or $\exp(-\frac{n^2\pi^2 Dt}{L^2})$ and $\sin(\frac{n\pi x}{L})$ have dimensionless arguments, as they must.[2]

The point to be made is that in any physically or biologically motivated problem, there are parameters and variables that are measured in some units, or dimensions, and it is always possible to reduce the number of free parameters by rescaling. To see how this works in a slightly more complicated example, consider the diffusion equation with linear growth or decay which we introduced in the previous section,

$$(6.20) \qquad\qquad \frac{\partial u}{\partial t} = D\frac{\partial^2 u}{\partial x^2} \pm \alpha u,$$

on the domain $0 \leq x \leq L$, for which there are three dimensional parameters, L, the size of the domain, with units of length, $\alpha > 0$, the growth or decay rate, with units of inverse time, and D, the diffusion coefficient, with units of $(\text{length})^2/\text{time}$. To nondimensionalize this problem, we rescale space, setting $x = L\xi$, as before. However, the choice of rescaling for t is not unique, since there are two time scales in this problem, the diffusion time scale and the reaction time scale. If we set $t = \frac{L^2}{D}\tau$ as above, equation (6.20) becomes

$$(6.21) \qquad\qquad \frac{\partial u}{\partial \tau} = \frac{\partial^2 u}{\partial \xi^2} \pm \mu u,$$

where $\mu = \frac{\alpha L^2}{D}$ is dimensionless. If, instead, we set $t = \frac{\tau}{\alpha}$, equation (6.20) becomes

$$(6.22) \qquad\qquad \frac{\partial u}{\partial \tau} = \frac{1}{\mu}\frac{\partial^2 u}{\partial \xi^2} \pm u.$$

There may be other considerations which make one choice preferable to another, but, regardless, both of these equations are nondimensional and depend on only the one dimensionless parameter μ, rather than the three dimensional parameters of the original equation. This is significant as it simplifies the analysis (i.e., the bookkeeping) of this problem considerably. Nondimensionalization is an important feature of analysis in the remainder of this book.

6.1.3. End of Interlude. Because of nondimensionalization, solving equation (6.3) with $\sigma = 1$ on the domain $0 < x < L$, subject to boundary conditions $u(0,t) = u(L,t) = 0$ is equivalent to solving (6.21) with the plus sign on the interval $0 \leq \xi \leq 1$, where $\mu = \frac{\alpha L^2}{D}$. This we can do using separation of variables. We try a solution $u(\xi,\tau) = \exp(\lambda\tau)U(\xi)$ and find that

$$(6.23) \qquad\qquad U'' + (\mu - \lambda)U = 0,$$

---

[2] $\sin(x)$ and $\exp(x)$ do not make sense and cannot be evaluated if x has dimensional units; $\exp(2) = 7.3891$, but $\exp(2s)$ or $\exp(2m)$ are not defined and cannot be evaluated.

with λ some constant to be determined. Because of the Dirichlet boundary conditions it must be that

(6.24) $$U(\xi) = \sin(n\pi\xi),$$

with $\lambda = \lambda_n = \mu - n^2\pi^2$ for any integer $n > 0$. Since (6.21) is a linear equation, the general solution is the linear superposition of all possible solutions

(6.25) $$u(\xi, \tau) = \sum_n a_n \exp(\lambda_n \tau) \sin(n\pi\xi).$$

We learn from this that the solution decays to zero if $\lambda_1 < 0$ but grows exponentially if $\lambda_1 > 0$. In other words, growth occurs only if

(6.26) $$\mu = \frac{\alpha L^2}{D} > \pi^2,$$

i.e., if the growth rate and domain size are large enough compared to the diffusion coefficient. Thus, there is a critical size for the domain below which the population decays and above which the population grows and survives. Another way to think about this critical size is as the threshold for *sustainability*.

6.2. Growth with a Carrying Capacity—Fisher's Equation

Now we consider a diffusing and reproducing population for which there is population size-dependent death. We can represent this by the two reactions

(6.27) $$U \xrightarrow{\alpha} 2U, \qquad U + U \xrightarrow{\beta} U.$$

For these reactions, the conservation equation is

(6.28) $$\frac{\partial u}{\partial t} = D\frac{\partial^2 u}{\partial x^2} + \alpha u - \beta u^2.$$

It is common to write this equation in the slightly different form

(6.29) $$\frac{\partial u}{\partial t} = D\frac{\partial^2 u}{\partial x^2} + \alpha u(1 - \frac{u}{K}),$$

where $K = \frac{\alpha}{\beta}$ is called the *carrying capacity*. Rescaling the variables by setting $u = \frac{\alpha}{\beta}v = Kv$, $t = \frac{\tau}{\alpha}$, and $x = \sqrt{\frac{D}{\alpha}}\xi$, the equation simplifies to

(6.30) $$\frac{\partial v}{\partial \tau} = \frac{\partial^2 v}{\partial \xi^2} + v - v^2,$$

with no free parameters.

A second derivation of this equation is related to SIR epidemic models. Here we suppose that there are two populations, denoted by S and I, representing susceptible and infected populations, respectively. A susceptible individual can become infected by contact with another infected individual, but there is no possible recovery from the infection; an infected individual is permanently contagious. This process can be represented by the reaction

(6.31) $$S + I \xrightarrow{\alpha} 2I,$$

and the conservation equations for these two populations are

$$\text{(6.32)} \qquad \frac{\partial s}{\partial t} = D_s \frac{\partial^2 s}{\partial x^2} - \alpha s i, \qquad \frac{\partial i}{\partial t} = D_i \frac{\partial^2 i}{\partial x^2} + \alpha s i.$$

Under the assumption that the diffusion coefficient for both populations is the same, $D_s = D_i$, the quantity $s + i$ satisfies the diffusion equation and so has steady, constant solutions $s + i = S_0$. With this conserved quantity, the equation for i becomes

$$\text{(6.33)} \qquad \frac{\partial i}{\partial t} = D_i \frac{\partial^2 i}{\partial x^2} + \alpha i (S_0 - i).$$

Rescaling the variables by setting $i = S_0 v$, $t = \frac{\tau}{\alpha S_0}$, $x = \sqrt{\frac{D_i}{\alpha S_0}} \xi$, the equation simplifies to (6.30).

Equation (6.30) is well known, and is usually referred to as *Fisher's equation* (named after the geneticist R. A. Fisher, 1890–1962). Fisher [20] derived this equation to model the spread of an advantageous genetic feature in a population, an application which we do not discuss here. However, Fisher's equation is important in many other contexts as it describes the spread of a population whose growth is resource limited, or whose growth is governed by the *logistic equation*.

A first step to gaining an understanding of this process is with a simulation. We take two approaches. First, for the spread of an infection, we use an agent-based simulation, which will give us some insight into the stochastic features of this process. Second, we solve Fisher's equation by means of numerical integration.

How can we do an agent-based simulation? Recall from Chapter 4 that an agent-based simulation follows the position and state of a number of individual particles. Here there are two states, S and I, and the ordinary differential equation describing the change of state $S \to I$ is $\frac{ds}{dt} = -\alpha s i$, where s and i are concentrations. However, the change of state is a exponential process, so each individual particle in the S state can transition to the I state at rate αi, where i is the concentration of I particles in the vicinity of the S particle in question. So, an agent-based simulation of this process involves taking time steps of size Δt. First, move each of the particles diffusively (we know how to do this from Chapter 4). Then, determine which, if any, state transitions occur. Specifically, for each particle in the state S, estimate the local concentration of i by counting the number of I particles in some small neighborhood, and use this estimate $\tilde{i}$ to set the probability of transition in time step Δt to be $\alpha \tilde{i} \Delta t$. The transition occurs if $\alpha \tilde{i} \Delta t > R$, where R is a uniformly distributed random number $0 < R < 1$.

The Matlab code for this agent-based simulation in two dimensions is titled agent_SIR_2d.m, and in one dimension is agent_SIR_one_d.m. An example of the simulation for one dimensional spread is shown in Figure 6.4. For this simulation the parameters were $D = 1$, $\alpha = 1$, $S_0 = 1$, on a domain $0 < x < L = 100$, with time step $\Delta t = 0.01$. What we see is that the disease appears to spread in both directions from the place of the initial infection with (more or less) constant velocity. Of course, there are fluctuations to this rate of spread because the susceptible population has some spatial variations in its distribution. This observation becomes clearer with larger S_0, and the rate of spread also increases as S_0 increases. You should run this code for several

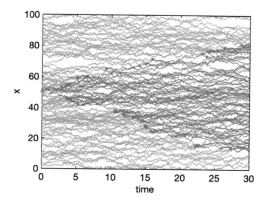

Figure 6.4. Example of spread of an epidemic with an agent-based simulation with parameters $D = 1$, $\alpha = 1$, $S_0 = 1$, on a domain $0 < x < L = 100$, with time step $\Delta t = 0.01$. (Green $= S$, Red $= I$.)

different values of parameters to get a better appreciation for these (and other) facts. (See Exercise 6.8.)

The second method is to solve Fisher's equation by means of numerical integration. For this, the Crank–Nicolson scheme for diffusion and forward Euler step for the reaction are the preferred methods. The Matlab code titled CN_Fisher.m is set up to integrate this with appropriate choice of parameters.

The numerical solution of this equation is shown in Figure 6.5. There we see that, following an initial transient, the solution appears to have a fixed shape moving with constant speed to the left and right. It is not difficult to verify (Exercise 6.11) using a comparison argument that if $0 \leq u(x,0) \leq 1$, then the solution of Fisher's equation satisfies $0 \leq u(x,t) \leq 1$ for all time $t > 0$.

Motivated by the numerical solution, we try to find traveling wave solutions of this equation. By a traveling wave solution, we mean a translation-invariant solution

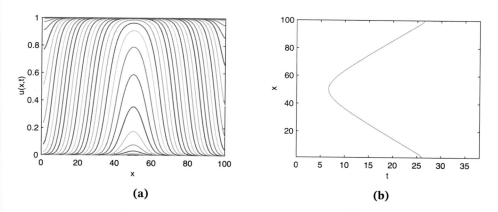

(a) **(b)**

Figure 6.5. (a) Solution of the Fisher equation (6.30) plotted as a function of position for equal time increments $\Delta t = 1$. (b) The $x - t$ locus of the level set $u(x,t) = 0.5$.

of (6.30) with a fixed form that provides a transition between the two rest states and translates with constant speed. That is, we seek a solution of (6.30) of the form $v(\xi, \tau) = U(\xi - c\tau)$, for some (yet to be determined) value of c, with the feature that $U(-\infty) = 1$, $U(\infty) = 0$. The new variable $\zeta = \xi - c\tau$, called the traveling wave coordinate, has the property that fixed values move in space-time with fixed speed c. When written as a function of ζ, the wave appears stationary.

To see if this is possible, we substitute this form into the governing equation (6.30) and find the ordinary differential equation for $U(\zeta)$,

$$(6.34) \qquad \frac{d^2 U}{d\zeta^2} + c \frac{dU}{d\zeta} + U(1 - U) = 0.$$

The challenge is to see if this ordinary differential equation has trajectories that connect $U = 1$ with $U = 0$, keeping U positive and U' negative, and the most natural way to approach this problem is using phase portrait analysis. To do so, we write the equation (6.34) as the first order system

$$(6.35) \qquad \frac{dU}{d\zeta} = \frac{W}{c}, \qquad \frac{dW}{d\zeta} = -c(W + U(1 - U)).$$

The phase portrait in Figure 6.6(a) (computed using Matlab code Fisher_waves_plot.m) shows the nullcline $\frac{dW}{d\zeta} = 0$ as a dashed curve.

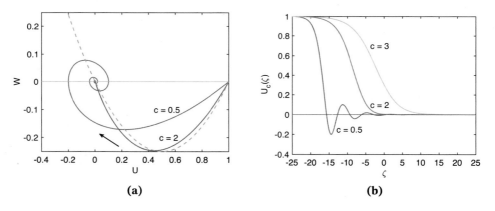

(a)   (b)

Figure 6.6. (a) Trajectories in the phase plane connecting the saddle point at $U = 1$ with the critical point at $U = 0$ with $c = 0.5$ and $c = 2.0$. (b) Traveling wave solution profiles $U_c(\zeta)$ plotted as a function of ζ, for $c = 0.5, 2.0$, and 3.0.

It is clear that there are exactly two critical points, namely, $W = 0$ and $U = 0$ or $U = 1$. The local linearized system, linearized around $U_0 = 0$ or 1 is

$$(6.36) \qquad \frac{du}{d\zeta} = \frac{w}{c}, \qquad \frac{dw}{d\zeta} = -cw - c(1 - 2U_0)u.$$

The nature of each critical point is determined by the eigenvalues of the Jacobian matrix

$$(6.37) \qquad J = \begin{pmatrix} 0 & \frac{1}{c} \\ c(-1 + 2U_0) & -c \end{pmatrix},$$

and these eigenvalues are the roots of the quadratic polynomial

(6.38) $$\lambda^2 + c\lambda + 1 - 2U_0 = 0,$$

which are

(6.39) $$\lambda = -\frac{c}{2} \pm \frac{1}{2}\sqrt{c^2 - 4(1 - 2U_0)}.$$

Clearly, with $U_0 = 1$, there are two real eigenvalues of opposite sign, so that the critical point at $U_0 = 1$ is a saddle point. The critical point $U_0 = 0$ is a node if $c > 2$, whereas it is a spiral point if $c < 2$. We conclude that there is a trajectory connecting the saddle point at $U_0 = 1$ with the critical point at $U_0 = 1$ for all values of $c > 0$. However, this trajectory has $U > 0$ and $U' < 0$ along the entire trajectory only if $c \geq 2$. The conclusion of this analysis is that Fisher's equation has nonnegative traveling wave solutions for all values of $c \geq 2$. However, which of these traveling wave solutions is the one that is seen following an initial transient, as in Figure 6.5?

To answer this question we invoke a comparison principle. Suppose $u(\xi, 0)$ is non-negative, strictly less than 1, and is zero for all x with $|x|$ sufficiently large. Then, it is possible to find a shift ϕ of the trajectory $U_c(\zeta)$ for any value of $c \geq 2$ so that $u(\xi, 0) \leq U_c(\xi + \phi)$. Now, we show that $u(\xi, t) \leq U_c(\xi + \phi - c\tau)$ for all $\tau \geq 0$. That is, let $v(\xi, \tau) = U_c(\xi + \phi - 2\tau) - u(\xi, \tau)$. Then, $v(\xi, 0) \geq 0$. Furthermore,

(6.40) $$\frac{\partial v}{\partial \tau} = \frac{\partial^2 v}{\partial \xi^2} + (1 - u - U_c)v.$$

It follows from the comparison theorem (Section 5.6) that $v(\xi, \tau)$ is nonnegative for all $t \geq 0$. Consequently, $u(\xi, 0)$ evolves into a profile which does not travel faster than speed $c = 2$.

In terms of original (dimensioned) variables, the solution $u(x, t)$ of (6.28) approaches $\frac{\alpha}{\beta}U(\sqrt{\frac{\alpha}{D}}(x - 2\sqrt{D\alpha}t))$ for large t, a traveling wave solution with speed $2\sqrt{D\alpha}$. Careful examination of Figure 6.5 (use a ruler to measure the distances between curves, or estimate the slope of the level set curve $u(x, t) = 0.5$) verifies that the speed of propagation for the computed solution is 2, as it should be.

6.2.1. On a Bounded Domain. Now we consider a slightly different problem, namely Fisher's equation (6.28) on the bounded one-dimensional domain $0 < x < L$ subject to homogeneous Dirichlet boundary conditions $u(0, t) = u(L, t) = 0$. In dimensionless terms, this corresponds to solving (6.30) on the domain $0 < \xi < Y$, where $Y = \sqrt{\frac{\alpha}{D}}L$. A biological situation for this may be the somewhat unreasonable situation of a game preserve with no constraints (i.e., fences) at the boundary and where animal occupants are killed immediately whenever they leave the preserve.

As usual, a preliminary analysis of this problem can be gained by numerical simulation. What is shown in Figure 6.7 are the solutions for two different domains, one with $Y = 2$ and the other for $Y = 5$, starting with initial data shown as dashed curves (computed using Matlab code CN_Fisher_w_Dirichlet.m). What is seen is that there are two different outcomes depending on the size of the domain. These are eventual extinctions ($v \to 0$) if Y is small, and long-term survival if Y is large enough.

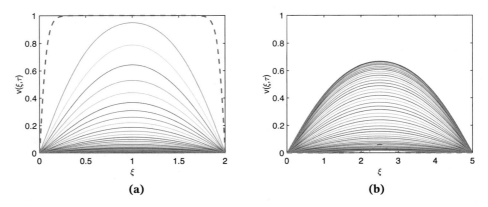

Figure 6.7. Time dependent solutions of Fisher's equation with Dirichlet boundary data on a domain with (a) $Y = 2$ and (b) $Y = 5$. The initial data profile shown as a dashed curve. Solutions in (a) decay to zero because the domain is too small, while solutions in (b) approach a positive steady state because the domain is sufficiently large.

To make the observation more precise, we do two things: first we do a linear stability analysis for the trivial solution $v = 0$, and then we look for steady solutions of the Fisher's equation. The linear stability analysis examines solutions of the linearized equation

$$(6.41) \qquad \frac{\partial v}{\partial \tau} = \frac{\partial^2 v}{\partial \xi^2} + v,$$

with homogeneous boundary conditions on the interval $0 < \xi < Y$. From above, we already know how to solve this equation using separation of variables and find that there are an infinite number of solution given by

$$(6.42) \qquad v_n(\xi, \tau) = \exp(\lambda_n \tau) \sin\left(\frac{n\pi\xi}{Y}\right),$$

where $\lambda_n = -\frac{n^2 \pi^2}{Y^2} + 1$. The solution with the largest growth rate has $n = 1$. Consequently, the solution $v = 0$ is stable if $\lambda_1 < 0$, i.e., if $Y < \pi$ and unstable if $\lambda_1 > 0$, i.e., if $Y > \pi$.

The search for steady solutions of the nonlinear equation is done by examining the steady equation (i.e., set $\frac{\partial v}{\partial \tau} = 0$)

$$(6.43) \qquad \frac{d^2 v}{d\xi^2} + v(1 - v) = 0, \qquad v(0) = v(Y) = 0,$$

in its phase portrait (shown in Figure 6.8, created using Matlab code Fisher_ss_pp.m),

$$(6.44) \qquad \frac{dv}{d\xi} = w, \qquad \frac{dw}{d\xi} = -v(1 - v).$$

Clearly, there are two critical points, with $w = 0$ and $v = v_0$ where $v_0 = 0$ or $v_0 = 1$. The linearized system is

$$(6.45) \qquad \frac{dV}{d\xi} = W, \qquad \frac{dW}{d\xi} = (2v_0 - 1)V,$$

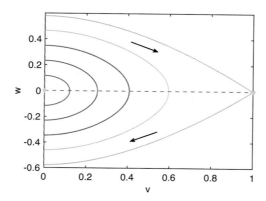

Figure 6.8. Phase portrait for the steady state Fisher's equation (6.43).

and the eigenvalues of the Jacobian matrix are

(6.46)
$$\lambda = \pm\sqrt{2v_0 - 1}.$$

Consequently, the critical point at $v_0 = 0$ is a center because the eigenvalues are purely imaginary, and the critical point at $v_0 = 1$ is a saddle point because the eigenvalues are real and of opposite sign. This means that there is a family of trajectories that encircle the origin, each having two intersections with $v = 0$. This family of trajectories is enclosed by a trajectory that intersects the saddle point exactly. These are the stable and unstable manifolds of the saddle point.

Close to the origin, these nearly circular trajectories are approximately described by

(6.47)
$$v(\xi) = \sin(\xi),$$

so the distance in ξ required to traverse between zeros is $\xi = \pi$. This suggests that at $Y = \pi$ there is a *bifurcation* of a nontrivial solution of the boundary value problem from the trivial (i.e., identically zero) solution of the boundary value problem.

The phase portrait trajectories can be found explicitly. Multiply the equation (6.43) by $\frac{dv}{d\xi}$ and integrate with respect to ξ once to find

(6.48)
$$\frac{1}{2}w^2 + F(v) = F(\hat{v}),$$

where $F(v) = \frac{v^2}{2} - \frac{v^3}{3}$, and $\hat{v}$ is the intercept of the trajectory on the v axis. The w intercept on the w-axis is

(6.49)
$$\hat{w} = \sqrt{2F(\hat{v})}.$$

We solve (6.48) for w and find

(6.50)
$$\frac{dv}{d\xi} = \sqrt{2F(\hat{v}) - 2F(v)},$$

so that

(6.51)
$$Y = 2\int_0^{\hat{v}} \frac{dv}{\sqrt{2F(\hat{v}) - 2F(v)}}.$$

The curve $Y = Y(\hat{v})$ is shown as a solid curve in Figure 6.9.

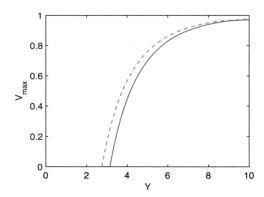

Figure 6.9. Plot of the maximum value of the steady solution of Fisher's equation as a function of dimensionless domain size $Y = \sqrt{\frac{\alpha}{D}}L$ with boundary conditions (6.57) with $\delta = \infty$ (solid curve) and $\delta = 5$ (dashed curve).

There is a practical matter associated with calculating this curve numerically that needs to be mentioned. As can be seen, the integral (6.51) is singular and therefore difficult to compute numerically. In fact, from a practical point of view, the formula (6.51) is effectively useless. A much better numerical algorithm is to compute phase plane trajectories by solving (6.45) as an initial value problem, starting at $v = 0$, $w = \hat{w}$ and terminating the integration when w hits zero, then recording the value of v and y at this v-axis intersection. This is how the curve in Figure 6.9 was calculated.

The conclusion of this analysis is interesting. It tells us that the organisms cannot survive on a preserve whose domain size L is too small, $L < \sqrt{\frac{D}{\alpha}}\pi$. Said another way, organisms for which D is large or α (their reproductive rate) is small require proportionately more terrain in order to survive.

6.2.1.1. *With a Robin Boundary Condition*. Rather than using the (rather draconian) Dirichlet condition, which requires instant death whenever an organism strays outside its growth domain, suppose that the organism has a niche-like growth rate, with logistic growth on the interior of a domain $0 < x < L$ and only decay outside this region. In mathematical language this is

$$(6.52) \qquad \frac{\partial u}{\partial t} = D\frac{\partial^2 u}{\partial x^2} + f(x, u),$$

where

$$(6.53) \qquad f(x, u) = \begin{cases} \alpha u - \beta u^2 & 0 < x < L \\ -ku & \text{elsewhere.} \end{cases}$$

It is again useful to introduce dimensionless variables as before, setting $u = \frac{\alpha}{\beta}v$, $t = \frac{\tau}{\alpha}$, and $x = \sqrt{\frac{D}{\alpha}}\xi$, in terms of which the governing equation becomes

$$(6.54) \qquad \frac{\partial u}{\partial \tau} = \frac{\partial^2 v}{\partial \xi^2} + F(\xi, v),$$

where

(6.55)
$$F(\xi, v) = \begin{cases} v(1 - v) & 0 < \xi < Y \\ -\delta^2 v & \text{elsewhere,} \end{cases}$$

where $\delta^2 = \frac{k}{\alpha}$, $Y = \sqrt{\frac{D}{\alpha}} L$.

We are looking for steady solutions of this equation, and so for ξ outside the niche domain,

(6.56)
$$v(\xi) = \begin{cases} v_0 \exp(\delta \xi) & \xi < 0 \\ v_Y \exp(-\delta(\xi - Y)) & \xi > Y, \end{cases}$$

which can be related to the Robin boundary conditions

(6.57)
$$v_\xi(0) = \delta v(0), \qquad v_\xi(Y) = -\delta v(Y).$$

Now, the search for steady solutions reduces to exactly the same phase-portrait equations, but now hitting the curve $w = \delta v$ at $\xi = 0$ and hitting the curve $w = -\delta v$ at $\xi = Y$ (see Figure 6.10).

A linearized analysis reveals the bifurcation point. That is, for small v,

(6.58)
$$v'' + v = 0,$$

so that $v = v_0 \cos(\xi - \frac{Y}{2})$, and then to satisfy the two Robin boundary conditions, it must be that

(6.59)
$$\sin(\frac{Y}{2}) = \delta \cos(\frac{Y}{2}),$$

which happens when

(6.60)
$$Y = Y_0(\delta) \equiv 2 \tan^{-1} \delta.$$

Notice that $\lim_{\delta \to \infty} Y(\delta) = 2$, as it should be. Clearly, sustainability is easier to achieve with a Robin condition than with a Dirichlet condition.

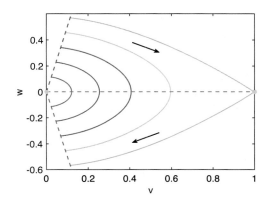

Figure 6.10. Phase portrait for the steady state Fisher's equation (6.43) with Robin boundary conditions (6.57) shown dashed, shown for $\delta^2 = 5$.

6.2.1.2. *With a Moving Niche.* The data are very convincing that we Earth dwellers are in a phase of global warming. One of the interesting questions related to global warming and global climate change is how populations of plants or animals will be able to adapt to changing environmental conditions. There are two possible ways that organisms can survive this environmental change. They could adapt through genetic mutation and selection to the gradually changing environment, or they could migrate along with the migrating niche in which they prosper. To study this second possibility, we use a simple model of a moving niche, by assuming that the population diffuses and grows but that the favorable environmental niche is moving. Thus, we take for the dynamics (in nondimensional units)

$$\frac{\partial v}{\partial \tau} = \frac{\partial^2 v}{\partial \xi^2} + F(\xi - C\tau, v),$$

(6.61)

where $F(\xi, v)$ is specified in (6.55) and $c = \sqrt{D\alpha}C > 0$ is the constant speed with which the niche is moving.

To determine if the population can survive this change, we look for solutions of the form $v(\xi, \tau) = U(\xi - C\tau)$ and find that $U(\xi)$ must satisfy the ordinary differential equation

$$\frac{d^2U}{d\xi^2} - C\frac{dU}{d\xi} + f(\xi, U) = 0.$$

(6.62)

Once again, we have an equation that we can study using phase plane techniques.

First, for $\xi < 0$, the solution takes the form

$$U(\xi) = U_0 \exp(\lambda_+ \xi),$$

(6.63)

and for $\xi > Y$, the solution takes the form

$$U(\xi) = U_Y \exp(\lambda_-(\xi - Y)),$$

(6.64)

where $\lambda_\pm$ are the roots of the quadratic polynomial $\lambda^2 + C\lambda - \delta^2 = 0$, i.e.,

$$\lambda_\pm = \frac{1}{2}(-C \pm \sqrt{C^2 + 4\delta^2}).$$

(6.65)

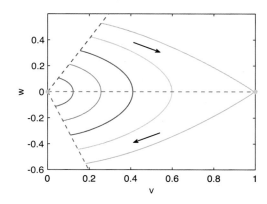

Figure 6.11. Phase portrait for the equation (6.62) with boundary conditions (6.66) shown dashed with $C = 1.0$ and $\delta^2 = 2.5$.

Consequently, the matching conditions at $\xi = 0$ and $\xi = Y$ are

$$(6.66) \qquad U'(0) = \lambda_+ U(0), \qquad U'(L) = \lambda_- U(L).$$

For $0 < \xi < Y$, the governing equation is

$$(6.67) \qquad 0 = U'' + CU' + U(1 - U).$$

The phase portrait for the solutions we seek is shown in Figure 6.11.

We can determine the bifurcation point above which the population survives by solving the linearized problem

$$(6.68) \qquad 0 = U'' + CU' + U.$$

We take $C < 2$, so that the origin is a spiral point rather than a saddle point. This means that the solution is

$$(6.69) \qquad U(\xi) = U_0 \exp(-\frac{C}{2}\xi) \sin(\mu\xi - \phi),$$

where $\mu = \frac{1}{2}\sqrt{4 - C^2}$. The two matching conditions are

$$(6.70) \qquad \frac{C}{2} \sin(\phi) + \mu \cos(\phi) = -\beta \sin(\phi),$$

$$(6.71) \qquad -\frac{C}{2} \sin(\mu Y - \phi) + \mu \cos(\mu Y - \phi) = \lambda_- \sin(\mu Y - \phi).$$

Eliminate ϕ from these equations and one finds (after applying some trigonometric identities) that

$$(6.72) \qquad \tan(\frac{\mu Y}{2}) = \sqrt{\frac{4\delta^2 + C^2}{4 - C^2}},$$

which implies that

$$(6.73) \qquad Y = \frac{4}{\sqrt{4 - C^2}} \tan^{-1} \sqrt{\frac{4\delta^2 + C^2}{4 - C^2}}.$$

Notice that in the limit $C \to 0$ this reduces to (6.60), as it must. A plot of this curve is

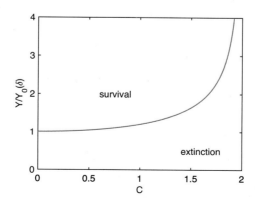

Figure 6.12. Plot of critical value of the length of the domain $\frac{Y}{Y_0(\delta)}$ as a function of niche velocity C, shown for $\delta^2 = 5$.

shown in Figure 6.12. It is not surprising that Y is an increasing function of C, since this implies that the domain size needed to survive a changing environment is larger than required in a static environment. Furthermore, as $C \to 2$, the required domain size increases to infinity, and the organisms cannot survive if $C > 2$ ($c > 2\sqrt{D\alpha}$), i.e., if the speed of the moving environment is larger than the natural spreading speed of the organism.

6.2.1.3. *On a Two-Dimensional Domain.* Now we have to face the inconvenient fact that no animal preserves are one dimensional, but they are two-dimensional with irregular boundaries. We expect that, as with one-dimensional domains, there is a threshold for the critical size of the domain in order to guarantee survival, but determination of this critical size is more challenging than in the one-dimensional case.

What are some of the challenges? First of all, we might like to do a numerical simulation. However, doing so requires discretization of the Laplacian operator on an irregular, two-dimensional grid, and this requires some extra thought, especially if the domain is not rectangular. The second challenge comes in determining if there is a threshold size, and if so, what it is. In one spatial dimension, the threshold analysis could be done using phase plane techniques. In higher dimensions, no such analysis is possible.

To illustrate, let's consider the case where the domain is a square with equal sides of length L. The governing Fisher's equation is

$$(6.74) \qquad \frac{\partial u}{\partial t} = D\left(\frac{\partial^2 u}{\partial x^2} + \frac{\partial^2 u}{\partial y^2}\right) + \alpha u - \beta u^2,$$

to be solved on the domain $0 < x, y < L$, and is subject to Dirichlet boundary conditions $u(0, y) = u(L, y) = u(x, 0) = u(x, L) = 0$. As usual, it is convenient to introduce the dimensionless variables (slightly different than above) $x = L\xi, y = L\eta, t = \frac{L^2}{D}\tau, u = \frac{\alpha}{\beta}v$, in terms of which Fisher's equation (6.74) becomes

$$(6.75) \qquad \frac{\partial v}{\partial \tau} = \frac{\partial^2 v}{\partial \xi^2} + \frac{\partial^2 v}{\partial \eta^2} + \mu(v - v^2),$$

where $\mu = \frac{L^2}{D}\alpha$, on the domain $0 < \xi, \eta < 1$, subject to the homogeneous boundary conditions $v(0, \eta) = v(1, \eta) = v(\xi, 0) = v(\xi, 1) = 0$. This is convenient because there is only one free parameter in the problem, namely $\mu = \frac{L^2}{D}\alpha$.

Numerical simulation of this problem requires that we discretize the equation (6.75). The natural discretization is to denote $v_{i,j} = v(ih, jh)$, where $h = \frac{1}{N}$ is the discrete grid size, and $0 \le i, j \le N$. Then, the natural discretization of the Laplacian is

$$(6.76) \qquad \left(\frac{\partial^2 v}{\partial \xi^2} + \frac{\partial^2 v}{\partial \eta^2}\right)_{i,j} \approx \frac{1}{h^2}(v_{i,j+1} + v_{i,j-1} + v_{i+1,j} + v_{i-1,j} - 4v_{i,j}).$$

Coding this in Matlab is a bit more complicated than for a one-dimensional grid, but that is what can be found in the Matlab code CN_Fisher_w_Dirichlet_2d.m. You are welcome to run this code to see that there is a survival threshold.

To determine the threshold analytically, we do a linear stability analysis. The linearized equation is

$$(6.77) \qquad \frac{\partial u}{\partial \tau} = \frac{\partial^2 v}{\partial \xi^2} + \frac{\partial^2 v}{\partial \eta^2} + \mu v,$$

and, using separation of variables, we find solutions of the form

$$(6.78) \qquad v_{m,n} = \exp(\lambda_{m,n}\tau)\sin(n\pi\xi)\sin(m\pi\eta),$$

where $\lambda_{m,n} = -\pi^2(m^2 + n^2) + \mu$. The largest growth rate is for $m = n = 1$, and so the zero solution is stable if $\lambda_{1,1} < 0$ while it is unstable if $\lambda_{1,1} > 0$. Consequently, the zero solution is stable if $-2\pi^2 + \mu < 0$, and unstable if $-2\pi^2 + \mu > 0$, i.e., if $\frac{L^2}{D}\alpha > 2\pi^2$. If the origin is unstable, then a small population will grow and survive. Thus, $\frac{L^2}{D}\alpha = 2\pi^2$ is the survival threshold.

The corresponding analysis for a circular domain is in Exercise 6.14.

6.3. Resource Consumption

Now consider the situation in which organisms, say bacteria, consume a resource substrate, such as glucose, of which there is a finite supply. For example, suppose bacteria are grown on an agar gel on a Petrie dish. The reaction describing this is

$$(6.79) \qquad U + S \xrightarrow{\alpha} 2U.$$

The units on U and S are such that one unit of S converts into one unit of U. We assume that both the glucose and the bacteria move by diffusion. Consequently, the differential equations describing this evolution (in one spatial dimension) are

$$(6.80) \qquad \frac{\partial u}{\partial t} = D_u \frac{\partial^2 u}{\partial x^2} + \alpha us,$$

$$(6.81) \qquad \frac{\partial s}{\partial t} = D_g \frac{\partial^2 s}{\partial x^2} - \alpha us,$$

where s represents the concentration of the resource substrate (i.e., the glucose). Numerical simulation of this system of equations is shown in Figure 6.13. The Matlab code for this simulation is titled CN_diffusion_gluc_micro_X.m. This simulation again suggests that there should be a traveling wave solution. The first step of the analysis is to simplify the equations by introducing scaled variables $t = \frac{\tau}{\alpha}$, $x = \sqrt{\frac{D_u}{\alpha}}\xi$, in terms of which the equations become

$$(6.82) \qquad \frac{\partial u}{\partial \tau} = \frac{\partial^2 u}{\partial \xi^2} + us,$$

$$(6.83) \qquad \frac{\partial s}{\partial \tau} = \delta \frac{\partial^2 s}{\partial \xi^2} - us.$$

where $\delta = \frac{D_g}{D_u}$.

Now, to examine the possibility of traveling wave solutions, we look for a solution of the form $u(\xi, \tau) = U(\xi - c\tau)$, $s(\xi, \tau) = S(\xi - c\tau)$, and find the system of ordinary

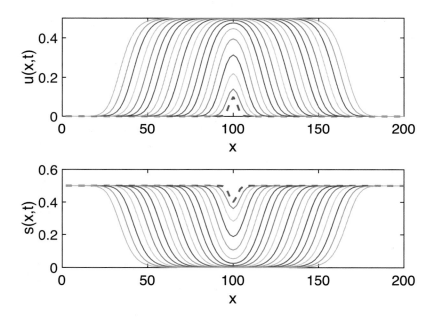

Figure 6.13. Solution of the bacteria-glucose system (top and bottom images, respectively), with initial profile for each shown dashed. For this simulation $D_u = D_g = 0.01$, $\alpha = 0.01$.

differential equations

$$(6.84) \qquad 0 = \frac{d^2U}{d\zeta^2} + c\frac{dU}{d\zeta} + US,$$

$$(6.85) \qquad 0 = \delta\frac{d^2S}{d\zeta^2} + c\frac{dS}{d\zeta} - US,$$

where $\zeta = \xi - c\tau$. Before we dive into a full-fledged analysis of these equations, let's examine the special case with equal diffusion coefficients $\delta = 1$. Then, adding the two equations together yields

$$(6.86) \qquad \frac{d^2}{d\zeta^2}(U + S) + c\frac{d}{d\zeta}(U + S) = 0.$$

This can be integrated once to get

$$(6.87) \qquad \frac{d}{d\zeta}(U + S) + c(U + S) = c,$$

where, without loss of generality, we assume that $\lim_{\zeta\to\pm\infty}(U + S) = 1$. In fact, the only bounded solution of (6.87) is $U + S = 1$. Substituting this into the equation for U, we find

$$(6.88) \qquad \frac{d^2U}{d\zeta^2} + c\frac{dU}{d\zeta} + U(1 - U) = 0,$$

which is Fisher's equation in traveling wave form. It follows that traveling wave solutions exist for $c \geq 2$.

Now let's try the general case. As before, add the two equations together and integrate once to get

(6.89)
$$\frac{d}{d\zeta}(U + \delta S) + c(U + S) = c.$$

We cannot solve this equation as before, so we write the two governing equations as a third order system by introducing the variable W,

(6.90)
$$\frac{dU}{d\zeta} = W,$$

(6.91)
$$\delta\frac{dS}{d\zeta} = c - W - c(U + S),$$

(6.92)
$$\frac{dW}{d\zeta} = -cW - US.$$

The two critical points are at $W = 0$ with $U = 0$, $S = 1$, or $U = 1$, $S = 0$. The stability of these two critical points is found by examining the eigenvalues of the Jacobian matrix,

(6.93)
$$J = \begin{pmatrix} 0 & 0 & 1 \\ -\frac{c}{\delta} & -\frac{c}{\delta} & -\frac{1}{\delta} \\ -S_0 & -U_0 & -c \end{pmatrix}.$$

The eigenvalues of J are the roots of the cubic polynomial

(6.94)
$$p_0(\lambda) = -(\delta\lambda^2 + c\lambda - 1)(\lambda + c),$$

when $S_0 = 0$, $U_0 = 1$, and

(6.95)
$$p_1(\lambda) = -(\lambda^2 + c\lambda + 1)(\lambda + \frac{c}{\delta}),$$

when $S_0 = 1$, $U_0 = 0$. The polynomial p_0 has two negative roots (assuming $c > 0$) and one positive root, so that the critical point at $U_0 = 1$, $S_0 = 0$ is a saddle point. The eigenvector associated with the eigenvalue λ is

(6.96)
$$\phi = \begin{pmatrix} -1 \\ \lambda(c + \lambda) \\ -\lambda \end{pmatrix},$$

which, for the one positive eigenvalue, points in the U decreasing, S increasing, and W decreasing direction. On the other hand, the polynomial p_1 has three roots with negative real part, one of which is $\lambda = -\frac{c}{\delta}$. The other two roots are complex if $c < 2$ and real if $c \geq 2$. Consequently, if $c \geq 2$, there is a trajectory connecting the saddle point at $U = 1$, $S = 0$ to the node at $S = 1$, $U = 0$ for which S and U are always positive and W is always negative. We conclude that there is a traveling wave solution for $c \geq 2$, as with Fisher's equation. Therefore, as with Fisher's equation, the wave speed is $\sqrt{2D_u\alpha}$ in original dimensional variables. It is an easy matter to calculate this traveling wave profile numerically, and this is shown in Figure 6.14, calculated for $\delta = 20$, and $c = 2$ (calculated using the Matlab code resource_consumption_profiles.m).

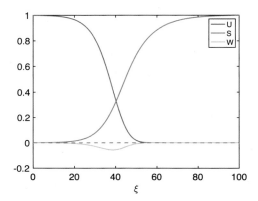

Figure 6.14. Plots of the traveling wave profile $U(\zeta)$, $S(\zeta)$, $W(\zeta)$ for the bacteria-glucose system as functions of ζ for $\delta = 20$, $c = 2$.

6.4. Spread of Rabies—SIR with Diffusion

It has been observed in England that rabid foxes tend to travel across much larger distances than rabies free animals. This observation has led to consideration of the spread of an infectious disease where the infected animals diffuse, but susceptible animals do not [**51**]. For this we consider the standard SIR disease dynamics

(6.97) $$S + I \xrightarrow{\alpha} 2I, \qquad I \xrightarrow{\beta} R,$$

where S represents the susceptible population, I represents the infected population, and R represents the recovered (or removed) population. The corresponding differential equations are

(6.98) $$\frac{\partial s}{\partial t} = -\alpha s i,$$

(6.99) $$\frac{\partial i}{\partial t} = \alpha s i - \beta i + D\frac{\partial^2 i}{\partial x^2}.$$

Introducing dimensionless variables $\sigma = \frac{s}{S_0}$, $u = \frac{i}{S_0}$, $t = \frac{\tau}{\alpha S_0}$, and $x = \sqrt{\frac{D}{\alpha S_0}}\xi$, we find the dimensionless equations

(6.100) $$\frac{\partial \sigma}{\partial \tau} = -\sigma u,$$

(6.101) $$\frac{\partial u}{\partial \tau} = \sigma u - \eta u + \frac{\partial^2 u}{\partial \xi^2},$$

depending on the single parameter $\eta = \frac{\beta}{\alpha S_0} = \frac{1}{R_0}$. A simulation of these equations is shown in Figure 6.15, and was computed using the Matlab code CN_diffusion_SIR.m.

As you can see from this figure, an initial amount of u grows and spreads as a traveling wave, leading to a permanent decrease in the amount of σ, while the spreading bulge of u is only temporary, as recovery eventually restores u to zero. We would like to determine how fast this infection spreads and how much of the initial susceptible population is affected by it.

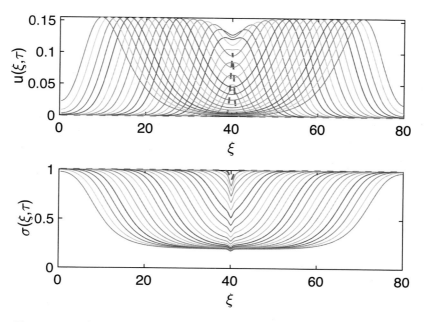

Figure 6.15. Solution of the SIR model system, with the initial profile for each shown dashed. For this simulation $\eta = 0.5$.

To answer these questions, as before, we look for traveling wave solutions of the form

$$(6.102) \qquad \sigma = S(\xi - c\tau), \qquad u = U(\xi - c\tau),$$

and find the system of equations

$$(6.103) \qquad c\frac{dS}{d\zeta} = SU,$$

$$(6.104) \qquad \frac{dU}{d\zeta} = W,$$

$$(6.105) \qquad \frac{dW}{d\zeta} = -cW + \eta U - SU,$$

where $\zeta = \xi - c\tau$.

The key to solving this system of equations is to first notice that with $\eta = 0$, $S + U + \frac{1}{c}W$ is a conserved quantity. To incorporate the η contribution, we try to find a conserved quantity of the form

$$(6.106) \qquad H = S + U + \frac{1}{c}W + G(S).$$

Since

$$(6.107) \qquad H' = S' + U' + \frac{1}{c}W' + G'(S)S' = \frac{1}{c}G'(S)SU + \frac{\eta}{c}U,$$

$H' = 0$, provided $G'(S)S = -\eta$ or $G(S) = -\eta \ln S$. In other words,

$$(6.108) \qquad H = S - \eta \ln S + U + \frac{1}{c}W$$

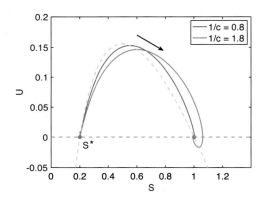

Figure 6.16. Phase portrait for the system (6.110)–(6.111) with $\eta = 0.497$, $S^* = 0.2$, and the $\frac{dU}{d\zeta} = 0$ nullcline shown as a dashed curve, with two trajectories leaving the saddle point at S^* and approaching $S = 1$, for parameters $\frac{1}{c} = 0.8$ and 1.8.

is a constant.

Now, suppose that the initial state has $S = 1$, $U = 0$, $W = 0$. Then,

$$(6.109) \qquad S - \eta \ln S + U + \frac{1}{c}W = 1$$

for all ζ so that the three variable system reduces to

$$(6.110) \qquad \frac{dS}{d\zeta} = \frac{1}{c}SU,$$

$$(6.111) \qquad \frac{1}{c}\frac{dU}{d\zeta} = 1 + \eta \ln S - S - U.$$

As with previous examples, we determine the behavior of this system by examining its phase portrait (see Figure 6.16, computed using the Matlab code SIR_wave_pp.m). First, the critical points have $U = 0$ and are roots of the equation $1 + \eta \ln S - S = 0$. One of these roots is $S = 1$, and there is a second root, $0 < S^* < 1$, provided $\eta < 1$. At this root, $S^* < \eta$.

For a linear stability analysis, we examine the linearized system

$$(6.112) \qquad \frac{dS}{d\zeta} = \frac{1}{c}S_0 U,$$

$$(6.113) \qquad \frac{1}{c}\frac{dU}{d\zeta} = \eta\frac{S}{S_0} - S - U,$$

where $S_0 = S^*$ or 1. The characteristic polynomial for this system is

$$(6.114) \qquad p(\lambda) = \lambda^2 + c\lambda + S_0 - \eta,$$

so that the eigenvalues are

$$(6.115) \qquad \lambda = -\frac{c}{2} \pm \frac{1}{2}\sqrt{c^2 - 4(S_0 - \eta)}.$$

Since $S^* < \eta$, the critical point at $S_0 = S^*$ is a saddle point, since the eigenvalues are of opposite sign. On the other hand, the critical point at $S_0 = 1$ is either a stable node or a stable spiral, a stable node if $c^2 \geq 4(1-\eta)$. It follows that there is a trajectory connecting $S = S^*$ with $S = 1$ for which $S \geq 0$ and $S^* \leq S \leq 1$, i.e., a traveling wave solution, for any value of c with $c^2 \geq 4(1 - \eta)$. The minimal speed is therefore $c = 2\sqrt{1 - \eta}$.

The implications of this are interesting, but not surprising. In original dimensioned coordinates, the speed of spread is

$$(6.116) \qquad\qquad 2\sqrt{D(\alpha s_0 - \beta)},$$

which is the speed of an SI disease (no recovery), decremented by an amount proportional to the recovery rate. In other words, rapid recovery reduces the rate of spread of the disease, which is no surprise. The fraction of the original susceptible population affected by the disease is $I^* = 1 - S^*$ where $1 + \eta \ln S^* - S^* = 0$. (This is exactly the same relationship as found with the ordinary differential equation SIR model in Chapter 1, (1.67).) It is an easy matter to make a plot of I^* vs. η to see that I^* is a decreasing function of η, with $I^* = 1$ when $\eta = 0$ and $I^* = 0$ when $\eta = 1$. In other words, the effect of the disease decreases as η increases, which is also not a surprise. A question that is unresolved by this analysis, however, is what happens if $\eta = \frac{\beta}{\alpha s_0} = \frac{1}{R_0} > 1$, and this is a question that can be explored by you (see Exercise 6.17).

6.5. Extras: Facilitated Diffusion

Why is the meat of a chicken breast white, while the meat of a duck breast is red? The simple answer is that duck meat gets its red color from myoglobin, which it has in much greater concentrations than in chicken meat. Ducks need a greater oxygen supply for their muscles than chickens do to enable their flight, and myoglobin facilitates oxygen diffusion. How is it that myoglobin helps supply this need?

Facilitated diffusion is an important example in which both diffusion and reaction play a role and occurs when the flux of a chemical is amplified by a reaction that takes place in the medium. We can tell from Table 5.1 that diffusion alone is inadequate to respond to changes in oxygen demand over distances larger than about a millimeter. This is why insects have long slender bodies, since their oxygen respiration is primarily by diffusion. (See Exercise 6.20.)

An example of facilitated diffusion occurs with the flux of oxygen in muscle fibers. In muscle fibers, oxygen is bound to myoglobin and is bound to and transported as oxymyoglobin, and this transport is greatly enhanced above the flow of oxygen in the absence of myoglobin [52],[75].

This well-documented observation needs further explanation, because at first glance it seems counterintuitive. Myoglobin molecules are much larger (molecular weight M=16,890) than oxygen molecules (molecular weight M=32) and therefore have a much smaller diffusion coefficient ($D = 4.4 \times 10^{-7}$ and $D = 1.2 \times 10^{-5}$cm^2/s for myoglobin and oxygen, respectively). The diffusion of oxymyoglobin would therefore seem to be much slower than the diffusion of free oxygen. Further, the diffusion of free oxygen would seem to be slowed by binding to myoglobin since there is less free oxygen to diffuse.

To anticipate slightly, the answer to this apparent paradox is that, at steady state, the total transport of oxygen is the sum of the free oxygen transport and additional oxygen that is transported by the diffusing myoglobin. If there is a lot of myoglobin, with a lot of oxygen bound to it, this additional transport due to the myoglobin can be substantial.

A simple model of this phenomenon is as follows. Suppose we have a tube of aqueous solution, divided into three subregions, separated by membranes across which oxygen readily diffuses but which is impermeable to myoglobin. We describe the location in the middle medium by the variable x, with $x = 0$ corresponding to the leftmost membrane and $x = L$ corresponding to the rightmost membrane, with separation length L. The middle region contains myoglobin. On the left (for $x \leq 0$) the oxygen concentration is held fixed at s_0, while on the right (for $x \geq L$) it is held fixed at s_L, which for convenience is assumed to be less than s_0.

If f is the rate of uptake of oxygen into oxymyoglobin, then equations governing the concentrations of $s = [O_2], e = [Mb], c = [MbO_2]$ are

$$(6.117) \qquad \frac{\partial s}{\partial t} = D_s \frac{\partial^2 s}{\partial x^2} - f,$$

$$(6.118) \qquad \frac{\partial e}{\partial t} = D_e \frac{\partial^2 e}{\partial x^2} - f,$$

$$(6.119) \qquad \frac{\partial c}{\partial t} = D_c \frac{\partial^2 c}{\partial x^2} + f.$$

It is reasonable to take $D_e = D_c$, since myoglobin and oxymyoglobin are nearly identical in molecular weight and structure. Since myoglobin and oxymyoglobin remain inside the slab, it is also reasonable to specify the no-flux boundary conditions $\partial e/\partial x = \partial c/\partial x = 0$ at $x = 0$ and $x = L$. For relative simplicity, we assume that the reaction of oxygen with myoglobin is governed by the reaction

$$O_2 + Mb \underset{k_-}{\overset{k_+}{\rightleftharpoons}} MbO_2,$$

so that (from the law of mass action) $f = -k_- c + k_+ se$. The total amount of myoglobin is conserved by the reaction, so that at steady state $e + c = e_0$ and (6.118) is superfluous.

We are interested in determining the steady state flux of oxygen across the slab. At steady state,

$$(6.120) \qquad 0 = s_t + c_t = D_s s_{xx} + D_c c_{xx},$$

and thus there is a second conserved quantity, namely the total flux

$$(6.121) \qquad D_s \frac{ds}{dx} + D_c \frac{dc}{dx} = -J,$$

which follows by integrating (6.120) once with respect to x. Integrating (6.121) with respect to x between $x = 0$ and $x = L$, we can express the total flux J in terms of boundary values of the two concentrations as

$$(6.122) \qquad J = \frac{D_s}{L}(s_0 - s_L) + \frac{D_c}{L}(c_0 - c_L),$$

although the values c_0 and c_L are as yet unknown.

To further understand this system of equations, it is useful to introduce dimensionless variables. Notice that k_+ has units of 1/(time · concentration), while k_- has units of 1/time, so that $\frac{k_-}{k_+}$ has units of concentration. We make the change of variables $s = \frac{k_-}{k_+}\sigma$, $c = e_0 u$, and $x = L\xi$, in terms of which (6.117) and (6.119) at steady state become

$$\text{(6.123)} \qquad \epsilon_s \frac{\partial^2 \sigma}{\partial \xi^2} = -u + \sigma(1 - u) = -\epsilon_c \frac{\partial^2 u}{\partial \xi^2},$$

where $\epsilon_s = \frac{D_s}{e_0 k_+ L^2}$, $\epsilon_c = \frac{D_c}{k_- L^2}$.

Reasonable numbers for the uptake of oxygen by myoglobin [74] are $k_+ = 1.4 \times 10^{10}\,\text{cm}^3\,\text{M}^{-1}\text{s}^{-1}$, $k_- = 11\,\text{s}^{-1}$, and $L = 0.022$ cm in a solution with $e_0 = 1.2 \times 10^{-5}\,\text{M/cm}^3$. (These numbers are for an experimental setup in which the concentration of myoglobin was substantially higher than what naturally occurs in living tissue.) With these numbers we determine that $\epsilon_s = 1.5 \times 10^{-7}$ and $\epsilon_c = 8.2 \times 10^{-5}$. Clearly, both of these numbers are quite small, suggesting that we can ignore them both in (6.123), and take

$$\text{(6.124)} \qquad u = \frac{\sigma}{1 + \sigma},$$

or in dimensional units,

$$\text{(6.125)} \qquad c = e_0 \frac{s}{K + s},$$

where $K = k_-/k_+$. Now we substitute (6.125) into (6.122) to find the total flux

$$
\begin{aligned}
\text{(6.126)} \qquad J &= \frac{D_s}{L}(s_0 - s_L) + \frac{D_c}{L} e_0 \left(\frac{s_0}{K + s_0} - \frac{s_L}{K + s_L} \right) \\
&= \frac{D_s}{L}(1 + \mu\rho)(s_0 - s_L),
\end{aligned}
$$

where $\rho = \frac{D_c}{D_s}\frac{e_0}{K}$, $\mu = \frac{K^2}{(s_0+K)(s_L+K)}$. In addition, we find expressions for the concentration $\sigma(\xi)$ by integrating (6.121) and expressing the result in dimensionless variables

$$\text{(6.127)} \qquad \sigma(\xi) + \rho \frac{\sigma(\xi)}{1 + \sigma(\xi)} = -(1 + \mu\rho)(\sigma_0 - \sigma_L)\xi + \sigma_0 + \rho \frac{\sigma_0}{1 + \sigma_0}.$$

Here we see how diffusion can be facilitated by an enzymatic reaction. In the absence of a diffusing carrier, $\rho = 0$ and the flux is purely Fickian. However, in the presence of a myoglobin carrier, diffusion is enhanced by the factor $\mu\rho$. The maximum enhancement possible is at zero concentration, when $\mu = 1$. In other words, the flux enhancement is largest when it is most needed. With the above numbers for myoglobin, this maximum enhancement is substantial, being $\rho = 560$.

If the oxygen supply is sufficiently high on the left side (near $x = 0$), then oxygen is stored as oxymyoglobin. Moving to the right, as the total oxygen content drops, oxygen is released by the myoglobin. Thus, even though the bound oxygen diffuses slowly compared to free oxygen, the quantity of bound oxygen is high (provided that e_0 is large compared to the half saturation level K), so that lots of oxygen is transported. Also, to take advantage of the myoglobin-bound oxygen, the concentration of oxygen must drop to sufficiently low levels on the right so that myoglobin releases its stored oxygen.

To explain it another way, note from (6.126) that the oxygen flux J is the sum of two terms, the usual Fickian flux term and an additional term that depends on the diffusion coefficient of MbO_2. The total oxygen flux is the sum of the flux of free oxygen and the flux of oxygen bound to myoglobin. Clearly, if oxymyoglobin is free to diffuse, the total flux is thereby increased. But since oxymyoglobin can only diffuse down its own gradient, the concentration of oxymyoglobin must be higher on one side than the other.

In Figure 6.17(a) are shown the dimensionless free oxygen concentration σ and the dimensionless bound oxygen concentration u plotted as functions of position. (These plots were made using equation (6.127) to determine ξ as a function of σ and then reversing the axes to find σ as a function of ξ. The Matlab code to make these plots is facilitated_diff_plots.m.) Notice that the free oxygen content falls at first, indicating higher free oxygen flux, and the bound oxygen decreases more rapidly at larger ξ. Perhaps easier to interpret is Figure 6.17(b), where the dimensionless flux of free oxygen and the dimensionless flux of bound oxygen are shown as functions of position. Here we can see that as the free oxygen concentration drops, the flux of free oxygen also drops, but the flux of bound oxygen increases. For large ξ, most of the flux is due to the bound oxygen. For these figures, $\rho = 10, \sigma_0 = 2.0, \sigma_L = 0.1$.

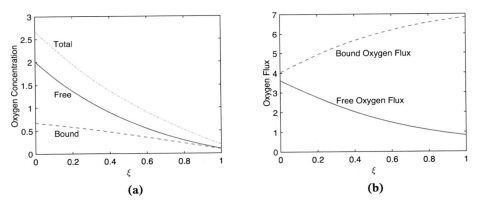

Figure 6.17. (a) Free oxygen content $\sigma(\xi)$ and bound oxygen content $u(\xi)$ plotted as functions of ξ. (b) Free oxygen flux $-\sigma'(\xi)$ and bound oxygen flux $-\rho u'(\xi)$ plotted as functions of ξ, using $\rho = 10, \sigma_0 = 2.0, \sigma_L = 0.1$.

6.5.1. Facilitated Diffusion in Muscle Respiration. Even at rest, muscle fibers consume oxygen. In humans, the oxygen consumption of live muscle tissue at rest is about 5×10^{-8} mol/cm^{3}s, and the concentration of myoglobin is about 2.8×10^{-7} mol/cm^3. Thus, when myoglobin is fully saturated (one oxygen molecule per molecule of myoglobin), it contains only about a 5 s supply of oxygen. Further, the oxygen at the exterior of the muscle cell must penetrate to the center of the cell to prevent the oxygen concentration at the center falling to zero, a condition called *oxygen debt*.

To explain how myoglobin aids in providing oxygen to a muscle cell and helps to prevent oxygen debt, we examine a model of oxygen consumption that includes the effects of diffusion of oxygen and myoglobin. We suppose that a muscle fiber is a long circular cylinder (radius $a = 2.5 \times 10^{-3}$ cm) and that diffusion takes place only in the radial direction. We suppose that the oxygen concentration at the outer boundary of the fiber is a fixed constant and that the distribution of species is radially symmetric. With these assumptions, the steady-state equations governing the diffusion of oxygen and oxymyoglobin are

$$(6.128) \qquad D_s \frac{1}{r} \frac{d}{dr} \left(r \frac{ds}{dr} \right) - f - g = 0,$$

$$(6.129) \qquad D_c \frac{1}{r} \frac{d}{dr} \left(r \frac{dc}{dr} \right) + f = 0,$$

where, as before, $s = [O_2]$, $c = [MbO_2]$, and $f = -k_- c + k_+ se$. The coordinate r is in the radial direction. The new term in these equations is the constant g, corresponding to the constant consumption of oxygen. The boundary conditions are $s = s_a$, $dc/dr = 0$ at $r = a$, and $ds/dr = dc/dr = 0$ at $r = 0$. For muscle, s_a is typically 3.5×10^{-8} mol/cm^3. Numerical values for the parameters in this model are difficult to obtain, but reasonable numbers are $D_s = 10^{-5}$ cm^2/s, $D_c = 5 \times 10^{-7}$ cm^2/s, $k_+ = 2.4 \times 10^{10}$ cm^3/mol $\cdot$ s, and $k_- = 65$/s [75].

Introducing nondimensional variables $\sigma = \frac{k_+}{k_-} s$, $u = c/e_0$, and $r = a\xi$, we obtain the differential equations

$$(6.130) \qquad \epsilon_s \frac{1}{\xi} \frac{d}{d\xi} \left(\xi \frac{d\sigma}{d\xi} \right) - \gamma = \sigma(1-u) - u = -\epsilon_c \frac{1}{\xi} \frac{d}{d\xi} \left(\xi \frac{du}{d\xi} \right),$$

where $\epsilon_s = \frac{D_s}{e_0 k_+ a^2}$, $\epsilon_c = \frac{D_c}{k_- a^2}$, $\gamma = g/k_-$. Using the parameters appropriate for muscle, we calculate that $\epsilon_s = 2.3 \times 10^{-4}$, $\epsilon_c = 1.2 \times 10^{-3}$, $\gamma = 3.3 \times 10^{-3}$. While these numbers $\epsilon_s = \frac{D_s}{e_0 k_+ a^2}$ and ϵ_c are not as small as for the experimental slab described earlier, they are small enough to warrant the assumption that the approximation (6.125) holds in the interior of the muscle fiber.

It also follows from (6.130) that

$$(6.131) \qquad \epsilon_s \frac{1}{\xi} \frac{d}{d\xi} \left(\xi \frac{d\sigma}{d\xi} \right) + \epsilon_c \frac{1}{\xi} \frac{d}{d\xi} \left(\xi \frac{du}{d\xi} \right) = \gamma.$$

We integrate (6.131) twice with respect to ξ to find

$$(6.132) \qquad \epsilon_s \sigma + \epsilon_c u = A \ln \xi + B + \frac{\gamma}{4} \xi^2.$$

The constants A and B are determined by boundary conditions. Since we want the solution to be bounded at the origin, $A = 0$, and B is related to the concentration at the origin, i.e., $B = \epsilon_s \sigma_0 + \epsilon_c u_0$.

Now suppose that there is just enough oxygen at the outer boundary to prevent oxygen debt. In this model, oxygen debt occurs if σ falls to zero. Marginal oxygen debt occurs if $\sigma = u = 0$ at the muscle center $\xi = 0$. For this boundary condition, we take $A = B = 0$. Then the concentration at the boundary must be at least as large as σ_0, where, using the approximation $\sigma(1-u) = u$,

$$(6.133) \qquad \sigma_0 + \rho \frac{\sigma_0}{\sigma_0 + 1} = \frac{\gamma}{4\epsilon_s},$$

and where $\rho = \epsilon_c/\epsilon_s$. Otherwise, the center of the muscle is in oxygen debt.

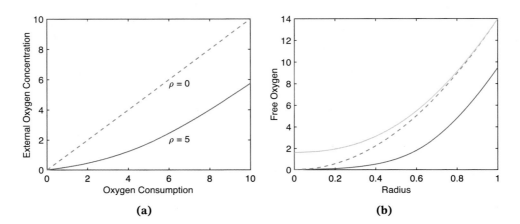

Figure 6.18. (a) Critical concentration σ_0 plotted as a function of oxygen consumption $\frac{\gamma}{4\epsilon_s}$, for $\rho = 5$ (solid curve) and $\rho = 0$ (dashed curve). (b) Free oxygen σ as a function of radius ξ. Solid curves show oxygen concentration in the presence of myoglobin ($\rho = 5$), the lower of the two having exactly the critical external oxygen concentration. The dashed curve shows the oxygen concentration without facilitation at the critical external concentration level. For this figure, $\frac{\gamma}{4\epsilon_s} = 14$.

The critical concentration σ_0 is a decreasing function of ρ, indicating a reduced need for external oxygen concentration because of facilitated diffusion by myoglobin. A plot of this critical concentration σ_0 as a function of the scaled consumption $\frac{\gamma}{4\epsilon_s}$ is shown in Figure 6.18(a). For this plot $\rho = 5$, which is a reasonable estimate for muscle. The dashed curve is the critical concentration when there is no facilitated diffusion ($\rho = 0$). The easy lesson from this plot is that facilitated diffusion decreases the likelihood of oxygen debt, since the external oxygen concentration necessary to prevent oxygen debt is smaller in the presence of myoglobin than without.

A similar lesson comes from Figure 6.18(b), where the internal free oxygen content σ is shown, plotted as a function of radius ξ. The solid curves show the internal free oxygen with facilitated diffusion, and the dashed curve is without. The smaller of the two solid curves and the dashed curve have exactly the critical external oxygen concentration, showing clearly that in the presence of myoglobin, oxygen debt is less likely at a given external oxygen concentration. The larger of the two solid curves shows that myoglobin produces an oxygen surplus at the center of the muscle fiber in the situation where there is only enough external oxygen for a myoglobin-free fiber to survive. For this figure, $\rho = 5$, $\frac{\gamma}{4\epsilon_s} = 14$.

Exercises

6.1. Suppose a chemical species u diffuses and decays at rate α on a semi-infinite domain $0 < x < \infty$. At the boundary at $x = 0$, there is a flux of u that is diffusive, that is, $-D\frac{du}{dx}|_{x=0} = \delta(A - u(x = 0))$, where A is held constant and δ represents the porosity of the boundary. Find the steady state profile of the concentration of u.

6.2. Suppose a chemical species u diffuses and decays at rate α outside a spherical cell of radius r. Inside the cell, the concentration is held at constant level A. The chemical diffuses across the cell wall, so that the flux across the wall is proportional to the difference between inside and outside concentrations. In math language, $Dr^2\frac{du}{dr}|_{r=R} = \delta(A - u(r = R))$. Find the steady state distribution of the chemical species outside of the sphere.

6.3. Suppose that a chemical species A is irreversibly converted from one form to another, i.e., $A \xrightarrow{\alpha} B$, at the boundaries of a one dimensional domain of length L, starts with a uniform concentration of A and no B at time $t = 0$, and the diffusion coefficient of both species is the same. Determine (numerically) the concentration of B at the center of the domain as a function of time. *Hint.* Species A diffuses with Robin boundary conditions. Assuming A and B have the same diffusion coefficient, show that $[A] + [B]$ satisfies the diffusion equation with homogeneous Neumann boundary conditions so that $[A] + [B] = [A]_{t=0}$. Be sure to nondimensionalize this problem before setting up the numerical simulation. The Matlab code CN_diffusion_NR.m (from Chapter 5) can be readily adapted to solve this problem.

6.4. A particle diffuses (with diffusion coefficient D) in a region $0 < x < L$ after being released from $x = 0$. The particle can degrade with degradation rate α. The goal of this exercise is to determine the probability that the particle reaches the boundary at $x = L$ *before* it decays.

  (a) The answer is a function of what single nondimensional parameter?

  (b) Do a stochastic simulation of this problem to get a numerical estimate of the answer for several parameter values.

  (c) The probability that the particle reaches the boundary before degrading is $\pi(0)$ where $\pi(x)$ satisfies the differential equation

$$D\pi_{xx} - \alpha\pi = 0, \qquad \pi'(0) = 0, \qquad \pi(L) = 1.$$

  Calculate the probability that the particle reaches the boundary before decaying and compare this with what you found from your numerical simulation.

6.5. **Dropping like flies:** Suppose a large number of insects are released from some point and when they are released they are also sprayed with a chemical poison that is known to kill the insects by a Poisson process with rate α. The insects move by two dimensional diffusion with diffusion coefficient D until they drop and land on the ground.

(a) What are the differential equations describing the evolution of the density of flying insects $ru(r,t)$ and the density of dead insects $rv(r)$?

(b) Do a stochastic simulation of this two dimensional diffusion-decay process to find the distribution of dead insects as a function of the radius r from the release site.

(c) Find an analytical expression for the distribution of dead insects as a function of radius.

Hint. You will need to make use of the integral formula

$$\int_0^\infty \frac{1}{t} \exp(-\frac{a^2}{t} - t)dt = 2K_0(2|a|),$$

where $K_n(x)$ is the modified Bessel function of the second kind of order n, and is known by Matlab as besselk(n,x). The important feature of $K_0(x)$ for this exercise is that it is an exponentially decaying function, $K_0(x) \sim \sqrt{\frac{\pi}{2x}} \exp(-x)$ for large x and $\int_0^\infty K_0(x)xdx = 1$.

Reminder. In two dimensions, the functions $u(r,t)$ and $v(r)$ are scaled in such a way that $2\pi \int_0^\infty u(r,t)rdr$ and $2\pi \int_0^\infty v(r)rdr$ are particle totals. This means that $rv(r)$, and not $v(r)$, is a density per radial increment dr.

6.6. A passive cable is a nerve axon for which the transmembrane ion current is ohmic, of the form $I_{\text{ion}} = \frac{V}{R_m}$, where R_m is the membrane resistance. A typical value for R_m is $R_m = 4 \text{ k}\Omega \text{ cm}^2$. Using values from Tables 3.1 and 3.2, determine time and length constants for sciatic nerve and squid giant axon.

6.7. A large number of molecules are released from the center of a spherical cell of radius R. The molecules diffuse with diffusion coefficient D and degrade at rate α. The goal of this exercise is to determine the percentage of the molecules that reach the boundary at $r = R$ before they decay.

(a) How many nondimensional parameters are there for this problem?

(b) Do a stochastic simulation of this problem.

(c) The probability that a particle reaches the boundary before degrading is $\pi(0)$ where $\pi(r)$ satisfies the differential equation

$$\frac{D}{r^2}\frac{d}{dr}(r^2\frac{d\pi}{dr}) - \alpha\pi = 0,$$

subject to boundary conditions $\pi(R) = 1$, $\pi'(0) = 0$. Find $\pi(0)$.

(d) Compare the results of your simulation with the analytical result.

6.8. Find the speed of a traveling wave in dimensional units for the spread of a *SI* disease (6.31).

6.9. A dingo population which lives in the eastern parts of Australia is prevented from invasion to the west by a fence that runs north-south. Imagine that the fence breaks somewhere at time $t = 0$. A farm is located on the west side of the fence, exactly 100 miles west of the hole in the fence. The farmers would like to know how long it will take the dingoes to reach their farm. Model the spread of dingoes by

$$u_t = Du_{xx} + ku(1 - \frac{u}{K}),$$

with $k = 1$ (1/month), and $K = 1$ (in units of u).

(a) The region between the fence and farm is flat and the diffusion coefficient is $D_1 = 100$ (miles^2/month). When does the dingo population reach the farm? (*Hint.* Consider a traveling wave and calculate the wave speed.)

(b) How will the time of arrival change if the diffusion constant is

$$D_2 = 50 \text{ miles}^2/\text{month}$$

due to some rock and slope in the region?

6.10. (a) Use scaling arguments to derive that the minimal speed of propagation of traveling wave solutions of the equation $u_t = DU_{xx} + ku(U_0 - u)$ is $c = 2\sqrt{kU_0 D}$.

(b) Use the Matlab code CN_Fisher.m to verify numerically that the speed of propagation of traveling wave solutions of the equation $u_t = DU_{xx} + ku(U_0 - u)$ is $c = 2\sqrt{kU_0 D}$. How does the accuracy of the answer you find numerically depend on discretization parameters?

6.11. Use a comparison argument to prove that the solution of Fisher's equation with $0 \le u(x, 0) \le 1$ satisfies $0 \le u(x, 0) \le 1$ for all $t \ge 0$.

6.12. Suppose the population of some organism is governed by the Fisher's equation

$$u_t = Du_{xx} + \alpha u(1 - u)$$

on the interval $0 < x < L$ subject to boundary conditions $u_x = 0$, at $x = 0$ and $u = 0$ at $x = L$. Use linear stability analysis to determine under what conditions on the parameters D, L, and α such a population can survive. (The solution of this problem depends on what dimensionless combination of parameters?)

6.13. Do a linear stability analysis of Fisher's equation on a rectangular domain with homogeneous Dirichlet boundary conditions. What are the dimensions of the smallest rectangle that can support survival?

6.14. (a) Use the Matlab code CN_Fisher_w_Dirichlet_radial.m to estimate the critical size of a circular domain of radius R necessary for survival for the Fisher's equation with homogeneous boundary conditions.

Remark. For this it is necessary to discretize the radially symmetric Laplacian operator $\nabla^2 v = \frac{1}{r}\frac{\partial}{\partial r}(r\frac{\partial v}{\partial r})$. Suppose we let $r_j = jh$, where $h = \frac{R}{N}$, $0 < j \le N$. Then, the natural discretization of the Laplacian is

$$\left(\frac{1}{r}\frac{\partial}{\partial r}(r\frac{\partial v}{\partial r})\right)_j = \frac{1}{jh^2}\left((j + \frac{1}{2})v_{j+1} - 2jv_j + (j - \frac{1}{2})v_{j-1}\right).$$

This is the discretization used in the code CN_Fisher_w_Dirichlet_radial.m.

(b) Do a linear stability analysis of the Fisher's equation on a circular domain with homogeneous boundary conditions to determine the threshold size for survival.

Remark. The solution of this problem requires use of the Bessel function $J_0(x)$. What you need to know is that the Bessel function $J_0(\alpha x)$ satisfies the differential equation

$$\frac{1}{x}\frac{d}{dx}(x\frac{du}{dx}) + \alpha^2 u = 0,$$

and has an infinite number of zeros, denoted μ_n, for which $J_0(\mu_n) = 0$. The smallest zero is $\mu_1 = 2.4048$.

(c) Which type of domain is more efficient, i.e., requires the least area for sustainability: a square domain or a circular domain?

6.15. An SIS disease is one for which recovery from the infection renders a person susceptible again, with no immunity, and is described by the reaction

$$S + I \xrightarrow{\alpha} 2I, \qquad I \xrightarrow{\beta} S.$$

Suppose the species S and I diffuse with the same diffusion coefficient.

(a) Show that there is a critical value of the total population S_0 above which the disease is endemic, i.e., a steady state solution that has a positive amount of I. What is the fraction of the population that is infected in the endemic state?

(b) Show that if S_0 is above the critical population level, there is a traveling wave of infection progression that introduces the disease to an initially disease-free population. What are the differential equations describing these dynamics? What is the dimensionless scaling that converts this into Fisher's equation? What is the speed of propagation of the traveling wave in dimensional units?

6.16. Make a plot of the fraction of susceptible individuals affected by an epidemic $I^* = 1 - S^*$ where $1 + \eta \ln S^* - S^* = 0$. Verify that I^* is a decreasing function of η, with $I^* = 1$ when $\eta = 0$ and $I^* = 0$ when $\eta = 1$.

6.17. Use numerical simulation to determine what happens with the SIR epidemic when $\eta = \frac{\beta}{\alpha S_0} > 1$.

6.18. Suppose diffusing bacteria u consume a stationary resource s and consequently grow at rate $f(s) = \frac{ks}{K+s}$, and decay at rate γ. Find the minimal speed of propagation of a traveling wave solution invading a substrate at level $s = s_0$. How much of the resource remains after the wave of invading bacteria has passed?

Hint. In traveling wave coordinates, find a first integral (invariant of the motion) of the form $H = s + G(s) + au + bu'$, and then analyze the phase portrait of the reduced system.

6.19. Suppose diffusing bacteria u consume a stationary resource s and consequently grow at rate $f(s) = \frac{ks^2}{K^2+s^2}$, and decay at rate γ. Find the minimal speed of propagation of a traveling wave solution invading a substrate at level $s = s_0$. How much of the resource remains after the wave of invading bacteria has passed?

Hint. In traveling wave coordinates, find a first integral (invariant of the motion) of the form $H = s + G(s) + au + bu'$, and then analyze the phase portrait of the reduced system.

6.20. (a) Oxygen is supplied to insects through branched tubular structures called trachea. Movement of oxygen through these tubes is primarily by diffusion (although some larger insects expand and contract their trachea to enhance the flow). Consider the flow of oxygen through a one dimensional tube of length L, with oxygen consumed at a constant metabolic rate g everywhere along the tube, no-flux of oxygen at the distal end of the tube at $x = L$, and a constant concentration of oxygen u_0 at the body surface $x = 0$. Determine the critical consumption rate g for which there is oxygen debt exactly at the distal end $x = L$.

(b) Suppose the atmospheric oxygen concentration were to double (think prehistoric times). How much larger could insects be with the same consumption rate but longer trachea, and not be in oxygen debt?

6.21. Suppose that the cancer cells in a solid tumor metabolize oxygen at a constant rate g, if there is available oxygen, but otherwise die and become necrotic. For a spherical solid tumor of radius R immersed in tissue in which the surrounding concentration of oxygen is c_0:

(a) Find the concentration of oxygen at the center of the tumor assuming there is no necrosis.

(b) Find a polynomial equation for the size of the necrotic core. Under what conditions on the parameters is the necrotic core size positive?

(c) Use the same parameter values as used for muscle in Section 6.5.1 to estimate the maximum size of a tumor without a necrotic core.

Hint. At the boundary of the necrotic core, both the oxygen concentration and the flux of oxygen must be zero.

6.22. Find the maximal enhancement for diffusive transport of carbon dioxide via binding with myoglobin using $D_s = 1.92 \times 10^{-5} \, \text{cm}^2/\text{s}$, $k_+ = 2 \times 10^8 \, \text{cm}^3/\text{M} \cdot \text{s}$, $k_- = 1.7 \times 10^{-2}/\text{s}$. Compare the amount of facilitation of carbon dioxide transport with that of oxygen at similar concentration levels.

Chapter 7

The Bistable Equation — Part I: Derivations

The next equation we consider is the *bistable equation,*

(7.1)
$$\frac{\partial u}{\partial t} = D\frac{\partial^2 u}{\partial x^2} + kf(u),$$

where k is a rate (with units 1/time), and $f(u)$ is a function (having the same units as u) with three zeros, $f(u_0) = f(u_1) = f(u_2) = 0$, with $u_0 < u_1 < u_2$, $F'(u_0) < 0$, $f'(u_1) > 0$, and $f'(u_2) < 0$. This equation is called the *bistable equation* because the two equilibria u_0 and u_2 are stable equilibria of the ordinary differential equation $\frac{du}{dt} = kf(u)$. (This equation has also been referred to as the Nagumo equation, [53], [45], in reference to the electrical engineer Nagumo who, as well as Fitzhugh [22], [21], used this equation as a simplified model of action potential propagation.)

There are numerous biological situations in which this equation is relevant. These include the spread of the spruce budworm in northeastern forests, the spread of *Wolbachia* infection in mosquitoes, the propagation of action potentials along nerve axons, and the propagation of post-fertilization calcium waves in frog eggs. These are described in more detail in the following sections.

7.1. Spruce Budworm

The spruce budworm is a moth that in its larval form is one of the most destructive insects of fir and spruce forests throughout Canada and the eastern United States. It attacks these trees in the forests of eastern North America in large outbreaks every 30 to 50 years. Most years its population level is relatively low, but in some years it exhibits outbreaks in which the population may increase by a factor of 1000. During an outbreak, budworm larvae may eat enough new needles in an evergreen forest to kill 80% of the trees and effectively destroy the forest. However, the destruction of the forest also eliminates the budworms' food supply, causing the eventual collapse of the budworm population, after which the forests can begin a slow recovery.

To model a budworm invasion, we let u denote the budworm population size. The equation governing u, proposed by Ludwig [**42**], is

$$(7.2) \qquad \frac{\partial u}{\partial t} = D\frac{\partial^2 u}{\partial x^2} + f_g - f_d,$$

f_g being the rate of growth, and f_d being the rate of destruction of the budworms by predators. For f_g we take a logistic-type growth model

$$(7.3) \qquad f_g = r_B u(1 - \frac{u}{K_B}),$$

where r_B is the intrinsic growth rate, and K_B is the carrying capacity. The carrying capacity is related to the health of the forest through

$$(7.4) \qquad K_B = K_u S,$$

where S is the available branch surface area on which the larvae can feed, and K_u is the carrying capacity in terms of larvae per branch surface area.

Next, we assume that the spruce budworm is subject to predation by birds, predation which is modeled by the Hill function of order 2,

$$(7.5) \qquad f_d = \frac{\beta u^2}{\alpha^2 S^2 + u^2}.$$

This is chosen to be a saturating function of u since, for a finite, and relatively constant, bird population, the birds will be glutted with larvae when the larvae population is very high, so consumption will approach a constant rate. The term S^2 in the denominator is because the rate of consumption should be a function of $\frac{u}{S}$ (larvae per branch area), since that is what the birds actually see. We treat S as a constant since we are only concerned with the initial spread of the spruce budworm. While it is true the larvae defoliate trees, reducing S, this is not relevant for the dynamics of the initial spread. Typical parameter values are shown in Table 7.1.

Plots of $f = f_g - f_d$ are shown in Figure 7.1(a) for several different values of $\sigma = \frac{r_B K_u}{\beta} S$, and it can be seen to be bistable for appropriate parameter values. This plot was made using Matlab code spruce_budworm_rhs.m.

Table 7.1. Typical parameter values for the spruce-budworm model.

r_B	1.5 year^{-1}
K_u	355 larvae branch^{-1}
β	43200 larvae acre^{-1}year^{-1}
α	1.11 larvae branch^{-1}
r_s	0.1 year^{-1}

We would like to determine the parameter values for which the equation

(7.6) $$0 = f_g - f_d = r_B u(1 - \frac{u}{K_u S}) - \frac{\beta u^2}{\alpha^2 S^2 + u^2} \equiv F(u),$$

has three nonnegative roots. This is equivalent to determining the roots of the cubic polynomial obtained after clearing the denominators in (7.6). Crucially, cubic polynomials can have either one or three real roots. The boundary in parameter space between three real roots and one real root of $F(u)$ occurs when $F(u)$ has a double zero, i.e., when $F(u)$ and $F'(u)$ have simultaneous zeros. Since $F(u)$ and $F'(u)$ are rational functions, this is equivalent to finding when the polynomial numerators of $F(u)$ and $F'(u)$ have simultaneous zeros.

The general way to find when two polynomials $f(u)$ and $g(u)$ have simultaneous zeros is with use of the *resultant*. The resultant is the determinant of the *Sylvester matrix*. While you don't actually need to know this for what follows, given two polynomials,

(7.7) $$f(u) = a_n u^n + a_{n-1} u^{n-1} + \cdots + a_0, \quad g(u) = b_m u^m + a_{m-1} u^{m-1} + \cdots + b_0,$$

the *Sylvester matrix* is defined as the $(n + m) \times (n + m)$ matrix

(7.8) $$S = \begin{pmatrix} a_n & a_{n-1} & a_{n-2} & \cdots & 0 & 0 & 0 \\ 0 & a_n & a_{n-1} & \cdots & & & \\ 0 & 0 & a_n & \cdots & a_1 & a_0 & 0 \\ & & & & & a_1 & a_0 \\ b_m & b_{m-1} & b_{m-2} & \cdots & 0 & & \\ 0 & b_m & b_{m-1} & \cdots & & & \\ 0 & 0 & & & b_1 & b_0 & 0 \\ & & & & & b_1 & b_0 \end{pmatrix}.$$

Then, the resultant of f and g is defined as

(7.9) $$R(f, g) = \det(S).$$

Now, the important theorem is

Theorem. *Suppose* $f(u) = a_n \prod_{i=1}^{n}(u - \xi_i)$ *and* $g(u) = b_m \prod_{j=1}^{m}(u - \eta_j)$. *Then*

(7.10) $$R(f, g) = a_n^m b_m^n \prod_i \prod_j (\xi_i - \eta_j).$$

In general, it is very difficult to calculate the resultant of two polynomials, because the Sylvester matrix is an $(n + m) \times (n + m)$ matrix, and no one I know enjoys calculating the determinant of matrices larger than about 3×3. But fortunately, both Maple and Mathematica have routines that calculate it with ease. In Maple, the appropriate command is

(7.11) $$R := \text{factor}(\text{resultant}(f, g, u));$$

For this problem, one finds that the resultant of the numerators of $F(u)$ and $F'(u)$ is proportional to

(7.12) $$R = 4\kappa^2(\kappa^2 + 1)^2 \sigma^3 + 4\kappa^2(3\kappa^2 - 5)\sigma^2 + (12\kappa^2 - 1)\sigma + 4,$$

where $\sigma = \frac{r_B K_u}{\beta} S, \kappa = \frac{\alpha}{K_u}$. The curve $R = 0$ is shown plotted in Figure 7.1(b). In the region I, there is only one nonnegative root, while in region II there are three nonnegative roots; the function is bistable.

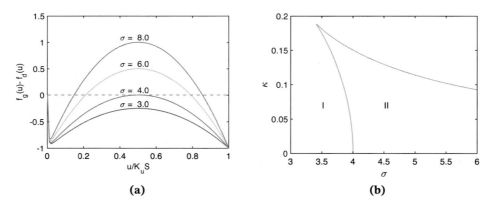

Figure 7.1. (a) Plot of $f_g(u) - f_d(u)$ as a function of $\frac{u}{K_u S}$ for $\sigma = \frac{r_B K_u}{\beta} S =$ 3.0, 4.0, 6.0, 8.0, and $\kappa = \frac{\alpha}{K_u} = 0.0031$. (b) Plot of the curve $R = 0$ with R given by (7.12), dividing κ-σ parameter space into regions for which $f_g - f_d$ has one nonnegative root (region I) and for which it has three nonnegative roots (region II).

7.2. *Wolbachia*

Dengue fever is a mosquito-borne disease that affects up to 500 million people a year, primarily in tropical climates. So far, efforts to control dengue through eradication of the mosquitoes have failed. However, one promising strategy for eradicating this disease is by means of the bacteria *Wolbachia*. *Wolbachia* are bacteria that live in insect cells and are passed from one generation to the next through the insects' eggs. *Wolbachia* is present in up to 60% of all the different species of insects in the world, including some species of mosquitoes that bite people, but not (at present) *Aedes aegypti*, the primary mosquito species involved in the transmission of dengue. When Wolbachia are introduced into mosquitoes, they interfere with pathogen transmission. However, different strains of *Wolbachia* have different effects on key life history traits such as lifespan that affect overall fitness, and consequently how readily (if at all) it will establish itself in the wild mosquito population. Thus, the current goal is to find or develop a strain of *Wolbachia* that has a reproductive advantage so that infected mosquitoes will dominate the *Aedes aegypti* mosquito population and will simultaneously prevent the transmission of dengue [31], [46].

Wolbachia infection is by female-transmission. That is, the offspring of a *Wolbachia*-infected female mosquito will all (or almost all) be *Wolbachia*-infected, whereas mating with a *Wolbachia*-infected male does not transmit the bacteria infection to the offspring mosquitoes. However, mating of infected male mosquitoes with uninfected female mosquitoes produces eggs that will not hatch, through a mechanism called *cytoplasmic incompatibility*. This results in a reproductive advantage for the infected females compared to the uninfected females, because of the presence of infected males. Of course, this advantage may be ameliorated by other negative effects of *Wolbachia* infection, such as lifespan shortening, so that the overall ability of *Wolbachia*-infection to spread is not immediately apparent [62].

This reproductive scenario is summarized by the "reaction scheme"

(7.13) $$U_f + U_m \xrightarrow{k_1} U,$$

(7.14) $$U_f + I_m \xrightarrow{k_2} \phi,$$

(7.15) $$I_f + U_m \xrightarrow{k_3} I,$$

(7.16) $$I_f + I_m \xrightarrow{k_4} I,$$

where U and I refer to Uninfected and Infected, respectively, and the subscripts m and f refer to male and female, respectively.

To build a model for the spread of *Wolbachia* [4], let U represent the uninfected female mosquito population density, and let I represent the infected female mosquito population density, and then $N = U + I$ is the total female population density. For simplicity, we make the reasonable assumption that the male populations and female populations are the same. Thus, the dynamics of U and I are governed by the equations

(7.17) $$\frac{\partial U}{\partial t} = D\nabla^2 U + k_1 \frac{U}{N} U + k_2 \frac{I}{N} U - k_d(N)U,$$

(7.18) $$\frac{\partial I}{\partial t} = D\nabla^2 I + k_3 \frac{U}{N} I + k_4 \frac{I}{N} I - k_d(N)I,$$

where k_1, k_2, k_3, and k_4 are the rates of reproduction coming from mating of uninfected males with uninfected females, infected males with uninfected females, uninfected males with infected females, and infected males with infected females, respectively. Mating between infected males and uninfected females produces eggs that do not hatch as a result of *cytoplasmic incompatibility*, so $k_2 = 0$. Here we make the simplifying assumption that the death rates of infected and uninfected mosquitoes are the same and that all differences in fitness are reflected by differences in the reproduction rates. (Derivation and analysis of a model in which infection by *Wolbachia* shortens the lifespan of a mosquito can be found in [62]).

We introduce the variables $i = \frac{I}{N}$, $u = \frac{U}{N}$ as the fraction of infected females and uninfected females, respectively, and calculate that

(7.19) $$\frac{\partial i}{\partial t} = D\nabla^2 i + 2D\nabla i \cdot \frac{\nabla N}{N} + k(i - \alpha)i(1 - i),$$

where $\alpha = \frac{k_1 - k_3}{k_4 + k_1 - k_3}$, $k = k_4 + k_1 - k_3$. Under the assumption that the total mosquito population is spatially uniform (so that $\frac{\nabla N}{N}$ can be ignored), this is the bistable equation if $0 < \alpha < 1$, i.e., if $k_3 < k_1$.

7.3. Nerve Axons

In their groundbreaking papers in 1952, Hodgkin and Huxley [30] (A. L. Hodgkin, 1914–1998, and A. F. Huxley, 1917–2012) proposed mathematical models for the ion channels responsible for the transmembrane currents in the giant axon of squid. (Recall the cable equation (3.41) with transmembrane currents I_{ion}.) For these nerve cells, there are three types of ion channels, namely sodium, potassium, and chloride ion

channels (although they called the third a leak current), with current-voltage relationships for all of these that are of the form

(7.20) $I_j = g_j(V - V_j)$,

with j =Na, K, or L. The quantity V_j is called the Nernst potential, and g_j is the conductance. One important aspect of many ion channels is that g_j is not constant but
varies in a time dependent fashion in response to the transmembrane potential V. In
particular, Hodgkin and Huxley determined that

(7.21) $g_{Na} = \bar{g}_{Na} m^3 h$, $g_K = \bar{g}_K n^4$,

where m, n, and h satisfy differential equations of the form

(7.22) $\dfrac{du}{dt} = \alpha_u(1 - u) - \beta_u u$,

for $u = m, n, h$, where

(7.23) $\alpha_m = 0.1 \dfrac{-25 - V}{\exp\left(\frac{25-v}{10}\right) - 1}$, $\beta_m = 4 \exp\left(\dfrac{-V}{18}\right)$,

(7.24) $\alpha_h = 0.07 \exp\left(\dfrac{-V}{20}\right)$, $\beta_h = \dfrac{1}{\exp\left(\frac{30-V}{10}\right) + 1}$,

(7.25) $\alpha_n = 0.01 \dfrac{10 - V}{\exp\left(\frac{10-V}{10}\right) - 1}$, $\beta_n = 0.125 \exp\left(\dfrac{-V}{80}\right)$.

For these expressions, the potential V is measured in units of mV, current density is in
units of μA/cm^2, conductances are in units of mS/cm^2, and capacitance is in units of
μF/cm^2. The remaining parameters are

(7.26) $\bar{g}_{Na} = 120$, $\bar{g}_K = 36$, $\bar{g}_L = 0.3$, $C_m = 1$,

with Nernst potentials $V_{Na} = 115$ mV, $V_K = -12$ mV, and $V_L = -10.6$ mV.[1]

The Hodgkin–Huxley equations are used to describe the dynamics of action potentials, which consist of a rapidly rising *upstroke* followed by a less rapid downstroke
eventually returning to rest, i.e., steady state. The interest here is in the initial upstroke
phase, which can be reasonably modeled by setting $h = h_0$ and $n = n_0$ to be constant
($h_0 = 0.596$, $n_0 = 0.318$), and taking $m = m_\infty(V)$, where

(7.27) $m_\infty(V) = \dfrac{\alpha_m}{\beta_m + \alpha_m}$.

The result is that

(7.28) $I_{ion} = \bar{g}_{Na} h_0 m_\infty^3(V)(V - V_{Na}) + \bar{g}_K n_0^4(V - V_K) + g_L(V - V_L)$.

A plot of $-I_{ion}$ is shown in Figure 7.2 (made using the Matlab code HH_up-
stroke_rhs.m). This function is bistable as there are three zeros, at $V_0 = 0$, $V_1 = 2.6$,

---

[1]The Hodgkin–Huxley equations have the unfortunate "feature" that the rest potential (i.e. the steady state solution
for V), when there is no input current, is zero. This, of course, is not correct for nerve axons, as a typical rest potential for
real nerves is about -65 mV. So, to make the Hodgkin–Huxley equations take on realistic physiological values, one must shift
the potentials, including the Nernst potentials, by -65 mV. While this "feature" is a bit of a nuisance, this comment should
not be taken as a criticism. They did, after all, win the Nobel Prize for their work, and deservedly so.

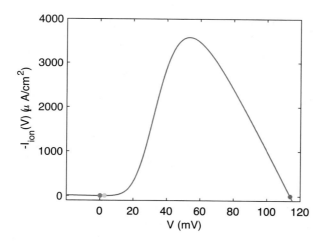

Figure 7.2. Plot of $-I_{ion}(V)$ for the Hodgkin–Huxley upstroke model (7.28).

and $V_2 = 114$ (denoted with dots in Figure 7.2), the smallest and largest of which are stable solutions of the ordinary differential equation $C_m \frac{dV}{dt} = -I_{ion}(V)$.

A model for action potential propagation along a nerve axon is obtained by using the description (7.28) of the ionic current in the cable equation (3.41), yielding another important example of the bistable equation.

7.4. Calcium Handling

Calcium ions (Ca^{++}) play an important role in much of the signaling that is done by cells. For example, calcium is necessary for neurotransmitter release by nerves at their synapses, for contraction of skeletal muscle and cardiac cells, for insulin secretion by β cells in the pancreas, for hormone secretion by endocrine glands, and for light adaptation by photoreceptors. Calcium waves are also known to play an important role in post-fertilization signaling. For example, the eggs of *Xenopus laevis* (African claw-toed frog) show calcium release waves that propagate from the site of fertilization throughout the rest of the cell and act to prevent multiple fertilization sites.

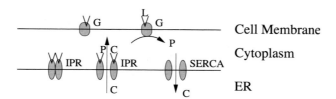

Figure 7.3. Diagram of calcium handling. Ligand in the extracellular space (L) binds with a G-protein (denoted by G), causing the production of IP$_3$ (denoted by P). IP$_3$ binds to an IP$_3$ receptor (IPR) activating the IPR. When open, the IPR allows the flux of calcium, denoted by C, from the ER into the cytoplasm. Calcium can also bind to the IPR, further activating the IPR. Calcium is pumped from the cytoplasm into the ER by SERCA pumps.

Calcium enters the cytoplasm of the cell from internal calcium stores called *endoplasmic reticulum* (ER) through calcium channels, called IP_3 receptors, or IPR. IP_3 (Inositol triphosphate) is a chemical that is produced at the cell membrane by activated G-proteins and binds with IP_3 receptors to activate calcium release from the ER. Calcium is taken back up into the ER through calcium pumps, called SERCA (Sarco and Endoplasmic Reticulum ATPase) pumps. (The SR is the Sarcoplasmic Reticulum, the equivalent of the ER but for cardiac cells.) Consequently, we can model the dynamics of calcium in the cytoplasm (denoted by c) with the equation

$$(7.29) \qquad \frac{\partial c}{\partial t} = D\nabla^2 c + J_{\text{IPR}} - J_{\text{SERCA}}.$$

Release of calcium from IPR is by a mechanism called CICR (Calcium-Induced Calcium Release) and is reasonably modeled by the Fickian flux

$$(7.30) \qquad J_{\text{IPR}} = k_f P_o(c_e - c),$$

where c_e is the ER calcium concentration, k_f is the total channel conductance, and P_O is the probability that a channel is open, taken to be the function of the c and p,

$$(7.31) \qquad P_O = P\left(\frac{c}{c + K_2}\right)^3, \qquad P = \left(\frac{p}{p + K_1}\right)^3,$$

where $p = [IP_3]$. An important feature of this function is its calcium dependence, namely that the open probability increases as calcium increases, and this is the feature (i.e., the positive feedback) that gives rise to CICR.

A common model for the SERCA pump is the Hill function of order 2,

$$(7.32) \qquad J_{\text{SERCA}} = \frac{V_p c^2}{K_p^2 + c^2}.$$

Finally, since calcium moves back and forth between the ER and the cytoplasm, we take the simple relationship between c and c_e,

$$(7.33) \qquad c + \frac{c_e}{\gamma} = c_t,$$

where γ is the ratio of cytoplasmic volume to ER volume.

Parameter values for this model are given in Table 7.2.

A plot of the total calcium flux $J_{\text{tot}} = J_{\text{IPR}} - J_{\text{SERCA}}$, plotted as a function of calcium concentration is shown in Figure 7.4, for several values of IP_3 concentration p (made using the Matlab code calcium_CICR_rhs.m). It is apparent that the function J_{tot} is

Table 7.2. Typical parameter values for IP_3 calcium release model.

V_p	$=$	$0.9\,\mu\text{Ms}^{-1}$	K_p	$=$	$0.1\mu\text{M}$
k_f	$=$	$1.11\,\text{s}^{-1}$	γ	$=$	5.5
c_t	$=$	$2\,\mu\text{M}$			
K_1	$=$	$0.13\mu\text{M}$	K_2	$=$	$0.082\mu\text{M}$

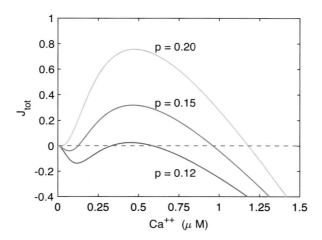

Figure 7.4. Plot of total calcium flux $J_{tot} = J_{IPR} - J_{SERCA}$ as a function of calcium Ca^{++}, for several values of IP_3 concentration p.

bistable provided p is sufficiently large, and consequently, equation (7.29) provides us with another example of the bistable equation.

Exercises

7.1. Under what conditions on the parameters a, b, and c do the two quadratic polynomials $x^2 + a = 0$ and $x^2 + bx + c = 0$ have simultaneous roots?

7.2. Under what conditions on the parameters a and b does the cubic polynomial $x^3 + ax + b = 0$ have a double root?

7.3. Under what conditions on the parameters a, b, and c does the quartic polynomial $x^4 + ax^2 + bx + c = 0$ have a double root?

7.4. (a) Find rescaled (dimensionless) variables for which the spruce budworm problem becomes

$$\frac{\partial v}{\partial \tau} - \frac{\partial^2 v}{\partial \xi^2} = \sigma v(1 - v) - \frac{v^2}{\kappa^2 + v^2} \equiv g(v).$$

What are σ and κ in terms of original parameters?

(b) Show that this is the bistable equation for a range of the parameter values σ and κ as follows. Find the steady state solutions by plotting σ as a function of v on the range $0 < v < 1$, and then reverse the axes.

(c) Determine the range of κ values for which the function $\sigma = f(v)$ is triphasic.

Hint. The curve $\sigma = f(v)$ is either triphasic or monophasic (monotone). The separation between these occurs when $f'(v)$ and $f''(v)$ have simultaneous zeros. Calculate the resultant of two appropriate polynomials to find the value (or values) of κ for which this occurs.

(d) *Extra challenge.* Find (and plot) the curve in κ-σ parameter space that divides the space into two regions, one for which the function $g(v)$ has a single positive root and one for which it has three positive roots.

(e) Show that, if σ is such that $g(v)$ has a single positive zero, call it v_0, then this equation is similar to Fisher's equation since $g(0) = 0$ and $g(v) > 0$ for $0 < v < v^*$. Show that this happens both for σ sufficiently small and for σ sufficiently large.

7.5. Consider the spruce-budworm equation (7.2). For all parameter values, the equation is like Fisher's equation since for $f = f_g - f_d$, $f(0) = 0$ and $f(u) > 0$ for $0 < u < u_0$, where u_0 is the smallest positive zero of $f(u)$. Calculate the speed of propagation for this Fisher-like wave.

7.6. (a) Find rescaled (dimensionless) variables for which the calcium problem (7.29) becomes

$$\frac{\partial u}{\partial \tau} = \frac{\partial^2 u}{\partial \xi^2} + u^2 g(u),$$

where $g(u) = \rho \frac{u}{(u+\kappa_2)^3}(\gamma(1-u)-u) - \frac{1}{u^2+\kappa_1^2}$. What are ρ, κ_1, and κ_2 in terms of original parameters?

(b) Show that this is the bistable equation for a range of the parameter values ρ as follows. Find the steady state solutions by plotting ρ as a function of u on the range $0 < u < \frac{\gamma}{\gamma+1}$, and then reverse the axes. For what values of ρ is this bistable?

Chapter 8

The Bistable Equation — Part II: Analysis

To study the bistable equation (7.1), it is convenient to introduce the dimensionless variables $\tau = kt$, $\xi = \sqrt{\frac{k}{D}}x$, in terms of which we have

(8.1)
$$\frac{\partial u}{\partial \tau} = \frac{\partial^2 u}{\partial \xi^2} + f(u).$$

Now to get an idea about the behavior of the solution, it is useful to do a simulation. In Figure 8.1 are shown two simulations of the equation (8.1) with $f(u)$ the cubic function

(8.2)
$$f(u) = u(1 - u)(u - \alpha),$$

in this case with $\alpha = 0.25$ and starting from initial data $u_0(x) = a \operatorname{sech}^2(\frac{x}{\lambda})$, $\lambda = 4.1$ with $a = 0.41$ in Figure 8.1(a), and $a = 4.2$ in Figure 8.1(b). This simulation used the Matlab code CN_Bistable.m.

There are two features of these simulations that are noteworthy. First, while the initial data for these two simulations are nearly identical, the ultimate behavior of the solution is vastly different. On the left, the solution decays and goes to zero, while on the right the solution approaches what appears to be a fixed profile that moves to the right (a traveling wave), so that for any fixed ξ, $u(\xi, \tau) \to 1$ as $\tau \to \infty$. Thus, it appears that there are traveling waves solutions, but they are not initiated by all positive initial data, as it was for the Fisher equation.

8.1. Traveling Waves

By a traveling wave solution, we mean a translation-invariant solution of (8.1) with a fixed form that provides a transition between the two stable rest states (the largest and

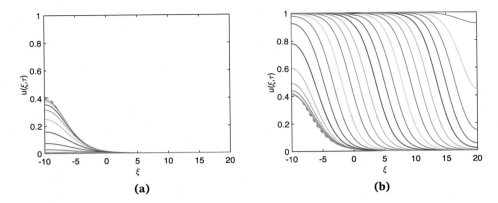

(a)   **(b)**

Figure 8.1. Solution of the bistable equation (8.1) with $f(u)$ given by (8.2) for $\alpha = 0.25$ starting from initial data (shown dashed) $u_0(x) = a \operatorname{sech}^2(\frac{x}{\lambda})$, $\lambda = 4.2$, with (a) $a = 0.41$, and (b) $a = 0.42$. Plots made using Matlab code bistable_threshold_simulation.m.

smallest zeros of the nonlinear function $f(u)$) and translates with constant speed. That is, we seek a solution of (8.1) of the form

$$(8.3) \qquad\qquad u(\xi, \tau) = U(\xi + c\tau) = U(\zeta),$$

for some (yet to be determined) value of c. Note that, because we use $\zeta = \xi + c\tau$ as the traveling wave coordinate, a solution with c positive corresponds to a wave moving from right to left. We could equally well use $\xi - c\tau$ as the traveling wave coordinate, to obtain waves moving from left to right (for positive c).

By substituting (8.3) into (8.1) it can be seen that a traveling wave solution must satisfy

$$(8.4) \qquad\qquad U_{\zeta\zeta} - cU_\zeta + f(U) = 0,$$

and this, being an ordinary differential equation, should be easier to analyze than the original partial differential equation. For $U(\zeta)$ to provide a transition between rest points, it must be that $f(U(\zeta)) \to 0$ as $\zeta \to \pm\infty$.

To study (8.4), it is convenient to write it as the two first order equations,

$$(8.5) \qquad\qquad U_\zeta = W,$$
$$(8.6) \qquad\qquad W_\zeta = cW - f(U).$$

To find traveling front solutions for the bistable equation, we look for a solution of (8.5) and (8.6) that connects the rest points $(U, W) = (0, 0)$ and $(U, W) = (1, 0)$ in the (U, W) phase plane. Such a trajectory, connecting two different steady states, is called a heteroclinic trajectory, and in this case is parametrized by ζ; the trajectory approaches $(0, 0)$ as $\zeta \to -\infty$ and approaches $(1, 0)$ as $\zeta \to +\infty$ (see the dashed line in Figure 8.2(a)). The steady states at $U = 0$ and $U = 1$ are both saddle points, while for the steady state $U = \alpha$, the real part of both eigenvalues have the same sign, negative if c is positive and positive if c is negative, so that this is a node or a spiral point. Since the points at $U = 0$ and $U = 1$ are saddle points, the goal is to determine whether

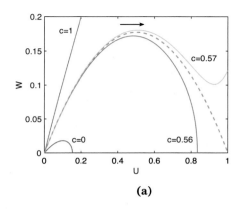
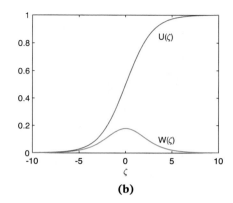

(a)   **(b)**

Figure 8.2. (a) Trajectories in the (U, W) phase plane leaving the rest point $U = 0$, $W = 0$ for the equation $U_{\zeta\zeta} - cU_\zeta + U(U - \alpha)(1 - U) = 0$, with $c = 0.0, 0.56,$ 0.57, and 1.0, and $\alpha = 0.1$. The dashed curve shows the connecting heteroclinic trajectory. (b) Profile of the traveling wave solution. In the original coordinates, this front moves to the left with speed $c = 0.5666$. This figure was made using Matlab code bistable_waves_pp.m.

the parameter c can be chosen so that the trajectory that leaves $U = 0$ at $\zeta = -\infty$ connects with the saddle point $U = 1$ at $\zeta = +\infty$, all while W is nonnegative. The mathematical procedure to do this is called *shooting*, and some sample trajectories are shown in Figure 8.2(a).

First, we can determine the sign of c. Supposing a monotone increasing ($U_\zeta > 0$) connecting trajectory exists, we multiply (8.4) by U_ζ and integrate from $\zeta = -\infty$ to $\zeta = \infty$ with the result that

$$c \int_{-\infty}^{\infty} W^2 d\zeta = \int_{-\infty}^{\infty} U_{\zeta\zeta} U_\zeta d\zeta + \int_{-\infty}^{\infty} f(U) U_\zeta d\zeta$$

(8.7)
$$= \frac{1}{2} U_\zeta^2 \Big|_{-\infty}^{\infty} + \int_0^1 f(u) du = \int_0^1 f(u) du.$$

In other words, if a traveling wave solution exists, then the sign of c is the same as the sign of the area under the curve $f(u)$ between $u = 0$ and $u = 1$. If this area is positive, then the traveling solutions move the state variable U from $U = 0$ to $U = 1$, and the state at $U = 1$ is said to be *dominant*.

Suppose $\int_0^1 f(u) du > 0$. We want to determine what happens to the trajectory that leaves the saddle point $U = 0, U_\zeta = 0$ for different values of c. With $c = 0$, an explicit expression for this trajectory is found by multiplying (8.4) by U_ζ and integrating to get

(8.8)
$$\frac{W^2}{2} + \int_0^U f(u) du = 0,$$

which is a relationship between U and W for the trajectory that goes through the origin. If this trajectory were to reach $U = 1$ for some value of $W \neq 0$, then

(8.9)
$$\frac{W^2}{2} + \int_0^1 f(u) du = 0,$$

which can occur only if $\int_0^1 f(u)du < 0$. Since this contradicts our assumption that $\int_0^1 f(u)du \geq 0$, we conclude that this trajectory cannot reach $U = 1$. Neither can this trajectory remain in the first quadrant, as $W > 0$ implies that U is increasing. Thus, this trajectory must intersect the $W = 0$ axis at some value of $U < 1$ (Figure 8.2(a)). It cannot be the connecting trajectory.

Next, let's see what happens when c is large. In the (U, W) phase plane, the slope of the trajectory leaving the rest point at $U = 0$ is the positive root of $\lambda^2 - c\lambda + f'(0) = 0$, which is always larger than c.[1] Let K be the smallest positive number for which $f(u) \leq Ku$ for all u on the interval $0 < u \leq 1$, and let σ be any fixed positive number. On the line $W = \sigma U$ the slope of trajectories satisfies

$$(8.10) \qquad \frac{dW}{dU} = c - \frac{f(U)}{W} = c - \frac{f(U)}{\sigma U} \geq c - \frac{K}{\sigma}.$$

By picking c large enough, we can be sure that $c - K/\sigma > \sigma$, so that trajectories cross the line $W = \sigma U$ from below. Thus, once a trajectory is above the line $W = \sigma U$, it will stay above it. We also know that for large enough c, the trajectory leaving the saddle point $U = 0$ has slope λ which is larger than c and therefore has slope larger than σ since $c > K/\sigma + \sigma > \sigma$. Therefore, the trajectory leaving the saddle point always stays above the line $W = \sigma U$, and therefore passes above the rest point at $(U, W) = (1, 0)$.

Now we have two trajectories, one with $c = 0$, which misses the rest point at $U = 1$ by crossing the $W = 0$ axis at some point $U < 1$, and one with c large, which misses the rest point by staying above it at $U = 1$. Since trajectories depend continuously on the parameters of the problem, there is a continuous family of trajectories depending on the parameter c between these two special trajectories, and therefore there is at least one trajectory that hits the point $U = 1, W = 0$, exactly.

The value of c for which this heteroclinic connection occurs is unique. To verify this, notice from (8.10) that the slope dW/dU of trajectories in the (U, W) plane is a monotone increasing function of the parameter c. Suppose at some value of $c = c_0$ there is known to be a connecting trajectory. For any value of c that is larger than c_0, the trajectory leaving the saddle point at $U = 0$ must lie above the connecting curve for c_0. However, with $c > c_0$, the trajectory approaching the saddle point at $U = 1$ as $\zeta \to \infty$ must lie below the connecting curve with $c = c_0$. A single curve cannot simultaneously lie above and below another curve, so there cannot be a connecting trajectory for $c > c_0$. By a similar argument, there cannot be a connecting trajectory for a smaller value of c, so the value c_0, and hence the connecting trajectory, is unique.

For most functions $f(u)$, it is necessary to calculate the speed of propagation of the traveling front solution numerically, and the exercises at the end of this chapter provide an opportunity to do so.

Functions for which the speed of propagation can be calculated analytically include the cubic function (8.2) and the piecewise-linear function [45]

$$(8.11) \qquad f(u) = -u + H(u - \alpha), \qquad 0 < \alpha < 1,$$

---

[1] Recall that for a saddle point, there are two trajectories that leave the critical point, i.e., approach the critical point in backwards time, $\zeta \to -\infty$, and two trajectories that approach the critical point as $\zeta \to \infty$. These special trajectories are in the direction of the eigenvectors of the Jacobian matrix corresponding to the positive and negative eigenvalues, respectively.

where $H(u)$ is the Heaviside function

(8.12)
$$H(u) = \begin{cases} 0 & u < 0, \\ 1 & u \geq 1. \end{cases}$$

This piecewise-linear function is not continuous, nor does it have three zeros, yet it is useful in the study of traveling wave solutions of the bistable equation because it is an analytically tractable model that retains many important qualitative features.

In the piecewise linear case (8.11) one calculates directly that

(8.13)
$$c = \frac{1 - 2\alpha}{\sqrt{\alpha - \alpha^2}}$$

(see Exercise 8.4).

Suppose $f(u)$ is the cubic polynomial

(8.14)
$$f(u) = -(u - u_0)(u - u_1)(u - u_2),$$

where the zeros of the cubic are ordered $u_0 < u_1 < u_2$. We want to find a heteroclinic connection between the smallest zero u_0, and the largest zero u_2, so we make the guess that

(8.15)
$$W = U' = -b(U - u_0)(U - u_2).$$

This is a reasonable guess, because $W = 0$ at $U = u_0$ and at $U = u_2$ and is of one sign in between, so the trajectory will be monotone. We substitute this guess into the governing equation (8.4), and find that we must have

(8.16)
$$b^2(2U - u_0 - u_2) - cb - (U - u_1) = 0.$$

This is a linear function of U that can be made identically zero only if we choose $b = \frac{1}{\sqrt{2}}$ and

(8.17)
$$c = \frac{1}{\sqrt{2}}(u_2 - 2u_1 + u_0).$$

It follows from (8.15) that

(8.18)
$$U(\zeta) = \frac{u_0 + u_2}{2} + \frac{u_2 - u_0}{2} \tanh\left(\frac{u_2 - u_0}{2\sqrt{2}}\zeta\right),$$

which is independent of u_1. In the case that $u_0 = 0, u_1 = \alpha$, and $u_2 = 1$, the speed reduces to

(8.19)
$$c = \sqrt{2}(\frac{1}{2} - \alpha),$$

showing that the speed is a decreasing function of α and the direction of propagation changes at $\alpha = 1/2$. The profile of the traveling wave in this case is

(8.20)
$$U(\zeta) = \frac{1}{2} + \frac{1}{2} \tanh\left(\frac{\zeta}{2\sqrt{2}}\right).$$

A plot of this traveling wave profile is shown if Figure 8.2(b).

A third bistable function that is useful for analytical reasons is the piecewise linear function

$$
(8.21) \qquad f = \begin{cases} -u & -\infty < u < \frac{\alpha}{2}, \\ u - \alpha & \frac{\alpha}{2} < u < \frac{1+\alpha}{2}, \\ 1 - u & \frac{1+\alpha}{2} < u < \infty. \end{cases}
$$

It is left as an exercise to calculate the speed of propagation for this function (see Exercise 8.6).

8.2. Threshold Behavior

The second important feature of the bistable equation is its threshold behavior. That is, an initial stimulus must exceed some threshold in order to initiate a traveling wave. This feature of the bistable equation is illustrated nicely by the simulations shown in Figure 8.1(a) and (b) (computed using Matlab code bistable_threshold_simulation.m). The solutions there are with initial data profile (shown dashed) $u_0(\xi) = a \operatorname{sech}^2(\frac{\xi}{\lambda})$, $\lambda = 4.2$, with (a) $a = 0.41$ and (b) $a = 0.42$. There is only a slight difference between the initial data curves for these two plots. However, for the smaller of the two initial profiles the solution decays to zero while for the larger of the two initial profiles, the solution approaches the traveling wave. The existence of a threshold is established by the following.

Theorem. *Any two solutions of the bistable equation that are initially ordered remain ordered for all time.*

Suppose $u_1(\xi, \tau)$ and $u_2(\xi, \tau)$ are two solutions of the bistable equation for which $u_1(\xi, 0) \leq u_2(\xi, 0)$. Define $v(\xi, \tau) = u_2(\xi, \tau) - u_1(\xi, \tau)$. Then $v(\xi, 0) \geq 0$ and $v(\xi, \tau)$ satisfies the differential equation

$$
(8.22) \qquad \frac{\partial v}{\partial \tau} = \frac{\partial^2 v}{\partial \xi^2} + v \int_0^1 f'(su_2 + (1 - s)u_1)\,ds.
$$

If $\int_0^1 f'(su_2 + (1 - s)u_1)\,ds$ is a bounded function (and it is if f is continuously differentiable), then $v(\xi, \tau) \geq 0$ for all τ.

Consequently, we have the following corollary.

Corollary. *If the solution $u(\xi, \tau)$ evolves into a traveling wave solution, then the solution $v(\xi, \tau)$ with $v(\xi, 0) \geq u(\xi, 0)$ also evolves into a traveling wave solution. Similarly, if the solution $u(\xi, \tau)$ approaches zero as $\tau \to \infty$, then the solution $v(\xi, \tau)$ with $v(\xi, 0) \leq u(\xi, 0)$ also approaches zero as $\tau \to \infty$.*

There are no simple formulas for this stimulus threshold but this feature can easily be determined numerically. The procedure for this is as follows: Choose a profile for $u_0(\xi)$ that is a monotone increasing function of a parameter, say a. For example, to generate Figure 8.1, the profile $u_0(\xi) = a \operatorname{sech}^2(\frac{\xi}{\lambda})$, which is monotone increasing in a for every value of space constant λ, was used. Pick two values of a, say a_L and a_U which are below and above threshold, respectively. Then, using the method of bisection, home in on the threshold value of a.

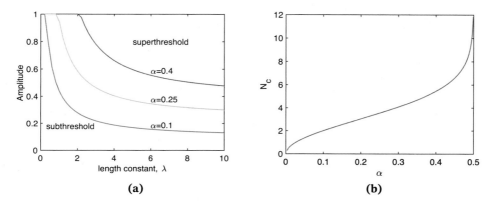

Figure 8.3. (a) Threshold curves amplitude a vs. length constant λ for the cubic bistable equation with $\alpha = 0.1, 0.25, 0.4$ for the initial data function $u_0(\xi) = a\,\text{sech}^2(\frac{\xi}{\lambda})$. (b) The threshold quantity N_c (8.23) plotted as a function of α for the cubic function (8.2).

The results of doing this for the function $u_0(\xi) = a\,\text{sech}^2(\frac{\xi}{\lambda})$ for the cubic function (8.2) for several values of α (using the Matlab codes bistable_thresholds.m and threshold_plotter.m) can be seen in Figure 8.3.

Another way to characterize the threshold is to realize that since $\int_{u_0}^{u_2} f(u)du > 0$, there is a nonconstant steady solution which is homoclinic to u_0 (meaning that $U(\xi) \to u_0$ in the limit $\xi \to \pm\infty$, see the $c = 0$ profile in Figure 8.2), and this solution profile is a threshold. Since there are no other steady profiles, any initial profile whose phase portrait lies entirely within this profile will result in decay to u_0 in the limit $\tau \to \infty$, while any initial profile whose phase portrait lies entirely outside this profile will evolve into traveling waves.

Considerations such as these can be used to determine how large a stimulus is necessary to initiate a traveling wave. In particular, if $U_0(\xi)$ is the steady homoclinic profile, then

$$(8.23) \qquad N_1 = \int_{-\infty}^{\infty} U_0(\xi)d\xi$$

gives an estimate of how much of the quantity u must be provided as a stimulus in order to initiate a traveling wave. It is a straightforward matter to calculate this quantity numerically (use the Matlab code bistable_threshold_integral.m). The results of this calculation are shown in Figure 8.3 for the cubic function (8.2), plotted as a function of α for $0 < \alpha < \frac{1}{2}$.

8.2.1. Thresholds in Two Dimensions. The simulations shown in Figure 8.1 show only the one dimensional spatial domain with $\xi > 0$. Symmetry of the bistable equation in ξ (the equation is invariant under the transformation $\xi \to -\xi$) implies that if the initial data are symmetric in ξ, then the solution is also symmetric in ξ for all τ. Consequently, for a superthreshold initial profile in one spatial dimension we expect to see two traveling wave profiles emerge, one moving to the right and one moving to the left.

There are many applications, such as the spruce budworm or *Wolbachia* problem where the natural physical domain is two dimensional. In this higher dimensional space, we also expect there to be threshold behavior. That is, suppose in a two dimensional space, the initial data are radially symmetric. We expect the solution to also be radially symmetric, governed by the equation

$$(8.24) \qquad \frac{\partial u}{\partial \tau} = \frac{1}{\xi} \frac{\partial}{\partial \xi} (\xi \frac{\partial u}{\partial \xi}) + f(u),$$

where ξ is the (dimensionless) radial coordinate.

It is easy to verify numerically that this equation exhibits threshold behavior, in that, if the initial profile is large enough, there results an outward moving wave profile which looks like the one dimensional traveling wave solution for large ξ. On the other hand, if the initial profile is small, the solution collapses to zero as $\tau \to \infty$.

One profile that separates super-threshold from sub-threshold behavior is the solution of the steady equation

$$(8.25) \qquad \frac{1}{\xi} \frac{d}{d\xi} (\xi \frac{du}{d\xi}) + f(u) = 0,$$

with $u'(0) = 0$, $\lim_{\xi \to \infty} u(\xi) = u_0$ and $u(0) > u_0$, analogous to the homoclinic trajectory in the one-dimensional case.

A direct way to solve this problem is with numerical shooting. That is, we rewrite the equation (8.25) as the first order system

$$(8.26) \qquad \frac{du}{d\xi} = -\frac{w}{\xi},$$

$$(8.27) \qquad \frac{dw}{d\xi} = \xi f(u),$$

then solve this as an initial value problem with initial conditions $u(0) = a$, $w(0) = 0$ for some value of a, with $u_1 < a < u_2$. Because we expect $u(\xi)$ to be a decreasing function of ξ (hence $w \geq 0$), if $w(\xi)$ becomes negative, the value of a is too small. On the other hand if $u(\xi)$ goes below u_0, the value of a is too large: Adjust the value of a until $u(\xi)$ stays close to u_0 for large ξ.

This seems like a perfectly good strategy for finding the standing profile. However, the astute reader will notice that there is a problem when trying to integrate this system starting at $\xi = 0$. This is because the righthand side of the first equation is zero divided by zero—not a good thing.

To avoid this problem it is necessary to start the integration at some small value of $\xi > 0$, and to do this, one must find a power series expansion for $u(\xi)$ for small ξ. Suppose $u(\xi) = a + b\xi^2 + \cdots$ for small ξ. Then, $w(\xi) = -2b\xi^2 + \cdots$, and for consistency, $\frac{dw}{d\xi} = \xi f(u)$ implies that $4b = -f(a)$. This, then, tells us to start the integration at some small value of $\xi > 0$, with initial data $u(\xi) = a - \frac{f(a)}{4} \xi^2$, and $w(\xi) = \frac{f(a)}{2} \xi^2$.

In Figure 8.4 are shown plots of the solutions of (8.26)–(8.27) for three different starting values a. Clearly, the smallest value $a = 0.23$ is too small and the largest value

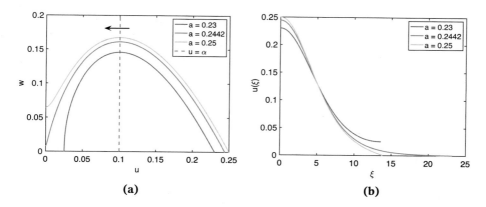

Figure 8.4. (a) Solution trajectories of the system (8.26)–(8.27) plotted in the u, w plane. (b) Showing $u(\xi)$ as a function of ξ, for three different starting values $u(0) = a$. For this plot, $f(u)$ is the cubic function (8.2) with $\alpha = 0.1$. For the trajectory with $a = 0.2442$, the area under the profile, (8.28), is $N_2 = 36.04$.

$a = 0.25$ is too large, while $a = 0.2442$ is quite close to the correct value for the threshold trajectory. This computation used the Matlab code bistable_two_d_threshold.m.

Once we have found the standing profile $U_0(\xi)$, an estimate of the size of the threshold stimulus is provided by the integral

$$(8.28) \qquad N_2 = 2\pi \int_0^\infty U_0(\xi)\xi\,d\xi,$$

which represents the area under the two-dimensional, rotationally symmetric, standing profile. The calculations to determine N_2 and the profiles in Figure 8.4 were done using the Matlab code bistable_two_d_threshold_number.m.

8.2.2. Meanwhile, Back at the Ranch. All of the results of the previous sections were derived in terms of dimensionless variables. This is valuable because it is *always* easier to work with dimensionless variables than with dimensional variables, if only because there are fewer variables and parameters to keep track of. However, in real life, for real world problems (down on the ranch, so to speak), we need to know speeds and thresholds in physical units.

Suppose that the dimensionless bistable equation has a traveling wave solution with (dimensionless) speed c, $u(\xi, \tau) = U(\xi - c\tau)$. We use the change of variables $\tau = kt$, $\xi = \sqrt{\frac{k}{D}}x$ to convert this into a solution of the dimensional bistable equation,

$$(8.29) \qquad U(\xi - c\tau) = U\left(\sqrt{\frac{k}{D}}x - ckt\right) = U\left(\sqrt{\frac{k}{D}}(x - \sqrt{Dk}ct)\right),$$

which being of the form $F(x - c_d t)$ implies that the speed of propagation in dimensional terms is

$$(8.30) \qquad c_d = \sqrt{Dk}c.$$

Notice that $\sqrt{Dk}$ has units of length/time, i.e. velocity.

To find the size of the threshold stimulus, we suppose that $U_d(x)$ is the homoclinic standing profile of the dimensional bistable equation in a one dimensional spatial domain. In dimensional units, if the variable u is a density, or concentration, then it has units of number per length. It follows that the threshold stimulus number is

(8.31)
$$N_s = \int_{-\infty}^{\infty} U_d(x)dx = \sqrt{\frac{D}{k}} \int_{-\infty}^{\infty} U_d(\sqrt{\frac{D}{k}}\xi)d\xi = \sqrt{\frac{D}{k}} \int_{-\infty}^{\infty} U_0(\xi)d\xi = \sqrt{\frac{D}{k}} N_1.$$

Notice that this has the correct units, since N_1 has the same units as U_0 (ξ is dimensionless), so the units of N_s are (length)·(number/length) = number.

In two dimensions, the units on u are number/area, and the threshold stimulus estimate is

(8.32)
$$N_s = 2\pi \int_0^{\infty} U_d(r)rdr = 2\pi\frac{D}{k} \int_0^{\infty} U_d(\sqrt{\frac{D}{k}}\xi)\xi d\xi = 2\pi\frac{D}{k} \int_0^{\infty} U_0(\xi)\xi d\xi = \frac{D}{k} N_2.$$

N_s again has the correct units, being (length)²· (number/(length)²) = number.

If u is a dimensionless quantity, then the dimensional variable, say U, is related to u through a dimensional scale factor, U_0, $U = U_0 u$, and the critical number N_s must also be scaled by U_0, that is,

(8.33)
$$N_s = \left(\frac{D}{k}\right)^{d/2} U_0 N_d, \quad d = 1, 2, 3$$

where $d = 1, 2, 3$ is the dimension of the physical space in which the wave is to propagate.

8.3. Propagation Failure

We now know that a bistable wave fails to propagate if

(8.34)
$$\int_{u_0}^{u_2} f(u)du \leq 0.$$

However there are additional reasons that a wave may fail to propagate, some of which we now describe.

8.3.1. Regions of Block.
Suppose there is a population that has bistable growth in most of space, but there is a region of space which cannot support this growth because the environment is not habitable, for example. This could be a paved road that does not support mosquito breeding or a firebreak in a forest that has no food source for spruce budworm. The question we ask here is how large a break will prevent the wave from spreading past the barrier.

Suppose that on the interval $0 < x < L$, the function u satisfies

(8.35)
$$\frac{\partial u}{\partial t} = D\frac{\partial^2 u}{\partial x^2} - k_d u,$$

whereas on the remainder of the real line, u satisfies

(8.36)
$$\frac{\partial u}{\partial t} = D\frac{\partial^2 u}{\partial x^2} + kf(u),$$

where $f(u)$ is a bistable function with $f(0) = f(\alpha) = f(1) = 0$. For all the plots and calculations in this section we used the cubic function (8.2).

We first nondimensionalize this problem by setting $x = \sqrt{\frac{D}{k}}\xi$, $\tau = kt$, so that the equations become

$$\text{(8.37)} \qquad \frac{\partial u}{\partial \tau} = \frac{\partial^2 u}{\partial \xi^2} - \kappa u,$$

$\kappa = \frac{k_d}{k}$ on the interval $0 < \xi < Y \equiv \sqrt{\frac{k}{D}}L$, whereas on the remainder of the real line, u satisfies

$$\text{(8.38)} \qquad \frac{\partial u}{\partial \tau} = \frac{\partial^2 u}{\partial \xi^2} + f(u).$$

What are the behaviors that need explanation? In Figure 8.5 are shown two simulations (made using the Matlab code CN_Bistable.m) both of the bistable equation with a region of block on $0 < \xi < Y$. On the left, for which $Y = 2.95$, the wavefront is slowed when it encounters the block region, but it manages to successfully propagate through. On the right, for which $Y = 3.0$, the solution fails to propagate through the block region and becomes a standing wave as $\tau \to \infty$.

So the strategy to study this problem is to determine conditions under which there is a standing profile $U(\xi)$ (i.e., with $\frac{\partial u}{\partial \tau} = 0$) like the final profile in Figure 8.5(b), having the feature that

$$\text{(8.39)} \qquad \lim_{\xi \to \infty} U(\xi) = 1, \qquad \lim_{\xi \to -\infty} U(\xi) = 0.$$

This means that we want to piece together a solution that satisfies

$$\text{(8.40)} \qquad U'' + f(U) = 0,$$

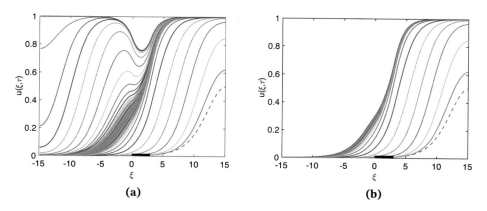

(a) **(b)**

Figure 8.5. Solution of the bistable equation with $\alpha = 0.25$, with a region of block for $0 < \xi < Y$ (shown as a black bar) in which $\kappa = 0.1$ is shown for (a) $Y = 2.95$ and (b) $Y = 3.0$. Dashed curves show the initial profile and waves are moving from right to left.

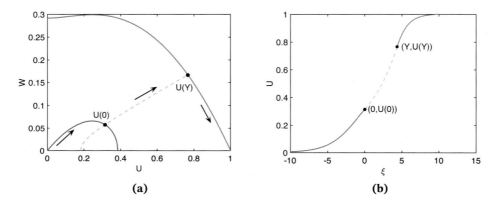

Figure 8.6. (a) Phase portrait for a standing blocked wave (increasing ξ direction shown by arrows). (b) Spatial profile for a blocked solution for the cubic function (8.2), $\alpha = 0.245$, $\kappa = 0.05$.

on the intervals $-\infty < \xi < 0$ and $Y < \xi < \infty$ and

$$(8.41) \qquad\qquad U'' - \kappa U = 0,$$

on the interval $0 < \xi < Y$, with U and U' continuous at the interfaces $\xi = 0$ and $\xi = Y$.

This is easily understood from a phase portrait analysis as follows (see Figure 8.6). Define $W = U'$. The trajectory with

$$(8.42) \qquad\qquad \frac{1}{2}W^2 + F(U) = 0,$$

where $F(U) = \int_0^U f(u)du$, is the trajectory that satisfies $U'' + f(U) = 0$ and approaches the origin as $\xi \to -\infty$ (the lower curve in Figure 8.6(a)), while the trajectory with

$$(8.43) \qquad\qquad \frac{1}{2}W^2 + F(U) = F(1)$$

is the trajectory that satisfies $U'' + f(U) = 0$ and approaches $U = 1$ as $\xi \to \infty$ (the upper curve in Figure 8.6(a)). Any trajectory of the form

$$(8.44) \qquad\qquad \frac{1}{2}W^2 - \frac{\kappa}{2}U^2 = K$$

is a solution $U'' - \kappa U = 0$ (for example, shown dashed in Figure 8.6(a)) that connects the first two trajectories is a candidate for the solution we seek. So, to find a candidate solution, pick any value for $U(0) = U_s$ that lies in the interval $0 < U_s < U_{\max}$, where $U_{\max}$ is the unique positive root of $F(U) = 0$. (This is the range on which $F(U) \leq 0$.) For this value of U_s, determine W_s so that $\frac{1}{2}W_s^2 + F(U_s) = 0$, i.e., that intersects the lower trajectory. Now solve the initial value problem

$$(8.45) \qquad U' = W, \quad W' = \kappa U, \quad U(0) = U_s, \quad W(0) = W_s,$$

terminating the integration when the solution intersects the upper integral curve, $\frac{1}{2}W(Y)^2 + F(U(Y))) = F(1)$. Since at the intersection of these two trajectories the

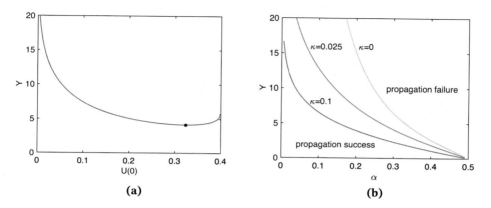

Figure 8.7. (a) Plot of the function $Y = Y(U(0))$ for the blocked solution for the cubic function (8.2), with $\alpha = 0.245$, $\kappa = 0.05$. The dot shows the smallest blocking region for which the blocked solution exists. (b) Critical length of blocking region as a function of α for the cubic function (8.2) with $\kappa = 0, 0.025, 0.1$.

values of W are the same, it must be that the terminal value of U, $U = U(Y)$, satisfies the equation

$$(8.46) \qquad \frac{\kappa}{2}U^2 + F(U) - F(1) = -K = -\frac{1}{2}W_s^2 + \frac{\kappa}{2}U_s^2.$$

Thus, knowing $U(Y)$ allows us to determine the value of Y for this trajectory, and provides a recipe for determining the length Y as a function of U_s, $Y = Y(U(0))$. (See Exercise 8.13). A plot of this function is shown in Figure 8.7(a).

8.3.2. Traumatic Brain Injury.
One of the concerns of football players, or anyone who receives frequent blows to the head (this could also include combat soldiers in the vicinity of loud explosions), is the effect of these blows to the nerves of the brain. Injury to the brain from these blows is commonly called a concussion or traumatic brain injury (TBI). A primary result of these traumatic events is mechanical damage to nerve axons by shearing or stretching. This can result in the interruption of axonal transport, further resulting in accumulation of transported materials as axonal swellings within a few hours of the trauma. Commonly, these swellings appear in a regular arrangement along the length of an axon near the site of injury, classically referred to as axonal varicosities. A more widely recognized axonal pathology found shortly after TBI is a large single swelling described as an axonal bulb, also referred to as focal axonal swellings. These regions of swelling can cause disruptions to the propagation of action potentials along the axon [65], [44].

To study what happens when a region of an axon is swollen, we need a reminder of the effect of axonal cross-sectional area on action potentials. This we find in the derivation of the cable equation (3.41) and we write the governing equation for the transmembrane potential as

$$(8.47) \qquad p\left(C_m \frac{\partial V}{\partial t}\right) = \frac{\partial}{\partial x}\left(\frac{A(x)}{R_c}\frac{\partial V}{\partial x}\right) - pI_{\text{ion}},$$

where $A(x)$ is the cross-sectional area of the axon, p is its perimeter, R_c is the cyto-plasmic resistivity, and we have taken the extracellular resistance to be zero. For this discussion we assume that only $A(x)$ is variable, and that the quantities pC_m and pI_{ion} are not affected by the swelling of the axon.

The first thing to notice is that the diffusion coefficient for this equation is $D = \frac{A}{pC_mR_c}$. Since the speed of propagation is proportional to $\sqrt{D}$, if all else is the same, then axons with larger cross-sectional area have faster propagation velocities. However, what happens if there is a small region with larger than normal cross-section?

To address this question, we assume that $A(x) = A_0$ for $x > L$ and $x < 0$, while $A(x) = A_s > A_0$ for $0 < x < L$, and try to determine if there are parameter values for which there is a standing wave profile. If there is a standing wave profile, then propagation is blocked.

We assume that the current pI_{ion} is proportional to the bistable function (and is not affected by the swelling) so that a standing profile satisfies the equation

$$(8.48) \qquad \frac{d}{dx}\left(A(x)\frac{dU}{dx}\right) + kf(U) = 0,$$

where $f(U_0) = f(U_1) = f(U_2) = 0$. (To keep the notation the same as in the above problem, we replace V by U). Next, we introduce the dimensionless space variable $\xi = \sqrt{\frac{k}{A_0}}x$, so that the governing equation is

$$(8.49) \qquad A_rU'' + f(U) = 0, \quad 0 < \xi < Y, \qquad U'' + f(U) = 0, \quad \xi < 0, \xi > Y,$$

where $Y = \sqrt{\frac{k}{A_0}}L, A_r = \frac{A_s}{A_0}$.

Finally, we specify conditions for the blocking solution at $\xi = \pm\infty$ as

$$(8.50) \qquad \lim_{\xi \to \infty} U(\xi) = U_2, \qquad \lim_{\xi \to -\infty} U(\xi) = U_0.$$

The trajectories we seek have U continuous at the interfaces as well as $U'(0^-) = A_rU'(0^+)$ and $U'(Y^+) = A_rU'(Y^-)$. These conditions follow from the fact that the axial current defined in (3.33), i.e., the flux, is continuous.

The integral curves for $\xi < 0$ and for $\xi > Y$ are

$$(8.51) \qquad \frac{1}{2}W^2 + F(U) = F(U_0) = 0, \quad \xi < 0, \qquad \frac{1}{2}W^2 + F(U) = F(U_2), \quad \xi > Y,$$

denoted the lower curve and upper curve, respectively, where $F(U) = \int_{U_0}^{U} f(u)du$, $W = U'$, in the $W - U$ plane.

For the intermediate region, there are many options. For any $U_s, 0 < U_s < U_1$, we set $W = A_rU'$, so that $WW' + A_rU'f(U) = 0$ for which there is an integral curve

$$(8.52) \qquad \frac{1}{2}W^2 + A_rF(U) = \frac{W_s^2}{2} + A_rF(U_s)$$

that intersects the first trajectory, so that

$$(8.53) \qquad \frac{1}{2}W^2 + A_rF(U) = (A_r - 1)F(U_s).$$

The largest value of W on this curve is at $U = U_1$, for which

(8.54)
$$\frac{1}{2}W_{\max}^2 = (A_r - 1)F(U_0) - A_r F(U_1).$$

If this value of W is the same or bigger than the W value on the upper curve at $U = U_1$, i.e.,

(8.55)
$$\frac{1}{2}W_{\max}^2 \geq F(U_2) - F(U_1),$$

then we are assured that the intermediate trajectory provides a connection between the lower and upper curves. This will occur provided $A_r \geq A_r^*$, where

(8.56)
$$A_r^* = \frac{F(U_2) - F(U_1) + F(U_s)}{F(U_s) - F(U_1)}.$$

It remains to determine the value of Y for this connecting trajectory. This is done algorithmically (numerically) as follows. For a given value of U_s, pick $A_r = A_r^*$ as in (8.56). Solve the initial value problem

(8.57)
$$U' = \frac{W}{A_r}, \quad W' = -f(U), \quad U(0) = U_s, \quad W(0) = W_s,$$

where $\frac{1}{2}W_s^2 + F(U_s) = 0$. Then, Y is that value of ξ for which $U(\xi) = U_1$.

The interesting feature of this calculation is that we now have the critical curve for $A_r - Y$. That is, above and to the right of this curve, propagation failure is assured.

Plots of this curve are shown in Figure 8.8(b), computed using the Matlab code TBI_block.m with the cubic nonlinearity (8.2). What this shows quantifies what we intuitively suspected, namely that a large enough swelling over a long enough section of axon can cause propagation failure. Furthermore, the less excitable the axon (larger α), the easier it is for a block to occur.

While this discussion described a block only for a static cable, the real situation is much more dynamic. In particular, nerve action potentials consist of an upstroke, described by the bistable equation, and a recovery phase, during which the potential

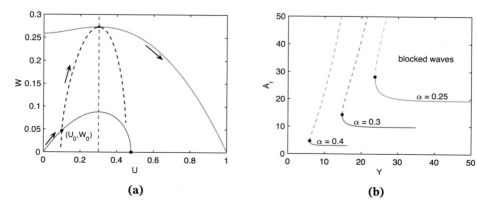

(a)   (b)

Figure 8.8. (a) Phase portrait for a standing blocked wave for TBI for the cubic function (8.2), $\alpha = 0.25$. (b) Critical curves above and to the right of which a standing blocked wave is assured, for $\alpha = 0.25, 0.3, 0.44$.

returns to rest and the medium recovers to await another action potential. One can envision the recovery process as causing dynamic, slowly varying changes to α. That is, immediately after an action potential passes, α is reset to a large value, blocking another immediate action potential. As the medium recovers, the value of α gradually returns to its low, preaction potential state. Now the apparent consequence of Figure 8.8(b) is that the recovery to allow a subsequent action potential takes longer when there is TBI than when there is not, since the critical value of α at which propagation is blocked is lower for TBI than not. Consequently, TBI allows only low frequency action potential sequences and disallows high frequency sequences, depending, of course, on the severity of the injury. Obviously, this can have serious consequences on neural signal processing.

8.3.3. Discrete Cells. The cable equation was derived (in Section 3.3) under the assumption that a nerve cell axon was a long, homogeneous, cylindrical membrane structure. Other excitable cells, in particular cardiac cells, are not like this. Instead, cardiac cells are bricklike, about 100 μm long and about 15 μm wide, connected at their ends (the junctional regions) with protein structures called *gap junctions* (see Figure 8.9(a)). Gap junctions are tiny pores in the membrane that connect the intracellular space of one cell with the intracellular space of its neighbor. In this diagram, we show just one large gap junction when in fact there are many distributed across the end face of the cell; The junctional space between the cells is quite narrow, on the order of 10–20 nm.

Gap junctions act electrically like resistors, and so can be modeled as obeying Ohm's law (the electrical equivalent of Fick's law). That is, we suppose that the current between two coupled cells i and j is $I = \frac{1}{r_g}(V_i - V_j)$, where V_i and V_j are the intracellular potentials of (isopotential) cells i and j, respectively, and r_g is the effective gap junctional resistance. So, for the nth cell in a long connected line of cells (Figure 8.9(b))

$$(8.58) \qquad A_s C_m \frac{dV_n}{dt} + A_s I_{\text{ion}}(V_n) = \frac{1}{r_g}(V_{n+1} - 2V_n + V_{n-1}),$$

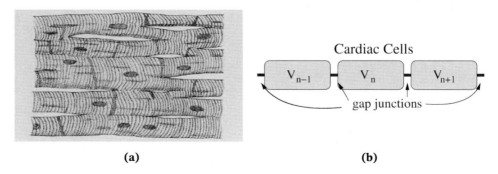

(a)   (b)

Figure 8.9. (a) Depiction of cardiac cellular tissue and (b) schematic diagram of gap-junctionally coupled cells. In (a), dark ovals represent the cell nucleus, dark vertical stripes represent the junctional regions where cells are coupled, and the faint thin lines represent Z-bands, which bound the sarcomeres and tether muscle fibers. (See Chapter 9 for a discussion of muscle contraction.)

where V_n is the nth intracellular potential, and A_s is the total surface area of a cell. We let R_m be the membrane resistance (see Exercise 8.9) and then set $t = R_m C_m \tau$, $V = u$ so that (8.58) becomes

(8.59)
$$\frac{du_n}{d\tau} = d(u_{n+1} - 2u_n + u_{n-1}) + f(u_n),$$

where $f(u) = -R_m I_{ion}(u)$ and $d = \frac{R_m}{A_s r_g}$. This equation looks like a discretized version of the cable equation that one would get via the method of lines, with the identification $d = \frac{D}{\Delta x^2}$, and indeed, we discuss this below. We refer to this equation as the *discrete bistable equation*.

In Figure 8.10 are shown the results of simulating the discrete bistable equation (using the Matlab code discrete_bistable_via_MOL.m) with the cubic bistable function (8.2), $\alpha = 0.25$, $d = 0.02$ on the left and $d = 0.018$ on the right, and both starting with initial data $u_n(0) = 0.5$ for $n < 0$ and $u_n(0) = 0$ for $n \geq 0$. On the left we see that the solution is a traveling wave. For the discrete bistable equation, a traveling wave solution has the feature that the solution for the $(n + 1)$-st cell is exactly the same as for the nth cell, delayed by some fixed amount $\delta\tau$, i.e., $u_{n+1}(t) = u_n(t - \delta\tau)$ for all n.

On the right, however, the solution approaches a steady profile, so that propagation fails. Propagation fails for all smaller values of d.

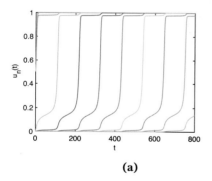
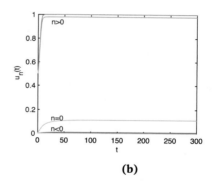

(a)   (b)

Figure 8.10. $u_n(t)$ plotted as a function of time for the discrete bistable equation (8.59) with $\alpha = 0.25$, and with (a) $d = 0.02$ and (b) $d = 0.018$.

To verify that propagation fails, we look for a standing solution of the bistable equation (8.59). The existence of a standing solution guarantees that propagation is blocked, since the discrete bistable equation admits a comparison theorem as does the continuous version (recall Section 8.2). A standing solution is a solution of the difference equation

(8.60)
$$d(u_{n-1} - 2u_n + u_{n+1}) + f(u_n) = 0,$$

subject to the conditions, $\lim_{n \to -\infty} u_n = 1$, $\lim_{n \to \infty} u_n = 0$. An example of this profile is shown in Figure 8.11. This standing profile is analogous to a heteroclinic trajectory between $u = 0$ and $u = 1$ that we found above for continuous equations using phase plane techniques.

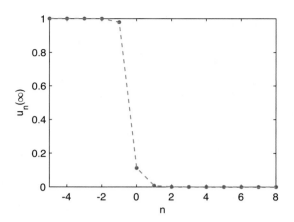

Figure 8.11. Standing profile for the discrete bistable equation.

It is not easy to find such solutions for general $f(u)$, but it is possible for the piecewise linear function (8.11). In particular, we take

(8.61)
$$u_n = \begin{cases} 1 - A\lambda^{-n} & n < 0, \\ B\lambda^n & n \geq 0, \end{cases}$$

where $0 < \lambda < 1$ is a root of the polynomial $\lambda^2 - (2 + \frac{1}{d})\lambda + 1 = 0$. Note that $u_n \to 1$ as $n \to -\infty$ and $u_n \to 0$ as $n \to \infty$. This choice of u_n satisfies the equation (8.60) for all n except $n = -1$ and $n = 0$. Assuming $B < \alpha$ and $1 - A\lambda > \alpha$, we have two additional conditions to satisfy, namely

(8.62)
$$n = 0: \quad 1 - A\lambda - 2B + B\lambda - \frac{k}{d}B = 0,$$

(8.63)
$$n = -1: \quad 1 - A\lambda^2 - 2(1 - A\lambda) + B + \frac{k}{d}A\lambda = 0,$$

which we solve for A and B to find

(8.64)
$$B = \frac{\lambda - \lambda^2}{\lambda^2 + 1}, \qquad A = 1 - B,$$

and then, the condition $B < \alpha$ leads to the requirement

(8.65)
$$d \leq \frac{\alpha(1 - \alpha)}{(2\alpha - 1)^2}.$$

A plot of this function is shown in Figure 8.12. Propagation fails for parameter values below this curve and it succeeds for parameter values above this curve (although we have not verified that propagation succeeds above this curve).

The implications of this are important, particularly for cardiac propagation. This implies that cardiac action potentials can fail when r_g is large, but not necessarily infinite. In other words, a decrease in the number or conductance of gap junctions can lead to a fatal failure of the heart.

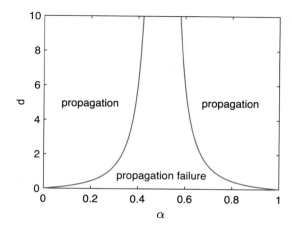

Figure 8.12. Plot of equation (8.65), made using Matlab code discrete_failure_plot.m.

8.3.3.1. *The Method of Lines, Revisited.* The observation that propagation for the discrete bistable equation fails if the coupling coefficient d is sufficiently small has important implications for numerical simulation by the method of lines. In particular, notice that the finite difference approximation to the continuous bistable equation (7.1) (i.e., the method of lines),

$$(8.66) \qquad \frac{du_n}{dt} = \frac{D}{\Delta x^2}(u_{n+1} - 2u_n + u_{n-1}) = f(u_n),$$

where $u_n(t) = u(n\Delta x, t)$ is *exactly* the discrete bistable equation (8.59) with coupling coefficient $d = \frac{D}{\Delta x^2}$. Using Taylor series, we can verify that

$$(8.67) \qquad \frac{1}{\Delta x^2}(u_{n+1} - 2u_n + u_{n-1}) = \frac{\partial^2 u}{\partial x^2} + O(\Delta x^2).$$

This implies the the speed of propagation calculated via the method of lines with spatial discretization Δx, say $C(\Delta x)$, will relate to the exact speed of propagation for the continuous bistable equation, called c_0, through

$$(8.68) \qquad C(\Delta x) = c_0 + O(\Delta x^2).$$

In other words, the speed of propagation will be well approximated in the limit $\Delta x \to 0$.

However, with real calculations one must always use fixed values of Δx; the limit $\Delta x \to 0$ can only be approximated. So, when we use the method of lines to simulate the continuous bistable equation, we are actually simulating the discrete bistable equation. We know that the discrete bistable equation exhibits propagation failure for larger Δx, i.e., $C(\Delta x) = 0$ for all Δx sufficiently large, even when the continuous version should propagate. The lesson to be learned is the cautionary note that solutions from numerical methods might be misleading.

8.3.4. Discrete Release Sites. A second example of the effects of discreteness can be seen with calcium release. Many models of calcium release from the ER assume that release is homogeneous in space. In fact, this is not the case. In *Xenopus* oocytes, for example, IPR are arranged into clusters with a density of about 1 per 30 mm^2, with each cluster containing about 25 IPR. Consequently, the propagation of Ca^{2+} waves in a cell is saltatory (from the Latin *saltare*, to hop or leap), with release "jumping" from one cluster of release sites to another.

In cardiac cells, muscle contraction is regulated by calcium release through ryanodine receptors that are spaced in aggregates along the length of the cardiac cell, separated by about $2\mu m$. (Muscle fibers contract when calcium is released and relax when calcium is resequestered.) Ryanodine receptors are also CICR receptors (similar to IPR's) in that they exhibit CICR, i.e., their open probability is an increasing function of calcium (as a reminder, see (7.31)). Each cluster of ryanodine receptors is separately controlled by voltage regulated calcium channels that release calcium into the cell only in the local vicinity of the RyR cluster. However, the calcium that is released from an individual cluster *could* stimulate a neighboring cluster, leading to a saltatory wave of calcium release from cluster to cluster. This would not be a good thing and is actually known to be the cause of certain dangerous cardiac arrhythmias. Thus, the spatial separation of ryanodine receptor clusters is an important safety feature of cardiac cells as it prevents propagation of calcium release waves, under normal circumstances,.

To explore the properties of this type of calcium wave, and to see the consequences of this discrete structure, we assume that calcium is released from discrete release sites but is removed continuously throughout space. We consider the equation for calcium concentration

$$(8.69) \qquad \frac{\partial c}{\partial t} = D_c \frac{\partial^2 c}{\partial x^2} - k_s c + L \sum_n \delta(x - nL) f(c).$$

The function f is your favorite description of calcium release, and L is the spatial separation between release sites.[2]

Unfortunately, the analysis of this model is, in general, difficult, so we make a simplifying assumption that makes analysis much more tractable. In this simplified model, we assume that when the calcium concentration $[Ca^{2+}]$ at a release site reaches a threshold value, c^*, that site *fires* by instantaneously releasing a fixed amount, σ, of calcium. Thus, a Ca^{2+} wave is propagated by the sequential firing of release sites, each responding to the Ca^{2+} diffusing from neighboring release sites. Hence, this model is known as the *fire-diffuse-fire* model [13], [37], [57], [59].

For this model, we assume that the Ca^{2+} concentration c satisfies the reaction diffusion equation

$$(8.70) \qquad \frac{\partial c}{\partial t} = D_c \frac{\partial^2 c}{\partial x^2} - k_s c + \sigma \sum_n \delta(x - nL)\delta(t - t_n),$$

where, as before, L is the spacing between release sites and k_s is the uptake rate. Although this equation looks linear, appearances are deceptive. Here, t_n is the time at which c first reaches the threshold value c^* at the nth release site. When this happens,

---

[2]The Dirac delta function, $\delta(x)$, is not truly a function but has the meaning that $\delta(x) = 0$ if $x \neq 0$, and $\int_{0-}^{0+} \delta(x)dx = 1$. It is also true that $\delta(ax) = \frac{1}{|a|}\delta(x)$. This follows from the formal calculation with integrals, $\int_{0-}^{0+} \delta(ax)dx = \frac{1}{a}\int_{0-}^{0+} \delta(ax)adx = \frac{1}{|a|}\int_{0-}^{0+} \delta(y)dy = \frac{1}{|a|}$. Another way of stating these is with $H'(x) = \delta(x)$, or $\int_{-\infty}^{x} \delta(x)dx = H(x)$, where H is the Heaviside function, but here differentiation and integration must be understood formally, not rigorously. The rigorous verification of these and other facts rely on generalized function theory, a topic that is beyond the scope of this text, but which can be found in [34], for example.

the nth release site releases the fixed amount σ. Thus, t_n depends in a complicated way on c.

Let's first nondimensionalize this problem. The natural length constant is L and a natural time constant is $\frac{L^2}{D_c}$ so we introduce the dimensionless variables $\xi = \frac{x}{L}, \tau = \frac{D_c t}{L^2}$, and find the dimensionless equation

$$(8.71) \qquad \frac{\partial c}{\partial \tau} = \frac{\partial^2 c}{\partial \xi^2} - \beta^2 c + \frac{\sigma}{L} \sum_n \delta(\xi - n)\delta(\tau - \tau_n),$$

where $\beta^2 = \frac{k_s L^2}{D_c}$.

We know from (6.10) that the profile resulting from the firing of a single site at $\xi = 0$ at time $\tau = 0$ with total amplitude 1 is given by

$$(8.72) \qquad u_0(\xi, \tau) = \frac{H(\tau)}{\sqrt{4\pi\tau}} \exp(-\frac{\xi^2}{4\tau} - \beta^2\tau),$$

where H is the Heaviside function (8.12). It follows that the calcium profile resulting from a release at position $\xi = n$ at time $\tau = \tau_n$ is given by

$$(8.73) \qquad c_n(\xi, \tau) = \frac{\sigma}{L} u_0(\xi - n, \tau - \tau_n).$$

If we superimpose the solutions from each site, we get

$$(8.74) \qquad c(\xi, \tau) = \sum_i c_i(\xi, \tau) = \frac{\sigma}{L} \sum_i u_0(\xi - i, \tau - \tau_i).$$

Notice that because of the instantaneous release, $c(\xi, \tau)$ is not a continuous function of time at any release site.

Now, suppose that sites $i = N, N - 1, \ldots$ have fired at known times with $\tau_N > \tau_{N-1} > \cdots$. The next firing time τ_{N+1} is determined implicitly by

$$(8.75) \qquad c(N + 1, \tau_{N+1}) = c^*, \qquad \frac{\partial}{\partial t} c(N + 1, \tau_{N+1}) > 0,$$

which is the time when c at $\xi_{N+1} = N + 1$ first reaches the threshold, c^*. Thus, τ_{N+1} must satisfy the equation

$$(8.76) \qquad c^* = \frac{\sigma}{L} \sum_{i \leq N} u_0(N + 1 - i, \tau_{N+1} - \tau_i).$$

A steadily propagating wave corresponds to having $\tau_i - \tau_{i-1} = \text{constant} = \delta\tau$ for all i, i.e., each site fires at a fixed time after its leftward neighbor fired. Note that the resulting wave does not have a constant spatial profile, but has a well-defined speed $\frac{1}{\delta\tau}$. If such a $\delta\tau$ exists, then $\tau_{N+1} - \tau_i = \delta\tau(N + 1 - i)$ and $\delta\tau$ is a solution of the equation

$$\theta \equiv \frac{c^* L}{\sigma} = \sum_{i \leq N} u_0(N + 1 - i, \delta\tau(N + 1 - i)).$$

$$(8.77) \qquad = \sum_{n=1}^{\infty} \frac{1}{\sqrt{4\pi n \delta\tau}} \exp\left(-\frac{n}{4\delta\tau} - \beta^2 n \delta\tau\right) \equiv g_\beta(\delta\tau).$$

This is a difficult (actually impossible) equation to solve directly. However, it is a straightforward matter (using Matlab) to determine θ as a function of the delay $\delta\tau$

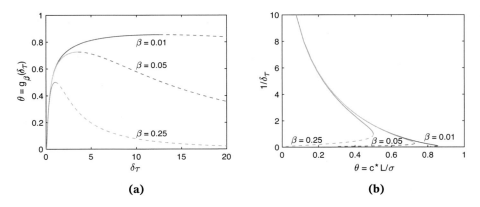

Figure 8.13. (a) Plots of $\theta = g_\beta(\delta\tau)$ vs. $\delta\tau$. (b) Plots of the dimensionless velocity $\frac{1}{\delta\tau}$ as a function of θ, for several values of $\beta = \sqrt{\frac{k_s L^2}{D_c}} = 0.01, 0.05, 0.25$.

as shown in Figure 8.13(a). Then, we easily plot the velocity $\frac{1}{\delta\tau}$ as a function of θ, as shown in Figure 8.13(b). These plots were made using the Matlab code fdf_plots.m.

Note that the function $g_\beta(\delta\tau)$ is not monotone, but has a maximal value, say $g_{\max}(\beta)$, which is a decreasing function of β. Furthermore, $g_\beta(\delta\tau) \to 0$ as $\delta\tau \to 0$ and as $\delta\tau \to \infty$. If $\theta > g_{\max}(\beta)$, no solution of (8.77) exists; there is propagation failure. On the other hand, if $\theta < g_{\max}(\beta)$, there are two solutions of (8.77), although, the physically meaningful solution is the smaller of the two, corresponding to the first time that $c(\xi, \tau)$ reaches c^*. (Realize that at any point in space, the calcium profile first increases and then decreases, so that if it hits the level θ, it does so twice, once on the way up and later on the way down.) The physically meaningful solution is shown as a solid curve, and the one that is not meaningful is shown dashed in Figure 8.13.

There are several interesting observations to be made here. First, the velocity is a monotone decreasing function of β and θ. This makes intuitive sense, since we should expect velocity to decrease if L or k_s or c^* increase, or if D_c or σ increase. Second, with $\beta \neq 0$, propagation ceases at a positive, not zero, velocity. The implications of this are that the transition from a stalled front to a moving front is dramatic, not gradual.

This has an interesting interpretation for an analogous problem, the rate of spread of fires in a forest or a fuel depository. Suppose there are a number of evenly spaced, highly explosive, heat sources, that explode and release a large amount of heat whenever the local ambient temperature exceeds some threshold. According to the above analysis, there is a critical spatial separation above which the accidental explosion of one of the fuel depositories will not spread. However, below this critical separation, explosions will spread rapidly, not gradually, even though the spatial separation may be only slightly below the critical value. This gives a possible explanation for why ever so slight changes of conditions can convert a controlled forest fire into one that is rapidly moving.

Exercises

8.1. Suppose u satisfies equation (7.1), with $f(u_0) = f(u_1) = f(u_2) = 0$. Find a change of variables that transforms this equation into the equation

$$\frac{\partial w}{\partial \tau} = \frac{\partial^2 w}{\partial \xi^2} + g(w),$$

where $g(0) = g(\alpha) = g(1) = 0$. What is $g(w)$ and what is α?

8.2. Suppose the bistable function $f(u)$ is such that $f(u) < 0$ for $u > u_2$ and $f(u) > 0$ for $u < u_0$, where $u_0 < u_2$. Use the comparison theorem (Section 5.6) to prove the following.

(a) Any solution of the bistable equation with bounded initial data remains bounded for all time.

(b) Any solution $u(x, t)$ with bounded initial data has $u_0 \leq \lim_{t \to \infty} u(x, t) \leq u_2$.

(c) Any solution $u(x, t)$ for which $u_0 \leq u(x, 0) \leq u_2$ has $u_0 0 \leq u(x, t) \leq u_2$, for all $t \geq 0$.

8.3. Consider the spruce-budworm equation (7.2). If $\kappa = \frac{\alpha}{K_u} \ll 1$ (which according to Table 7.1, it is), then the function $\frac{v^2}{\kappa^2 + v^2}$ is well-approximated by the step function

$$\frac{v^2}{\kappa^2 + v^2} \approx \begin{cases} 0 & v = 0, \\ 1 & v > 0. \end{cases}$$

Use this approximation to determine the value of S above which there are bistable traveling waves of spruce-budworm infestation.

8.4. Find the speed of propagation for the bistable equation with piecewise linear $f(u)$ (8.11).

Hint. To find traveling wave solutions, solve

$$U'' + cU' - U = 0, \qquad \zeta > 0$$

and

$$U'' + cU' - (U - 1) = 0 \qquad \zeta < 0$$

with boundary conditions $U(-\infty) = 1$, $U(\infty) = 0$ and matching conditions $u(0) = \alpha$ and $u'(0)$ continuous. To do so, take

$$U(\zeta) = \begin{cases} \alpha \exp(a\zeta) & \zeta > 0 \\ 1 + (\alpha - 1) \exp(b\zeta) & \zeta < 0, \end{cases}$$

and determine a and b so that the matching conditions are satisfied.

8.5. Consider the approximation for calcium release dynamics (7.29)

$$J_{SERCA}(c) = k_s c,$$

where $k_s = \frac{V_p}{2K_p}$ and

$$J_{IPR}(c) = \begin{cases} 0 & c < K_2, \\ k_f(c_T - c) & c > K_2. \end{cases}$$

Find the speed of propagation for calcium release waves using this approximation. For what values of k_f and c_T does propagation fail?

8.6. Find the speed of propagation for the bistable equation with the piecewise linear
bistable function

$$
f = \begin{cases} -u & -\infty < u < \frac{\alpha}{2}, \\ u - \alpha & -\frac{\alpha}{2} < u < \frac{1+\alpha}{2}, \\ 1 - u & \frac{1+\alpha}{2} < u < \infty. \end{cases}
$$

Hint. Find an implicit relationship for the speed c as a function of α, i.e,
find $\alpha = \alpha(c)$. Verify that $c = 2$ at $\alpha = 0$ and $c = -2$ at $\alpha = 1$.
Warning. This is a challenging calculation.

8.7. (a) Use the Matlab code CN_bistable.m to calculate the speed of spread for a
spruce-budworm invasion using the dimensionless equations from Exercise 7.4, for several values of σ.
(b) Use this to determine the speed of propagation for a spruce-budworm invasion as a function of S.

8.8. (a) Find an analytical representation for the speed of propagation for a *Wolbachia* mosquito infection in terms of the parameters D, k_1, k_3, and k_4.
(b) Different strains of *Wolbachia* have different kinetic parameters. The strain
wMel has been successfully established in three cities in Australia [**31**],
resulting in the estimate that $\alpha = \frac{k_1 - k_3}{k_4 + k_1 - k_3} = 0.3$. Using estimates of
$D = 500\text{m}^2/\text{day}$ [**62**], and $k_4 + k_1 - k_3 = 0.012/\text{day}$,
(i) Estimate the speed of propagation of a wave of *Wolbachia* infection.
(ii) Determine the width of a mosquito-free zone that will stop the wave.
Use that the natural death rate of mosquitoes is about $\frac{1}{40}/\text{day}$ [**62**].
(*Hint.* Make use of the Matlab code barrier_block.m.)
(iii) Suppose the natural density of mosquitoes is about 5 mosquitoes per
meter^2. Estimate how many infected mosquitoes need to be released
in order to initiate a wave of *Wolbachia* infection. *Hint.* Use the Matlab code two_d_threshold_number.m.

8.9. Find the speed of propagation for the cable equation (3.40) as a function of
physical parameters with ion currents defined by the Hodgkin–Huxley upstroke
(7.28) in the following steps.
(a) Nondimensionalize the cable equation (3.40) as follows: Define the *membrane resistance* R_m as the resistance per unit area of membrane by

$$
\frac{1}{R_m} = \frac{dI_{\text{ion}}}{dV}\Big|_{v=V_0},
$$

where V_0 is the smallest solution of $I_{\text{ion}} = 0$. Introduce scaled variables τ
and ξ so that the cable equation becomes

$$
\frac{\partial V}{\partial \tau} = \frac{\partial^2 V}{\partial \xi^2} - R_m I_{\text{ion}}(V).
$$

(b) Find the (nondimensional) traveling wave speed c_0 numerically for this scaled cable equation. (Use the Matlab codes CN_bistable.m and HH_upstroke_rhs.m to determine the speed of the Hodgkin–Huxley wavefront.)

(c) Determine the dimensional wave speed in terms of physical parameters and c_0.

8.10. (a) What percentage of sodium channels must be blocked in order for action potential propagation to fail? *Hint.* Use (8.7) and determine the critical value of $\bar{g}_{Na}$ so that the propagation speed is zero.

(b) TTX (tetrodotoxin = puffer fish toxin) is an extremely potent sodium channel blocker that works by binding with sodium channels and preventing them from opening. Suppose that the sodium channel conductance in (7.28) is modified by TTX binding by

$$\bar{g}_{Na} \rightarrow \bar{g}_{Na} \frac{1}{1 + \frac{[TTX]}{K_d}},$$

where $K_d \approx 5$ nM. What concentration of TTX will cause action potential propagation to fail?

8.11. Find the minimal level of P in (7.31) needed to guarantee that a calcium wave, described by (7.29), will spread.

Hint. To solve this problem, **do not** try to find the roots of $f(c)$ as a function of P. Rather, find the value of P for which $f(c) = 0$ for a given value of c. Then, calculate the integral $\int_0^c f(c)dc$ for the chosen value of c and corresponding value of P.

8.12. Find the critical number N_3 for the size of an initial stimulus at the center of a spherical domain necessary to initiate an outward propagating wave for a three dimensional medium with bistable cubic dynamics and $\alpha = 0.1$.

Hint. $N_3 = 4\pi \int_0^\infty U_0(\xi)\xi^2 d\xi$ where U_0 is the solution of the equation

$$\frac{1}{\xi^2}\frac{d}{d\xi}(\xi^2\frac{du}{d\xi}) + f(u) = 0,$$

with $u(0) = a$, $u'(0) = 0$ and $u(\xi) \rightarrow 0$, $u'(\xi) \rightarrow 0$ as $\xi \rightarrow \infty$.

8.13. Suppose U satisfies the differential equation $U'' - \kappa U = 0$, with initial data $U(0) = U_0$, $U'(0) = W_0$, and the final condition $U(Y) = U_Y$. Determine Y.

8.14. Find the critical curve relationship between A_r and Y for TBI block in the case that $f(u) = -u + H(u - \alpha)$. Verify that this curve satisfies $\lim_{Y \to \infty} A_r = \frac{1-\alpha}{\alpha}$ and $\lim_{A_r \to \infty} Y = \frac{1-2\alpha}{\alpha}$.

Hint. Solve the differential equation $A_r U'' - U = 0$, subject to the four conditions $U(0) = U_0$, $A_r U'(0) = U_0$, $U(Y) = \alpha$, and $A_r U'(Y) = 1 - \alpha$. Why is this the correct problem to solve?

8.15. Find the critical TBI curve, equivalent to those in Figure 8.8(b), for the Hodgkin–Huxley upstroke model (7.28).

Hint. Modify the Matlab code TBI_block.m using the ionic currents of HH_upstroke_rhs.m, and the nondimensionalization of Exercise 8.9.

Warning. Because the bistable function has a very large amplitude, this problem requires a bit of numerical "tweaking" to get the algorithm to work. It is easier to use smaller values of $\bar{g}_{Na}$ to get things working.

8.16. An infinitely long axonal cable has crossectional area A_+ for $x > 0$ and A_- for $x < 0$. Suppose that pC_m and pI_{ion} are identical for all x, and suppose that $I_{ion} = f(v)$ is bistable with $f(U_0) = f(U_0) = f(U_2) = 0$, $U_0 < U_1 < U_2$. Find the value of $A_r = \frac{A_-}{A_+}$ above which waves traveling from right to left are blocked. Find and plot an analytical expression for A_r as a function of $U_1 = \alpha$ for the cubic bistable function (8.2).

8.17. Simulate the discrete bistable equation (8.59) with cubic nonlinearity (8.2) and coupling coefficient d to find and plot the speed (in units of number of cells or nodes per time) as a function of d. How does this curve compare with the speed of propagation for the continuous bistable equation with diffusion coefficient d? Using the same data, plot the speed in units of length per unit of time assuming the cells are distance Δx apart and $d = \frac{D}{\Delta x^2}$. Does the speed converge to the correct speed as $\Delta x \to 0$?

    Hint. Modify the Matlab code discrete_bistable_via_MOL.m.

8.18. A large number of small heat sensitive explosive devices are to be stored along a long underground tunnel. Suppose for these devices it is known that $\theta = \frac{c^*\sigma}{L} = 0.5$. How far apart should piles of these devices be placed, and how large (or small) should the piles be to assure that an accidental spontaneous explosion will not propagate along the entire length of the passageway?

8.19. Ryanodine receptors are known to exhibit spontaneous (random) release events, the frequency of which increases with increasing SR calcium concentration. Calcium overload is the condition in which the SR calcium concentration of the cell is larger than normal.

    (a) Based on the model for calcium release (7.30), what is the effect of increased SR (or ER) calcium concentration on the amount of calcium released from ryanodine receptors?

    (b) What do you suspect, based on the analysis of the fire-diffuse-fire model, is the effect of calcium overload on cardiac cell behavior?

Chapter 9

Advection and Reaction

Now we begin to study problems in which transport (or advection) plays an important role.

9.1. Simple Advection

The first example is the simplest possible case. Suppose a material with density u is transported at constant velocity v, so that the flux is $J = vu$, and the conservation law reads

$$(9.1) \qquad \frac{\partial u}{\partial t} = -\frac{\partial}{\partial x}(vu).$$

It is reasonable to believe that the quantity u is simply translated at velocity v, and so it is reasonable to look for a translationally invariant solution of the form $u(x, t) = U(\xi)$, where $\xi = x - vt$. In fact, this is a solution of (9.1) for any differentiable function $U(\xi)$, as can be readily verified by direct substitution.

9.2. Advection with Decay

Suppose that a toxic chemical is dumped from a factory into a stream that is flowing at velocity v and that the chemical degrades naturally at rate λ. How much chemical flows into the lake at the end of the stream at distance L from the factory?

We model this problem by letting u be the concentration of chemical in the stream and then, invoking our well-used conservation law (2.4), write that

$$(9.2) \qquad \frac{\partial u}{\partial t} = -\frac{\partial}{\partial x}(vu) - \lambda u.$$

We suppose that at the factory outlet (at $x = 0$), the flux of chemical because of the factory is $vu(0, t) = vu_0(t)$, a function of time (maybe they dump more at night than during the day).

There are (at least) two ways to solve this problem. The first is to realize, as we did with the diffusion equation, that it may be possible to simplify the equation by making the guess $u(x, t) = f(t)U(x, t)$. Upon substitution into (9.2), we get

$$(9.3) \qquad f\frac{\partial U}{\partial t} + U\frac{df}{dt} = -f\frac{\partial}{\partial x}(vU) - \lambda f U,$$

and realize that if we set $\frac{df}{dt} = -\lambda f$, the equation reduces nicely to

$$(9.4) \qquad \frac{\partial U}{\partial t} = -\frac{\partial}{\partial x}(vU),$$

which we already know how to solve. It follows that

$$(9.5) \qquad u(x, t) = U(x - vt)\exp(-\lambda t).$$

It is actually more convenient to write the solution equivalently as

$$(9.6) \qquad u(x, t) = U(t - \frac{x}{v})\exp(-\lambda t),$$

and then the boundary condition at $x = 0$ is easier to deal with and becomes

$$(9.7) \qquad u(0, t) = U(t)\exp(-\lambda t) = u_0(t),$$

which implies that

$$(9.8) \qquad U(t) = \exp(\lambda t)u_0(t)$$

or

$$(9.9) \qquad u(x, t) = u_0(t - \frac{x}{v})\exp(-\lambda\frac{x}{v}).$$

The flux of chemical into the lake is given by

$$(9.10) \qquad J = vu(L, t) = vu_0(t - \frac{L}{v})\exp(-\lambda\frac{L}{v}).$$

The quantity $\frac{L}{v}$ is called the *residence time*, and accordingly, the flux of chemical into the lake is $\exp(-\lambda\frac{L}{v})$ times the flux out of the factory $\frac{L}{v}$ units of time previously.

The solution method we used here, of reducing the problem to one we have solved before, is wonderful when it works, but it is of limited practical usefulness. Instead, we need a solution method that is easily generalizable to more complicated problems. That method is called the *method of characteristics*.

The idea of the method of characteristics is to look for solutions of the equation (9.2) along special curves, called *characteristic curves*, of the form $x = X(t)$. For the example above, those curves were described by the coordinate $\xi = x - vt$, that is, curves of the form $x = X(t) = vt - \xi$, however, in general $X(t)$ is yet to be determined. Now, along the curve $x = X(t)$, the chain rule applied to $u(X(t), t)$ gives

$$(9.11) \qquad \frac{du}{dt} = \frac{\partial u}{\partial x}\frac{dX}{dt} + \frac{\partial u}{\partial t}.$$

If we pick $\frac{dX}{dt} = v$, then according to the partial differential equation (9.2),

$$(9.12) \qquad \frac{du}{dt} = \frac{\partial u}{\partial t} + \frac{\partial u}{\partial x}v = -\lambda u.$$

In other words, by this "trick", we have reduced the solution of the partial differential equation to the solution of the two ordinary differential equations

(9.13) $$\frac{dX}{dt} = v, \qquad \frac{du}{dt} = -\lambda u.$$

Next we need to figure out what to do about initial data. For this problem, initial data are $u(x = 0, t) = U_0(t)$. We represent the initial data as a curve in $x - u$ space parametrized by t_0, $x(t_0) = 0$, $u(t_0) = U_0(t_0)$ with t_0 viewed as parameterizing the initial data curve. Now we solve the two ordinary differential equations (9.13) subject to the initial data $x(t_0) = 0$, $u(t_0) = U_0(t_0)$, for all $t_0 \geq 0$. This solution is readily determined to be

(9.14) $$x = X(t) = v(t - t_0), \qquad u(t) = U_0(t_0) \exp(-\lambda(t - t_0)).$$

Finally, we undo the transformation of space by solving for t_0 as a function of x and t, i.e., $t_0 = t - \frac{x}{v}$, and then writing

(9.15) $$u(x, t) = U_0(t - \frac{x}{v}) \exp(-\lambda \frac{x}{v}),$$

as we found above.

9.3. Structured Populations

To properly understand the behavior of a population, it might be necessary to account for features of the organism, such as age or size, which can affect the growth of the population. In general a structured population is one for which there is some feature, called the structure variable, which characterizes individuals, and whose variation throughout the population affects the behavior of the population in an important way. In the sections that follow, we give two examples of structured populations whose dynamics are described by advection reaction kinetics.

9.3.1. Age Structure.
To begin with a simple example of a structured population, suppose $u(a, t)$ is a population density, so that $u(a, t)da$ represents the number of individuals in the population with ages between a and $a + da$. We might like to know how the demographics of the population changes over time, and if the population can be expected to survive.

To build a model of the population demographic dynamics, we ask how u can change. The obvious answer is that individuals can be born (at age zero), die, and age. To write down the conservation law for this population, we need to know the age flux. Since aging takes place at exactly the same rate at which time passes, the aging velocity is 1, and consequently the age flux is $J = u(a, t)$. This leads us to the conservation equation

(9.16) $$\frac{\partial u}{\partial t} = -\frac{\partial u}{\partial a} - \mu(a)u,$$

where $\mu(a) \geq 0$ is the death rate, possibly a function of age a.

In addition, we must specify the birthrate, that is, the rate of production of individuals of age $a = 0$. We specify

$$\text{(9.17)} \qquad U_0(t) = u(0, t) = \int_0^\infty \beta(x)u(x, t)dx.$$

Here $\beta(a)$ is the nonnegative age-dependent birthrate, in units of number of births per individual.

We begin to find the solution of this problem using the method of characteristics. The characteristic equations are

$$\text{(9.18)} \qquad \frac{dt}{da} = 1, \qquad \frac{du}{da} = -\mu(a)u,$$

subject to the data $u = U_0(t_0)$, $t = t_0$ when $a = 0$, a curve in $t - u$ space parametrized by t_0.

The solution is

$$\text{(9.19)} \qquad t = t_0 + a, \qquad u = U_0(t_0)P_S(a),$$

where $P_S(a) = \exp(-\int_0^a \mu(a)da)$ is the survival probability, i.e., the probability of survival until age a. We eliminate t_0 to find

$$\text{(9.20)} \qquad u(a, t) = U_0(t - a)P_S(a).$$

Now, we close this equation by requiring consistency via (9.17) to find

$$\text{(9.21)} \qquad U_0(t) = \int_0^\infty \beta(x)u(x, t)dx = \int_0^\infty \beta(x)P_S(x)U_0(t - x)dx.$$

Equation (9.21) is a linear integral equation for the (unknown) birthrate U_0 as a function of time. To get an idea of its solution, we try an exponential solution, $U_0(t) = \exp(\lambda t)$, and find upon substituting into (9.21),

$$\text{(9.22)} \qquad 1 = \int_0^\infty \beta(x)P_S(x)\exp(-\lambda x)dx \equiv F(\lambda),$$

which is called the characteristic equation for λ. We want to find the value of λ for which this equation is satisfied.

Clearly, the function $F(\lambda)$ is a monotone decreasing function of λ with

$$\text{(9.23)} \qquad F(0) \equiv \int_0^\infty \beta(x)P_S(x)dx,$$

and $F(\infty) = 0$, $F(-\infty) = \infty$. Therefore, if $F(0) > 1$ the solution has $\lambda > 0$, whereas, if $F(0) < 1$ the solution has $\lambda < 0$. In other words, the population grows exponentially, since $\lambda > 0$, (and is therefore sustainable) if $F(0) > 1$, whereas it decays exponentially, since $\lambda < 0$, if $F(0) < 1$. This all makes sense when one realizes that the quantity $F(0)$ represents the *fitness* of the population, i.e., the age structure-dependent, reproductive rate. A population is sustainable only if its fitness $F(0)$ is greater than 1.

9.3.2. Epidemics. The Kermack–McKendrick [39] model is an SIR model for the number of people infected with a contagious illness in a closed population over time. It was proposed to explain the rapid rise and fall in the number of infected patients observed in epidemics such as the plague (London 1665–1666, Bombay 1906) and cholera (London 1865).

The model can be represented by the reactions

$$(9.24) \qquad S + I \xrightarrow{\alpha} 2I, \quad I \xrightarrow{\beta} R,$$

where S represents susceptible individuals, I represents infected individuals and R represents the removed individuals, either by death or recovery with permanent immunity. If the reaction rates α and β are constants, then these reactions can be represented by the system of ordinary differential equations

$$(9.25) \qquad \frac{ds}{dt} = -\alpha s i, \quad \frac{di}{dt} = \alpha s i - \beta i;$$

analysis of this system is described in Chapter 1. Here, we suppose that the transmission rate is age dependent, meaning that the rate of infection depends on how long the infected individual has been infected (the infection age). This is actually typical of many viruses, including influenza A and SARS-CoV-2 (Severe Acute Respiratory Syndrome Coronavirus 2), for which the viral load and hence contagion is highest two to three days after initial infection and one or two days before the appearance of symptoms, and tapers off after that.[1] We also allow for the recovery rate β to be a function of the infection age of the infected individual. If this is the case, then the differential equation describing the evolution of the susceptible population S becomes

$$(9.26) \qquad \frac{ds}{dt} = -s \int_0^t \alpha(a) i(a, t) da,$$

where $i(a, t)$ is the age dependent population density of infected individuals. Here the upper limit of integration is t rather than ∞, since, if the process starts at time $t = 0$ when the first infected individuals are introduced into the population, then at time t, individuals cannot possibly have been infected for a time longer than t. The evolution of $i(a, t)$ is governed by the partial differential equation (the same as for the previous example of age dependent birth and death)

$$(9.27) \qquad \frac{\partial i}{\partial t} = -\frac{\partial i}{\partial a} - \beta(a) i,$$

and the rate of creation of newly infected individuals is the same as the rate of infection of susceptibles,

$$(9.28) \qquad i_0(t) = i(0, t) = -\frac{ds}{dt}.$$

To solve this problem, we must first solve the partial differential equation (9.27). This was done in the previous section using the method of characteristics, and gives

---

[1] In addition to age of infection, there may be other variables such as age of the individual, body mass index (BMI), blood type, sex, etc., which affect the transmission and death or recovery from the disease. To include these, a multivariable/multicompartment structure model could be formulated and studied.

that

(9.29) $$i(a,t) = i_0(t - a)P_S(a),$$

where $P_S(a) = \exp(-\int_0^a \beta(a)da)$ is the survival probability for the infection.

Now we use this information to simplify equation (9.26) for s to

(9.30) $$\frac{d}{dt}\ln(s) = -\int_0^t \alpha(a)P_S(a)i_0(t-a)da.$$

Since $i_0(t) = -\frac{ds}{dt}$, this is a nonlinear integral equation for $s(t)$ that we do not know how to solve. However, we can get some information about the solution by integrating both sides of the equation with respect to time. We find

$$\ln(\frac{s_\infty}{s_0}) = -\int_0^\infty \int_0^t \alpha(a)P_S(a)i_0(t-a)dadt$$

(9.31)
$$= -\int_0^\infty \alpha(a)P_S(a)da \int_0^\infty i_0(t)dt,$$

where the last expression is found following a change in the order of integration. But now we use that $i_0(t) = -\frac{ds}{dt}$, so that

(9.32) $$\ln(\frac{s_\infty}{s_0}) = B\int_0^\infty \frac{ds}{dt}dt = B(s_\infty - s_0),$$

where $B = \int_0^\infty \alpha(a)P_S(a)da$ is the effective transmission rate for the infection.

The solution of this transcendental equation determines the number of susceptible individuals remaining (s_∞) after the infection has run its course. It is useful to rewrite it as

(9.33) $$\ln(u) = Bs_0(u - 1),$$

where $u = \frac{s_\infty}{s_0}$, and notice that this equation is *exactly* the same form as (1.67) with Bs_0 replacing $\frac{\alpha s_0}{\beta}$. In fact,

(9.34) $$B = \int_0^\infty \alpha(a)P_S(a)da = \frac{\alpha}{\beta}$$

in the case that both α and β are constant, and $Bs_0 = R_0$ is the effective transmission rate known from Chapter 1 for an SIR ode epidemic model. It follows that there is a unique solution with $0 < u < 1$ if and only if $1 < Bs_0$. The interpretation of this is the same as for the ordinary differential equation model (9.25), and Figure 1.6(b) applies. Namely, there is a threshold for the initial susceptible population size s_0 below which the infection does not spread. Further, the fraction $u = \frac{s_\infty}{s_0}$ is a decreasing function of Bs_0. Thus, for the infection to spread, the effective transmission rate B times the initial susceptible population size s_0 must be greater than 1. On the other hand, an epidemic can be prevented from spreading if either B or s_0 can be reduced, say by quarantine to reduce B, or vaccination to reduce s_0.

9.3.3. Red Blood Cells. Adult humans have 20–30 trillion red blood cells and produce about 2 million red blood cells per second. Production of blood cells (also called erythrocytes) is controlled by an intricate array of soluble factors, that include hematopoietic growth and differentiation factors. Formation of these factors is itself controlled by other factors outside the bone marrow such as, in the case of red blood cells, low oxygen concentration for an extended period of time.

The feedback system that controls erythrocyte production is relatively well understood. The principal factor stimulating red blood cell production is the hormone *erythropoietin*. About 90% of the erythropoietin is secreted by renal tubular epithelial cells when blood is unable to deliver sufficient oxygen. The remainder is produced by other tissues (mostly the liver). When both kidneys are removed or destroyed by renal disease, the person invariably becomes anemic because of insufficient production of erythropoietin.

The role of erythropoietin in bone marrow is twofold. First, it stimulates the production of pre-erythrocytes, called *proerythroblasts*, and it also controls the speed at which the developing cells pass through the different stages. Normal production of red blood cells from stem cells takes 5–7 days, with no appearance of new cells before 5 days, even at high levels of erythropoietin. At high erythropoietin levels the rate of red blood cell production (number per unit time) can be as much as ten times normal, even though the maturation rate of an individual red blood cell varies much less.

Thus, in response to a drop of oxygen pressure in the tissues, an increased production of erythropoietin causes an increase in the rate of production of red blood cells, thus tending to restore oxygen levels. The control mechanisms that operate when the red blood cell count is too high (a condition called polycythemia or erythrocytosis) are less clear. Details of the regulatory system governing red blood cells can be found in Williams [73], while an excellent review of much of the material discussed here can be found in Haurie et al. [27].

Here we present a model of the red blood cell production cycle. We let $n(x, t)$ be the density of red blood cells at time t that are x units old, i.e., that were released into the bloodstream at time $t - x$. Red blood cells can die at any age, but for this discussion, we assume that they all die at some fixed age X (for normal humans this is about 120 days). Because aging takes place at velocity 1, hence the age flux of red blood cells is $J = n(x, t)$, the conservation law for red blood cells is the simple advection equation

$$(9.35) \qquad \frac{\partial n}{\partial t} = -\frac{\partial n}{\partial x}.$$

At any given time the total number of blood cells in circulation is

$$(9.36) \qquad N(t) = \int_0^X n(x, t)dx.$$

Now we suppose that the production of blood cells is controlled by N, and that once a cohort of cells is formed in the bone marrow, it emerges into the bloodstream as mature cells some fixed time d later, about 7 days for humans. Here we ignore the fact that at high levels of feedback (for example, at high levels of erythropoietin, which occurs when oxygen levels are low) cells mature more rapidly. Thus, we take

(9.37) $n(0, t) = F(N(t - d)),$

where F is a nonlinear production function that is monotone decreasing in its argument. The function F is related to the rate of secretion of growth inducer (erythropoietin, for example) in response to the blood cell population size.

Before going any further, it makes sense to rescale this problem. That is, we set $u = \frac{n}{N_0}$ and $U = \frac{N}{N_0}$, where N_0 is a typical number for the total red blood cells, say $N_0 = 24$ trillion. In these variables, the problem has

(9.38) $\dfrac{\partial u}{\partial t} = -\dfrac{\partial u}{\partial x},$

with

(9.39) $u(0, t) = f(U(t - d)), \quad U(t) = \displaystyle\int_0^X u(x, t) dx,$

where $f = \frac{F}{N_0}$.

The steady-state solution for this model is easy to determine. We set $\partial u / \partial t = 0$ and find that

(9.40) $u(x) = u(0), \quad x > 0,$

where $u(0)$ is yet to be determined. Since $U_0 = \int_0^X u(x) \, dx$ is the total number of cells in steady state, it follows that

(9.41) $U_0 = Xu(0).$

At steady state, $f(U_0) = u(0)$, and thus it follows that

(9.42) $f(U_0) = \dfrac{U_0}{X}.$

It is convenient to write this as

(9.43) $X = \dfrac{U_0}{f(U_0)},$

which determines X as a function of U_0. Since $f(U_0)$ is a monotone decreasing function of U_0, equation (9.42) is guaranteed to have a unique solution. Furthermore, the function $\frac{U_0}{f(U_0)}$ is a monotone increasing function of U_0, so that, because of (9.43), U_0 is a monotone increasing function of X. This implies that if the cell death age decreases, the cell population drops while the production of cells increases. An illustration of these facts is provided by the graph in Figure 9.1(b), where the two curves $\frac{f(U)}{f(0)}$ and $\frac{U}{Xf(0)}$ are plotted as functions of U. Here the function $f(U)$ is taken to be $f(U) = \frac{A}{1+U^7}$, as suggested by data from autoimmune-induced hemolytic anemia in rabbits [5]. The relationship between U_0 and X is shown plotted in Figure 9.1(a), and was found from (9.43) by computing X as a function of U_0, and then reversing the axes (using the Matlab code rbc_plots.m).

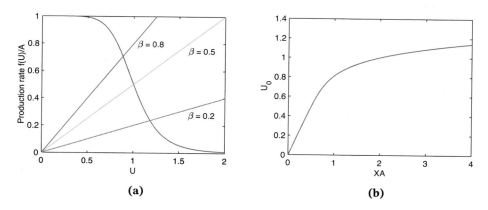

Figure 9.1. (a) Plot of $\frac{f(U)}{A}$ and βU as functions of U for three different values of $\beta = \frac{1}{AX}$ and for $f(U) = \frac{A}{1+U^7}$. (b) Plot of U_0 as a function of XA, using $f(U) = \frac{A}{1+U^7}$.

The next interesting question to ask is whether this steady solution is stable or unstable. It is convenient to integrate the partial differential equation (9.38) to get an ordinary differential equation. Integrating (9.38) from $x = 0$ to $x = X$ gives

$$\text{(9.44)} \qquad \frac{dU}{dt} = u(0, t) - u(X, t).$$

Since $u(0, t) = f(U(t - d))$ and $u(X, t) = u(0, t - X) = f(U(t - X - d))$, it follows that $U(t)$ is governed by the delay differential equation

$$\text{(9.45)} \qquad \frac{dU}{dt} = f(U(t - d)) - f(U(t - d - X)).$$

We now linearize around the steady state U_0 by looking for solutions of the form $U(t) = U_0 + \epsilon U_1(t)$. Substituting this form into (9.45), differentiating with respect to ϵ and taking the limit $\epsilon \to 0$, we find

$$\text{(9.46)} \qquad \frac{dU_1}{dt} = f'(U_0)\Big(U_1(t - d) - U_1(t - d - X)\Big).$$

Now we try a solution of the form $U_1 = \exp(\lambda t)$. It follows that λ must satisfy the characteristic equation

$$\text{(9.47)} \qquad \lambda + f'(U_0)e^{-\lambda(d+X)} - f'(U_0)e^{-\lambda d} = 0,$$

from which we learn that

$$\text{(9.48)} \qquad \frac{\lambda e^{\lambda d}}{1 - e^{-\lambda X}} = f'(U_0).$$

The roots λ of this equation determine the stability of the linearized solution. If all the roots have negative real part, then the steady solution U_0 is linearly stable, whereas if there are roots with positive real part, the steady solution U_0 is unstable. Notice that, since $f'(U_0) < 0$, and $\frac{\lambda e^{\lambda d}}{1-e^{-\lambda X}} > 0$ for all real λ, there can be no real roots of this equation; all roots are complex. It follows that even if the steady solution is stable, the return to steady state is oscillatory rather than monotone. Thus, following rapid disruptions of blood cell population, such as traumatic blood loss or transfusion, or a vacation at a high-altitude ski resort, the blood cell population oscillates about its steady state.

Necessarily, if there is a transition from stable to unstable solutions, it occurs only if a complex root changes the sign of its real part, leading to a *Hopf bifurcation*. If a Hopf bifurcation occurs, it occurs precisely when the complex roots are purely imaginary, $\lambda = i\omega$. We substitute $\lambda = i\omega$ into (9.48) and separate this into its real and imaginary parts to obtain

$$(9.49) \qquad f'(U_0)(\cos(\omega d) - \cos(\omega(d + X))) \;=\; 0,$$
$$(9.50) \qquad f'(U_0)(\sin(\omega d) - \sin(\omega(d + X))) \;=\; -\omega.$$

There are two ways to solve (9.49). Because cosine is symmetric about any multiple of π, we can take $n\pi - \omega d = n\pi + \omega(d + X)$, or $\omega(2d + X) = 2n\pi$, for any positive integer n. Because cosine is 2π periodic, we could also take $\omega X = 2n\pi$; however, since sine is also 2π periodic and $\omega \neq 0$, this fails to give a solution of (9.50). With $\omega(2d+X) = 2n\pi$, (9.50) becomes

$$(9.51) \qquad 2df'(U_0)\sin(\omega d) = -\omega d,$$

or, eliminating ω,

$$(9.52) \qquad 2df'(U_0) = -\frac{2n\pi}{2 + \frac{X}{d}}\,\frac{1}{\sin\left(\frac{2n\pi}{2+\frac{X}{d}}\right)}.$$

Finally, we use that $f(U_0) = U_0/X$ to write

$$(9.53) \qquad \frac{U_0 f'(U_0)}{f(U_0)} = -\frac{X}{d}\,\frac{n\pi}{2 + \frac{X}{d}}\,\frac{1}{\sin\left(\frac{2n\pi}{2+\frac{X}{d}}\right)}.$$

For each integer n, this equation defines a relationship between U_0 and X/d at which there is a change of stability and thus, a Hopf bifurcation. If we take f to be of the form

$$(9.54) \qquad f(x) = \frac{A}{1 + x^p},$$

we find that

$$(9.55) \qquad \frac{U_0 f'(U_0)}{f(U_0)} = -\frac{p U_0^p}{1 + U_0^p},$$

and (9.42) becomes

$$(9.56) \qquad dA = \frac{d}{X} U_0 (1 + U_0^p).$$

Equation (9.55) allows us to solve (9.53) for U_0 as a function of $\frac{X}{d}$ and then find dA as a function of X/d from (9.56). Shown in Figure 9.2 is this critical stability curve dA vs. $\frac{X}{d}$ for $n = 1$ and $p = 7$. The case $n = 1$ is the only curve of interest, since it is the first instability. That is, the steady state solution is unstable for all the critical stability curves with $n > 1$, and so these curves do not lead to physically relevant transitions.

The implications of this calculation are interesting. If the nondimensional parameters X/d and dA are such that they lie above the curve in Figure 9.2(a), then the steady

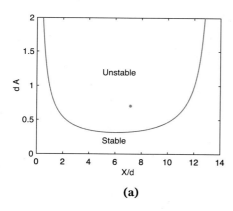
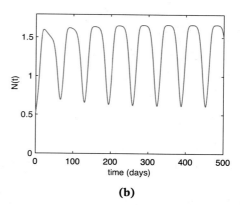

(a)   (b)

Figure 9.2. (a) Critical stability curve (Hopf bifurcation curve) for blood cell growth. (b) Time dependent solution of equations (9.38)–(9.39) for parameter values $X = 50$, $d = 7, A = 0.1$, shown as a dot on the left.

solution is unstable, and a periodic or oscillatory solution is likely (but not guaranteed by this analysis). On the other hand, if these parameters lie below or to the far right of this curve, the steady solution is stable.

From this we learn that there are three mechanisms by which cell production can be destabilized, and these are by changing the maximal production rate A, the expected lifetime X, or the production delay d. If X/d is sufficiently large ($> \approx 13$), the system cannot be destabilized. However, if X/d is small enough, increasing A is destabilizing. Increasing the delay d is also destabilizing. If A and X are held fixed, then changing d moves $y = dA$ and $x = X/d$ along the hyperbola $yx = $ constant. Thus, decreasing d is stabilizing, as it increases X/d, moving it out of and away from the unstable region.

For normal humans, with $d = 7$ days and $X = 120$ days, there is no instability, since $X/d = 17$. However, any mechanism that substantially shortens X can have a destabilizing effect and can result in oscillatory production of blood cells. Near the bifurcation, the period of oscillation is $T = \frac{2\pi}{\omega}$, where $\omega(2d + X) = 2\pi$, so that

(9.57) $$T = 2d + X.$$

Thus, for example, a disorder that halves the normal lifetime of blood cells to $X = 60$ days should result in oscillatory blood cell production with a period on the order of 74 days.

The human condition in which red blood cell counts oscillate is sometimes associated with chronic myelogenous leukaemia.

9.4. Simulation

It is always nice when problems have solutions that can be found with analytical techniques, but with biological applications this is rarely the case. This raises the question of how to best simulate advection equations. A natural starting place is with the example discussed above for red blood cell production.

Our goal here is to simulate equations (9.38)–(9.39), using the method of lines. We start by discretizing the age variable x by setting $u_j = u(j\Delta x, t)$, with $j = 0, 1, \ldots, N$, where $N\Delta x = X$. A natural discretization of (9.38) is

$$(9.58) \qquad \frac{du_j}{dt} = \frac{1}{\Delta x}(u_{j-1} - u_j),$$

for $j = 1, 2, \ldots, N$. To make this work, we need to know $u_0 = u(0, t) = f(U(t - d))$, which requires knowledge of $U(t - x)$ for $0 < x < d$. Of course, $U(t - x)$ satisfies the equation

$$(9.59) \qquad \frac{\partial U}{\partial t} = -\frac{\partial U}{\partial x},$$

and so it is once again natural to discretize this equation by setting $U_k = U(t - k\Delta y)$, $k = 0, 1, \ldots, K$, where $K\Delta y = d$, and then let

$$(9.60) \qquad \frac{dU_k}{dt} = \frac{1}{\Delta y}(U_{k-1} - U_k),$$

for $k = 1, 2, \ldots, K$. Now, we are finally able to close the system when we set $u_0 = f(U_K)$, and then

$$(9.61) \qquad U_0 = \Delta x \left(\frac{u_0}{2} + \sum_{j=1}^{N-1} u_j + \frac{u_J}{2}\right),$$

which is an approximation to the integral $\int_0^X u(x, t)dx$.

This algorithm is implemented in the Matlab code rbc_plots.m, and an example of the solution is shown in Figure 9.2(b).

9.4.1. Method of Lines; Upwinding. In the above section, where the goal was to simulate the partial differential equation

$$(9.62) \qquad \frac{\partial u}{\partial t} + \frac{\partial u}{\partial x} = 0,$$

the method proposed was to discretize $u(x, t)$ setting $u_j(t) = u(j\Delta x, t)$ and then replace the equation (9.62) with the discretized equation

$$(9.63) \qquad \frac{du_j}{dt} = \frac{1}{\Delta x}(u_{j-1} - u_j),$$

replacing the derivative $\frac{\partial u}{\partial x}$ with its backward finite difference. Notice, that we could have just as easily used the forward finite difference to get

$$(9.64) \qquad \frac{du_j}{dt} = \frac{1}{\Delta x}(u_j - u_{j+1}),$$

but we didn't! Why?

This question is partially answered by a simple observation, which is that at first glance (9.63) appears to have exponentially decaying solutions, while (9.64) has exponentially growing solutions. This follows simply from the fact that the equation $\frac{du}{dt} = -u + f$ has exponentially bounded solutions, while $\frac{du}{dt} = u + f$ exhibits exponentially growing behavior.

A more precise explanation is found by examining the numerical solutions of the advection equation

$$\frac{\partial u}{\partial t} + v\frac{\partial u}{\partial x} = 0, \tag{9.65}$$

where the velocity v is some constant. The method of lines with backward differences for this gives the equations

$$\frac{du_j}{dt} = \frac{v}{\Delta x}(u_{j-1} - u_j). \tag{9.66}$$

If we now choose to simulate this using forward Euler stepping in time, we get

$$u_j^{n+1} = u_j^n + \frac{v\Delta t}{\Delta x}(u_{j-1}^n - u_j^n), \tag{9.67}$$

or in matrix form

$$\mathbf{u}^{n+1} = \mathbf{u}^n + \frac{v\Delta t}{\Delta x}A\mathbf{u}^n, \tag{9.68}$$

where the matrix A has the form

$$A = \begin{pmatrix} -1 & 0 & 0 & \cdots & 0 \\ 1 & -1 & 0 & 0 & \cdots \\ & & \vdots & & \\ 0 & \cdots & 0 & 1 & -1 \end{pmatrix}. \tag{9.69}$$

Because A is a lower diagonal matrix, all of its eigenvalues are the diagonal elements -1, so that the eigenvalues of the matrix $I + \frac{v\Delta t}{\Delta x}A$ are all $1 - \frac{v\Delta t}{\Delta x}$. Hence, the numerical algorithm is stable only if $0 < \frac{v\Delta t}{\Delta x} < 2$.

This has important consequences. First, if $v < 0$, this scheme is always unstable which means that if $v < 0$ one must use forward, rather than backward, differences. This choice is called *upwinding* and refers to the fact that the difference is taken in the upwind direction, i.e., *into* the advective flow, toward or against the wind or the direction from which it is blowing.

The second consequence is that Δt must not be too large. This is referred to as a *CFL condition* (i.e., the Courant–Friedrichs–Levy condition).

The idea of upwinding requires a little extra thought when the velocity is not constant. To be specific, suppose we have the equation, written in conservation form,

$$\frac{\partial u}{\partial t} + \frac{\partial J}{\partial x} = 0, \quad J = v(x, u)u. \tag{9.70}$$

We define $J_{j-\frac{1}{2}}$ to be the discretized flux at position $x_{j-\frac{1}{2}}$ (halfway between grid points x_{j-1} and x_j, illustrated in Figure 9.3) where $v_{j-\frac{1}{2}} = v(x_j - \frac{\Delta x}{2}, \frac{1}{2}(u_{j-1} + u_j))$, and $H(v)$ is the Heaviside function (8.12). In words, if $v_{j-\frac{1}{2}} > 0$, we use the value of u to the left, u_{j-1}, to calculate the flux, whereas if $v_{j-\frac{1}{2}} < 0$ we use the value of u to the right, u_j, to calculate the flux, i.e.,

$$J_{j-\frac{1}{2}} = v_{j-\frac{1}{2}}\left(H(v_{j-\frac{1}{2}})u_{j-1} + H(-v_{j-\frac{1}{2}})u_j\right). \tag{9.71}$$

Figure 9.3. Diagram illustrating upwinding when velocity is positive (left) and negative (right).

With this definition for $J_{j-\frac{1}{2}}$, the method of lines approximation is

$$(9.72) \qquad \frac{\partial u_j}{\partial t} = -\frac{1}{\Delta x}(J_{j+\frac{1}{2}} - J_{j-\frac{1}{2}}).$$

Notice that this discretization correctly does upwinding and is also conserving, since $\frac{d}{dt}\sum_j u_j = 0$.

A Matlab code that implements this upwinding algorithm and can be used as a template for general problems is titled pde_upwind_MoL.m.

9.4.2. The Method of Characteristics. A second method to simulate advection equations uses the method of characteristics, which was described briefly in Section 9.2. Here we describe this method in more generality.

The general problem can be stated as follows. We seek a solution of the partial differential equation

$$(9.73) \qquad \frac{\partial u}{\partial t} + f(u, x, t)\frac{\partial u}{\partial x} = g(u, x, t),$$

with data specified for $u(x, t)$ along a curve in $x - t$ space, $x = X_0(t_0)$, $u(X_0(t_0), t_0) = U_0(t_0)$. (Notice that this is *not* written in conservation form if f is not a constant.) The idea, as stated above, is to look for curves in $x - t$ space along which the partial differential equation simplifies. So we examine the equation along the curve $x = X(t)$. Along any such curve $u = u(X(t), t)$, the chain rule implies that

$$(9.74) \qquad \frac{du}{dt} = \frac{\partial u}{\partial t} + \frac{\partial u}{\partial x}\frac{dX}{dt}.$$

Now, notice that if we set

$$(9.75) \qquad \frac{dX}{dt} = f(u, X, t),$$

the partial differential equation (9.73) reduces to the ordinary differential equation

$$(9.76) \qquad \frac{du}{dt} = g(u, X, t).$$

Thus, we have reduced the partial differential equation to the two ordinary differential equations

$$(9.77) \qquad \frac{du}{dt} = g(u, X, t),$$

$$(9.78) \qquad \frac{dX}{dt} = f(u, X, t),$$

which must be solved subject to initial data $X = X_0(t_0)$, $u = U_0(t_0)$, for all relevant values of t_0.

A Matlab code that can be used as a template for the method of characteristics is titled pde_by_moc.m.

The method of characteristics lends itself nicely to numerical simulation, since one can easily solve the system of differential equations numerically for a discretized grid of t_0 values, and be assured that this method is exact (i.e., equations (9.77)–(9.78) were derived with no approximations). The method has disadvantages, however, that need to be understood. First, unless the characteristic lines are all parallel, then what might start out as a uniform grid will compress or expand to be nonuniform, so that the representation of the function $u(x,t)$ as a function of x at a fixed time t could become highly nonuniform. What most people do in this situation is *regrid*, that is, from time to time, reinitialize the simulation using a uniform x-discretization, using a smoothed interpolated representation of the solution. The second disadvantage to this method is that it cannot be adapted to more difficult equations, such as equations with both advection and diffusion. This is a disadvantage that cannot be overcome, so when we get to those kinds of equations, a different method will be presented. Nonetheless, the method of characteristics is an extremely useful and important method, as we discover in the next section.

9.5. Nonlinear Advection; Burgers' Equation

No discussion of partial differential equations is complete without some mention of the inviscid Burgers' equation

$$(9.79) \qquad \frac{\partial u}{\partial t} + u\frac{\partial u}{\partial x} = 0.$$

A derivation of this equation for traffic flow is required for Exercise 2.10 and for a one dimensional inviscid compressible fluid in Exercise 2.11. Using it, one can study the evolution of traffic patterns, including traffic jams, flow at traffic signals, etc.; see [71]. Here instead, we provide an application of this equation that has more biological relevance, the formation of polymer gels [24], [76].

9.5.1. Derivation; Polymer Gels.
Gels play an important role in many biological contexts. Biofilm, the environment in which many bacteria reside, is a gel made up of secreted polymers. The mucus that lines the bronchial tubes and stomach consists of a polymer gel that is secreted from cells in the stomach or bronchial tube wall. Blood clots can also be viewed as gels of polymers (mainly fibrin) and the importance of appropriately formed blood clots is easy to recognize.

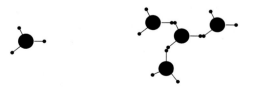

Figure 9.4. A monomer with three binding sites (left), and a tetramer (right).

Here we consider a simple polymer that consists of monomers all of which have k binding sites. We suppose that two monomers can bind to form a dimer by attaching to each other at one of the binding sites on each of the monomers. Similarly, a polymer consisting of n monomers can bind to another polymer with m monomers to form a polymer with $m + n$ monomers, by joining one (and only one) available binding site from each of the two polymers. This can be described as the chemical reaction

(9.80) $$C_n + C_m \rightarrow C_{n+m},$$

where C_n represents the chemical polymer species consisting of n monomers.

Depictions of a monomer and a tetramer, consisting of four monomers, with $k = 3$ are shown in Figure 9.4.

Now, we make a simplifying assumption that the polymers have a treelike structure and that there are no closed loops among binding site pairs. This simplification enables us to keep track of the number of free binding sites in a polymer consisting of n monomers. This is because, with n monomers there are a total of nk binding sites. Since each bond eliminates two binding sites, and there are exactly $n - 1$ binding pairs (this is where the no-loops restriction is imposed), there are

(9.81) $$r_n = nk - 2(n - 1)$$

remaining free binding sites. (Check for yourself in Figure 9.4 that for a tetramer, $n = 4$, with $k = 3$, there are $r_4 = 6$ free binding sites.)

Now, we can write down the differential equations governing this chemical reaction. Let c_n be the concentration of polymer species C_n. Then,

(9.82) $$\frac{dc_n}{dt} = \frac{k_b}{2} \sum_{i+j=n} r_i r_j c_i c_j - k_b R r_n c_n,$$

where R represents the concentration of all free binding sites. In words, this says that a C_n polymer is produced whenever a C_i and C_j molecule combine if $i + j = n$, and a C_n polymer is lost whenever it binds with anything else. These equations look like the law of mass action for a bimolecular reaction in that the rate of reaction between species C_i and C_j is the product of the concentration of reactive sites for species i, $r_i c_i$, and the concentration of reactive sites for species j, $r_j c_j$. There is one exception to this rule, however, for the reaction of two molecules both of size k. For this reaction, if this were the law of mass action, the rate of removal would include a factor 2, to indicate that when this reaction occurs, two molecules of size k are removed to turn into one molecule of size $2k$. The factor $\frac{1}{2}$ in front of the production term is to avoid double counting the number of reactions. The reaction rate k_b is the reaction rate for the individual binding sites. With a change of time scale we can always take $k_b = 1$.

There are several useful checks. First, it should be that the total amount of monomer in all forms is conserved. The total amount of monomer contained within the polymers is $M_1 = \sum_{n=1}^{\infty} n c_n$ and the total number of free binding sites in polymer is $R = \sum_k r_k c_k$. A direct calculation shows that

$$\frac{dM_1}{dt} = \frac{d}{dt} \sum_{n=1}^{\infty} n c_n$$

(substitute the definition of $\frac{dc_n}{dt}$)

$$= \sum_{n=1}^{\infty} n \left(\frac{1}{2} \sum_{i+j=n} r_i r_j c_i c_j - R r_n c_n \right)$$

(use that $i + j = n$ means $j = n - i$)

$$= \frac{1}{2} \sum_{n=1}^{\infty} \sum_{i=1}^{n} n r_i r_{n-i} c_i c_{n-i} - R M_1$$

(change the order of the summations)

$$= \frac{1}{2} \sum_{i=1}^{\infty} \sum_{n=i}^{\infty} n r_i r_{n-i} c_i c_{n-i} - R M_1$$

(substitute $j = n - i$)

$$= \frac{1}{2} \sum_{i=1}^{\infty} \sum_{j=0}^{\infty} (i + j) r_i r_j c_i c_j - R M_1$$

(notice that this is a product of single sums, and $c_0 = 0$)

$$= \sum_{i=1}^{\infty} i r_i c_i \sum_{j=1}^{\infty} r_j c_j - R M_1$$

(use the definitions of R and M_1)

(9.83) $$= 0.$$

In the calculations in this section, there is a change in the order of summation of double sums. In case it has been a while since you have done such a calculation, here is a reminder of how this works.

Consider the double sum $S = \sum_{n=1}^{N} \left(\sum_{i=1}^{n} a_{ni} \right)$. The first thing to do is to make a sketch of all the n and i values included in this sum. As depicted in Figure 9.5(a), this is the triangular region with $1 \leq i \leq n$ and $1 \leq n \leq N$, with $N = 10$ in the figure (made with the Matlab code double_sums.m). The vertical lines in Figure 9.5(a) correspond to the inner sum over i. To change the order of summation to sum first (the inner sum) over n and the outer sum over i, redraw the region of interest with horizontal lines to depict the first, or inner, sum, as shown in Figure 9.5(b). Now, it is easy to recognize that in order to include all of the points in the summation once and only once, we must have

(9.84) $$S = \sum_{n=1}^{N} \left(\sum_{i=1}^{n} a_{ni} \right) = \sum_{i=1}^{N} \left(\sum_{n=i}^{N} a_{ni} \right).$$

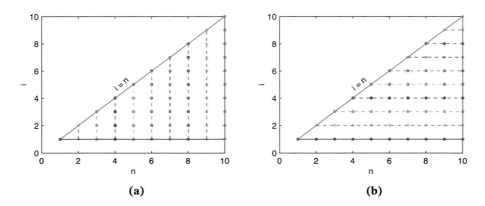

Figure 9.5. Illustration for change of summation order for a double sum.

Similarly, it is true that the concentration of reactive sites satisfies the differential equation $\frac{dR}{dt} = -R^2$, which can be verified by the calculation

$$\frac{dR}{dt} = \frac{d}{dt} \sum_{n=1}^{\infty} r_n c_n$$

(substitute the definition of $\frac{dc_n}{dt}$)

$$= \sum_{n=1}^{\infty} r_n \left(\frac{1}{2} \sum_{i+j=n} r_i r_j c_i c_j - R r_n c_n \right)$$

(use that $i + j = n$ means $j = n - i$)

$$= \sum_{n=1}^{\infty} \left(\frac{1}{2} \sum_{i=1}^{n} r_n r_i r_{n-i} c_i c_{n-j} - R r_n^2 c_n \right)$$

(change the order of the summations)

$$= \frac{1}{2} \sum_{i=1}^{\infty} \sum_{n=i}^{\infty} r_n r_i r_{n-i} c_i c_{n-j} - R \sum_{n=1}^{\infty} r_n^2 c_n$$

(substitute $j = n - i$, and $c_0 = 0$)

$$= \frac{1}{2} \sum_{i=1}^{\infty} \sum_{j=1}^{\infty} r_{i+j} r_i r_j c_i c_j - R \sum_{n=1}^{\infty} r_n^2 c_n$$

(use that $r_{i+j} = r_i + r_j - 2$)

$$= \frac{1}{2} \sum_{i=1}^{\infty} \sum_{j=1}^{\infty} (r_i + r_j - 2) r_i r_j c_i c_j - R \sum_{n=1}^{\infty} r_n^2 c_n$$

(rearrange terms)

$$= \sum_{i=1}^{\infty} r_i^2 c_i \sum_{j=1}^{\infty} r_j c_j - \left(\sum_{i=1}^{\infty} r_i c_i \right)^2 - R \sum_{n=1}^{\infty} r_n^2 c_n$$

(use the definition of R)

(9.85) $= -R^2.$

Finding the solution of an infinite system of differential equations is rarely easy. However, there is a technique that sometimes works, and that is to look for a *moment generating function* (see also Exercise 9.9). For this problem, we introduce the function

$$(9.86) \qquad g(z,t) = \sum_{n=1}^{\infty} z^{r_n} c_n,$$

and try to find its governing differential equation. Here is the calculation:

$$\frac{\partial g}{\partial t} = \sum_{n=1}^{\infty} z^{r_n} \frac{dc_n}{dt}$$

$$= \sum_{n=1}^{\infty} z^{r_n}\Big(\frac{1}{2}\sum_{i+j=n} r_i r_j c_i c_j - R r_n c_n\Big)$$

$$= \frac{1}{2}\sum_{n=1}^{\infty}\sum_{i=1}^{n} z^{r_n} r_i r_{n-i} c_i c_{n-i} - Rz\sum_{n=1}^{\infty} z^{r_n-1} r_n c_n$$

(change the order of the summation, recognize $\frac{\partial g}{\partial z}$)

$$= \frac{1}{2}\sum_{i=1}^{\infty}\sum_{n=i}^{\infty} z^{r_n} r_i r_{n-i} c_i c_{n-i} - Rz\frac{\partial g}{\partial z}$$

(substitute $j = n - i$, and $c_0 = 0$)

$$= \frac{1}{2}\sum_{i=1}^{\infty}\sum_{j=1}^{\infty} z^{r_{i+j}} r_i r_j c_i c_j - Rz\frac{\partial g}{\partial z}$$

(use that $r_{i+j} = r_i + r_j - 2$)

$$= \frac{1}{2}\sum_{i=1}^{\infty} z^{r_i-1} r_i c_i \sum_{j=0}^{\infty} z^{r_j-1} r_j c_j - Rz\frac{\partial g}{\partial z}$$

$$(9.87) \qquad = \frac{1}{2}\Big(\frac{\partial g}{\partial z}\Big)^2 - Rz\frac{\partial g}{\partial z}.$$

Wonderful! We found a partial differential equation for g.

Now, we introduce the change of variables

$$(9.88) \qquad W = zR - \frac{\partial g}{\partial z},$$

and following a direct calculation,

$$\begin{aligned}\frac{\partial W}{\partial t} &= z\frac{dR}{dt} - \frac{\partial^2 g}{\partial z\partial t}\\ &= z\frac{dR}{dt} - \frac{\partial}{\partial z}\Big(\frac{1}{2}\Big(\frac{\partial g}{\partial z}\Big)^2 - Rz\frac{\partial g}{\partial z}\Big)\\ &= -zR^2 - \frac{\partial}{\partial z}\Big(\frac{1}{2}(zR - W)^2 - Rz(zR - W)\Big)\\ &= -\frac{1}{2}\frac{\partial}{\partial z}(W^2),\end{aligned}$$

we find, as promised, Burgers' equation,

$$(9.89) \qquad \frac{\partial W}{\partial t} + W \frac{\partial W}{\partial z} = 0.$$

9.5.2. The Solution. Suppose there is an initial amount of monomer, $c_1(0) = C_0$ and no other polymer products. If this is the case, then $g(z, 0) = z^k C_0$, $R(0) = kC_0$, and $\frac{\partial g}{\partial z}(z, 0) = kz^{k-1}C_0$, so, consequently,

$$(9.90) \qquad W(z, 0) = C_0 k(z - z^{k-1}).$$

The case $k = 1$ is not very interesting, since then all monomers dimerize, and that is the end of it. The case $k = 2$ is also not interesting. All that can happen is that monomers combine into linear chains. Furthermore, in this case, $W(z, t) = 0$ for all t, and since $r_n = 2$ for all n, the generating function method fails. The case which is of interest is $k > 2$.

There are two possible ways to approach this problem, a numerical approach using the method of lines and an upwinding numerical discretization, or an exact approach using the method of characteristics. Following our usual approach, we begin with the numerical solution. Notice that equation (9.89) can be written in conservation form as

$$(9.91) \qquad \frac{\partial W}{\partial t} + \frac{\partial J}{\partial z} = 0, \qquad J = \frac{1}{2}W^2.$$

Since $J = \frac{1}{2}W^2 = vW$, we take $v = \frac{1}{2}W$ and this suggests the method of lines numerical scheme (from (9.72))

$$
\begin{aligned}
(9.92) \qquad \frac{dw_j}{dt} &= -\frac{1}{\Delta x}(J_{j+\frac{1}{2}} - J_{j-\frac{1}{2}}) = -\frac{1}{\Delta x}(v_{j+\frac{1}{2}}w_j - v_{j-\frac{1}{2}}w_{j-1}) \\
&= -\frac{1}{4\Delta x}\Big(w_j(w_{j+1} + w_j) - w_{j-1}(w_j + w_{j-1})\Big),
\end{aligned}
$$

where $w_j = W(j\Delta x)$, and we take $v_{j+\frac{1}{2}} = \frac{1}{2}(w_{j+1} + w_j)$.

The Matlab code to simulate this is titled gelation.m, and the results of the simulation are shown in Figure 9.6. One can see that while the simulation starts off fine, with the parabola $W(x, 0) = 3C_0(z - z^2)$ (for $k = 3$), as time progresses, the solution in the vicinity of $z = 1$ becomes ill-behaved. Something is seriously wrong with this numerical solution.

To understand what is going wrong with the numerical solution, we solve this problem analytically. To use the method of characteristics, we write the equation (9.89) in the form of (9.73), and thereby identify the characteristic equations as the system

$$(9.93) \qquad \frac{dZ}{dt} = W, \qquad \frac{dW}{dt} = 0,$$

subject to initial data $Z(0) = z_0$, $W(0) = 3C_0(z_0 - z_0^{k-1})$.

The solution of these equations is also easy to write down, namely,

$$(9.94) \qquad z = W(z_0)t + z_0 = z_0 + C_0 t(z_0 - z_0^{k-1}), \qquad w = W(z_0) = C_0 k(z_0 - z_0^{k-1}),$$

with z_0 a parameter. It is not possible to eliminate z_0 to find w as a function of z and t. However, because of the wonders of Matlab, it is an easy matter to plot the curve $z = W(z_0)t + z_0$, $w = W(z_0)$ for different values of t. This solution is shown in Figuref 9.7(a)

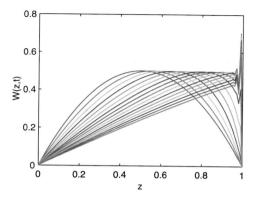

Figure 9.6. Numerical solution of Burgers' equation with initial data (9.90) and $k = 3$, $C_0 = \frac{2}{3}$.

with the characteristic curves shown in Figure 9.7(b). For a small time we see that the solution agrees nicely with the numerical solution. However, there is a time beyond which some characteristic curves intersect so that the solution is not uniquely defined for some values of $z \geq 1$, but is, in fact, multivalued.

The solution is well-behaved as long as the transformation $z = W(z_0)t + z_0$ is invertible, i.e., as long as there is exactly one value of z for each value of z_0 and t. The transformation fails to be invertible if the solution of $z = W(z_0)t + z_0$ for z_0 as a function of z is a double root, i.e., if the slope of the function $z = W(z_0)t + z_0$ is zero at the root, that is, if

(9.95) $$z = W(z_0)t + z_0, \qquad W'(z_0)t + 1 = 0.$$

These two equations define a curve in $z - t$ (parametrized by z_0), and is the envelope (or boundary) of the region in $z - t$ space where solutions are double valued.

Here is another excellent opportunity for you to get experience using the resultant. Notice that $W(z_0)$ is a $k-1$ order polynomial in z_0, so $W'(z_0)$ is a $k-2$ order polynomial.

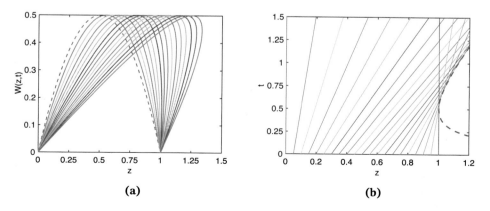

(a) $\qquad\qquad\qquad\qquad\qquad\qquad\qquad\qquad$ **(b)**

Figure 9.7. (a) Exact solution using the method of characteristics. (b) Characteristic curves for Burgers' equation with initial data (9.90) and $k = 3$, $C_0 = \frac{2}{3}$.

In the case $k = 3$, the resultant of the two polynomials (9.95) is

(9.96) $$R = 3C_0t(9C_0^2t^2 - 12C_0tz + 6C_0t + 1),$$

and the curve $R = 0$ is shown dashed in Figure 9.7(b). (See Exercise 9.15) The smallest value of z for which the double-valued solution appears is $z = z_0 = 1$, at

(9.97) $$t_c = \frac{1}{C_0k(k-2)}.$$

What is the meaning of this? According to the definition of W,

(9.98) $$\lim_{z \to 1^-} W(z,t) = R - \lim_{z \to 1^-} \frac{\partial g}{\partial z} = R - \sum_n r_n c_n \equiv R - R_s,$$

where R is the total concentration of free binding sites and $R_s = \sum_n r_n c_n$ is the total concentration of free binding sites contained in polymer. As long as $\lim_{z \to 1^-} W(z,t) = 0$, these two are the same. However, as soon as the solution $W(z,t)$ becomes double valued, $\lim_{z \to 1^-} W(z,t) > 0$ implies that there are some binding sites that are not contained in polymer. It is these that are identified as gel, and t_c is called the gel time, i.e., the first time at which gel appears.

To understand something about the growth of gel, it is useful to distinguish between the monomers that are in polymers and the monomers that are in the gel. In particular, the monomers in polymer are accounted for by

(9.99) $$M_1 = \sum_{n=1}^{\infty} n c_n.$$

Notice that

(9.100) $$\frac{\partial g(1,t)}{\partial z} = \sum_{n=1}^{\infty} r_n c_n = (k-1) \sum_{n=1}^{\infty} n c_n + 2 \sum_{n=1}^{\infty} c_n = (k-2)M_1 + 2g(1,t).$$

Since $g(0,t) = 0$, we calculate that

$$(k-2)M_1 = \frac{\partial g(1,t)}{\partial z} - 2g(1,t)$$

(using (9.88))

(9.101) $$= 2 \int_0^1 W(z,t)dz - W(1,t).$$

To evaluate this expression, it is useful to note that, from the method of characteristics,

(9.102) $$\int_0^1 W(z,t)dz = \int_0^{z_0^*} W(z_0)(W'(z_0)t + 1)dz_0,$$

where z_0^* is the function of t defined by $W(z_0^*)t + z_0^* = 1$.

Plots of the quantities R, R_s, M_1, and $R_g \equiv W(1,t)$ are shown plotted as functions of time in Figure 9.9 (found using the Matlab code gelation.m; see also Figure 9.8(b)). Several things to notice with this plot are that before gel time, M_1 is constant, and $R = R_s$, which shows that all the binding sites are in polymers. After gel time, however, R_s decreases dramatically, indicating that many of the binding sites are not in polymer

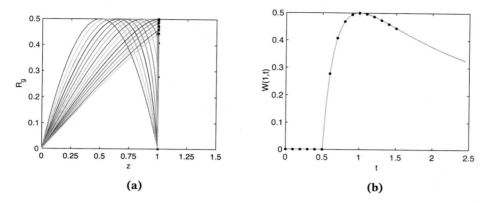

Figure 9.8. (a) Exact solution using the method of characteristics with $W(1,t) \equiv R_g$ denoted with asterisks. (b) Plot of $R_g = W(1,t)$ as a function of time with initial data (9.90) and $k = 3$, $C_0 = \frac{2}{3}$.

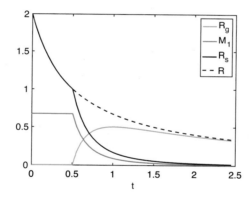

Figure 9.9. The quantities R, R_s, M_1, and $R_g \equiv W(1,t)$, with initial data (9.90) and $k = 3$, $C_0 = \frac{2}{3}$.

but in gel. Furthermore, after gel time, the amount of monomer in gel $(1\text{-}M_1)$ grows, until eventually, all the monomer is in gel (since $M_1 \to 0$).

What have we learned from this? Primarily, we have learned that Burgers' equation, and many nonlinear advection equations like it, can develop multivalued solutions in finite time. What to do with and how to interpret these multivalued solutions is entirely dependent on the physical process that is described. In the case of polymer gels, we found that polymer gels can form, and their growth can be followed by picking the correct branch of the multivalued solution. This procedure is applicable for more complicated processes, including the formation of blood clots as is described in [**23**].

9.6. Extras: More Advection-Reaction Models

9.6.1. Oxygen Exchange Between Capillaries. Solutes are exchanged between liquids by diffusion across their separating membranes. Since the rate of exchange is

affected by the concentration difference across the membrane, the exchange rate is increased if large concentration differences can be maintained. One important way that large concentration differences can be maintained is by the *countercurrent mechanism*. The countercurrent mechanism is important in many contexts, including renal function, the exchange of oxygen from water to blood through fish gills, the exchange of oxygen in the placenta between mother and fetus, and the exchange of oxygen in avian lungs. In nonbiological contexts, it is an important design feature for efficient heat exchangers, such as air conditioners and furnaces.

Suppose that two liquids containing a solute are flowing along parallel tubes of length L, separated by a permeable membrane. We model this in the simplest possible way as a one-dimensional problem, and we assume that solute transport between the tubes is a linear function of the concentration difference. Then the concentrations in the two one-dimensional tubes are given by

$$(9.103) \qquad \frac{\partial c_1}{\partial t} + v_1 \frac{\partial c_1}{\partial x} = d(c_2 - c_1),$$

$$(9.104) \qquad \frac{\partial c_2}{\partial t} + v_2 \frac{\partial c_2}{\partial x} = d(c_1 - c_2),$$

where the term $d(c_1 - c_2)$ represents the rate at which oxygen is lost from tube 1 and gained by tube 2. This exchange rate formula is a consequence of Fick's law for flux across a membrane with concentration c_1 on one side and concentration c_2 on the other (see Exercise 2.5).

The problem we face is to find the outflow fluxes, given the inflow flux, the length of the exchange chamber, and the flow velocities in each tube.

We assume that the flows are in steady state and that the input concentrations are c_1^0 and $c_2^0 = 0$. Then, if we add the two governing equations and integrate, we find that

$$(9.105) \qquad v_1 c_1 + v_2 c_2 = k,$$

with k an unknown constant. Next, we eliminate c_2 from (9.104) and find the differential equation for c_1,

$$(9.106) \qquad \frac{dc_1}{dx} = \frac{d}{v_1 v_2}(k - (v_1 + v_2)c_1),$$

which we can solve to learn that

$$(9.107) \qquad c_1(x) = \kappa + (c_1(0) - \kappa)e^{-\lambda x},$$

where $\kappa = \frac{k}{v_1 + v_2}$ and $\lambda = d\left(\frac{v_1 + v_2}{v_1 v_2}\right)$.

There are two cases to consider, namely when v_1 and v_2 are of the same sign and when they have different signs. If they have the same signs, say positive, then the input is at $x = 0$, and it must be that $c_1(0) = c_1^0$, $c_2(0) = c_2^0 = 0$, from which, using (9.105), it follows that $k = v_1 c_1^0$, and that

$$(9.108) \qquad \frac{c_1(L)}{c_1^0} = \frac{1}{1 + \rho} + \frac{\rho}{1 + \rho}e^{-\lambda L}, \quad \rho \frac{c_2(L)}{c_1^0} = \frac{\rho}{1 + \rho} - \frac{\rho}{1 + \rho}e^{-\lambda L},$$

where $\rho = v_2/v_1$, $\lambda L = dL\left(\frac{v_1 + v_2}{v_1 v_2}\right) = \Lambda(1 + \frac{1}{\rho})$, with $\Lambda = \frac{dL}{v_1}$ the nondimensional residence length.

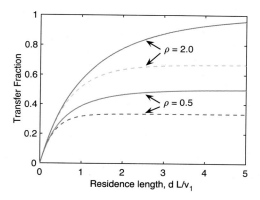

Figure 9.10. Transfer fraction for a cocurrent (dashed line) and a countercurrent (solid line) plotted as a function of residence length $\Lambda = \frac{dL}{v_1}$, for $\rho = 0.5, 2.0$.

On the other hand, in the case that v_1 and v_2 are of opposite sign, say $v_1 > 0$, $v_2 < 0$, the inflow for vessel 1 is at $x = 0$, but the inflow for vessel 2 is at $x = L$. In this case we calculate that (see Exercise 9.21)

$$(9.109) \qquad \frac{c_1(L)}{c_1^0} = \frac{e^{-\lambda L}(1-\rho)}{e^{-\lambda L} - \rho}, \qquad \rho \frac{c_2(0)}{c_1^0} = \rho \frac{e^{-\lambda L} - 1}{e^{-\lambda L} - \rho},$$

where $\rho = -v_2/v_1 > 0$, $\lambda L = \Lambda(1 - \frac{1}{\rho})$, with $\Lambda = \frac{dL}{v_1}$, provided that $\rho \neq 1$.

Finally, if $v_1 > 0$ and $v_2 = -v_1$, then $c_2(L) = 0$, and it follows that

$$(9.110) \qquad \frac{c_2(0)}{c_1^0} = \frac{\Lambda}{1 + \Lambda}.$$

The quantities of interest are $\rho \frac{c_2(L)}{c_1^0}$ if $v_2 > 0$ and $\rho \frac{c_2(0)}{c_1^0}$ if $v_2 < 0$, since these are the fractions of the total flux that flows out from tube 2, i.e., the transfer fraction. Plots of these quantities are shown in Figure 9.10 (made using the Matlab code co_counter_currents.m). The important observation is that the flux out of tube 2 is *always* greater with a countercurrent $v_2 < 0$ than with a cocurrent $v_2 > 0$. Notice also that with a cocurrent,

$$(9.111) \qquad \lim_{\Lambda \to \infty} \rho \frac{c_2(L)}{c_1^0} = \frac{\rho}{1 + \rho},$$

whereas with a countercurrent

$$(9.112) \qquad \lim_{\Lambda \to \infty} \rho \frac{c_2(0)}{c_1^0} = \begin{cases} 1, & \rho \geq 1, \\ \rho, & \rho < 1. \end{cases}$$

Clearly, the most efficient means of transfer is with a countercurrent. In fact, if $\rho \geq 1$, transfer is almost complete if Λ is large enough.

9.6.2. Protein Mediated Friction. We now turn our attention to an example of the effects of protein binding and unbinding from surfaces.

Platelets are cells in the blood stream that are normally transported with the blood flow throughout the circulatory system. However, if there is some damage to the endothelial wall of the vessel, the platelets are activated and proteins on their surfaces become "sticky" and readily bind to the endothelial surface. The purpose of this stickiness is to enable the platelets to attach to the surface and thereby initiate blood clot formation. Whether or not the platelets adhere is dependent on several factors, some of which we discuss now.

Consider the situation depicted in Figure 9.11 in which a cell, depicted here as a rectangular box, moves along a surface (the vessel wall) in response to forces applied to it by external forcing. These forces include the forcing of the moving fluid as well as the forces from proteins that are attached to the vessel wall. We assume that proteins can attach to or detach from the vessel wall according to

(9.113) $$U \underset{k_{\text{off}}(x)}{\overset{k_{\text{on}}(x)}{\rightleftarrows}} B,$$

where U represents the unbound state and B represents the bound state. The proteins are assumed to be flexible and act like springs when they are attached, providing a restoring force that resists the stretching of the spring. We let x denote the signed distance between the bond on the vessel wall and the attachment site on the cell, with x positive if the cell attachment site is to the right of the bond site on the wall. Note that if V, the velocity of the cell, is positive, then x for each bound protein is increasing at velocity V. Now we take $n(x, t)$ to be the density of attached binders with extension x. That is, x is a structure variable for the population of bound proteins. Since the density flux is $J = Vn(x, t)$, it follows from conservation that

(9.114) $$\frac{\partial n}{\partial t} = -V\frac{\partial n}{\partial x} + k_{\text{on}}(x)\left(N_T - \int_{-\infty}^{\infty} n(x, t)dx\right) - k_{\text{off}}(x)n,$$

where N_T is the total number of available (bound and unbound) binders, and $\int_{-\infty}^{\infty} n(x, t)dx$ is the total number of bound binders.

For simplicity, we take the binding rate to be

(9.115) $$k_{\text{on}}(x) = \alpha\delta(x),$$

meaning that bonds form only when they are unstretched, at extension $x = 0$. For the unbinding rate we take

(9.116) $$k_{\text{off}}(x) = \beta \exp(\kappa|x|),$$

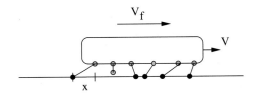

Figure 9.11. Diagram of a cell attached to a wall with flexible protein binders, moving with velocity V in a fluid moving with velocity V_f.

which means that the unbinding rate is exponentially growing in the extension x of the bond, a rate that is known as *Bell's law*. In words, this means that the more tension that is put on the bond, the more likely it is to break.

The force on the cell generated by the bound proteins is

$$(9.117) \qquad F = k \int_{-\infty}^{\infty} x n(x, t) dx,$$

where we assume that the force is linearly proportional to the extension of the bound linker proteins, with spring constant k. Finally, the motion of the cell is determined by Newton's law, which in this case is

$$(9.118) \qquad m \frac{dV}{dt} = \eta(V_f - V) - F,$$

for a cell in a moving fluid, where η is the drag coefficient for the fluid. The sign on F here is because a positive force from the binders resists the motion of the cell and so acts to decrease the velocity.

Although this is a time-dependent problem, we can learn a lot by looking for steady state solutions with $\frac{\partial n}{\partial t} = 0$, $\frac{dV}{dt} = 0$. Thus, we wish to solve the equation

$$(9.119) \qquad V \frac{dn}{dx} = \alpha \delta(x) \Big(N_T - \int_{-\infty}^{\infty} n(x) dx \Big) - \beta \exp(\kappa|x|) n.$$

Some thought needs to be given to how to solve this equation, since, because of the integral term, it is a nonlocal equation. First of all, notice that because of the binding rate, if $V > 0$, it is impossible to have binders with $x < 0$, i.e., $n(x) = 0$ for $x < 0$. Furthermore, because of the δ-function binding rate, there is a jump discontinuity in $n(x)$ at $x = 0$. We can determine $n(0)$ by integrating the equation (9.119) over a vanishingly small interval about $x = 0$, obtaining

$$\begin{aligned} V n(0^+) \quad &= \quad V \int_{0^-}^{0^+} \frac{dn}{dx} dx \\ &= \quad \int_{0^-}^{0^+} \alpha \delta(x) dx \Big(N_T - \int_{-\infty}^{\infty} n(x) dx \Big) - \int_{0^-}^{0^+} \beta \exp(\kappa|x|) n(x) dx \\ (9.120) \qquad &= \quad \alpha \Big(N_T - \int_{0}^{\infty} n(x) dx \Big), \end{aligned}$$

using the fact that $\int_{0^-}^{0^+} \delta(x) dx = 1$.

Now, we introduce a function $\bar{n}(x)$ that satisfies the differential equation

$$(9.121) \qquad V \frac{d\bar{n}}{dx} = -\beta \exp(\kappa x) \bar{n},$$

for $x \geq 0$, $\bar{n}(0) = 1$, and $\bar{n} = 0$ for $x < 0$, if $V > 0$, and $N(x)$, for which

$$(9.122) \qquad \frac{dN}{dx} = \kappa \bar{n},$$

with $N(0) = 0$. Then, the solution of the differential equation (9.119) is given by

$$(9.123) \qquad n(x) = n(0) \bar{n},$$

where, for consistency, from (9.120),

$$(9.124) \qquad Vn(0) = \alpha(N_T - n(0)\frac{N(\infty)}{\kappa}),$$

so that

$$(9.125) \qquad n(0) = \frac{\alpha N_T}{V + \alpha \frac{N(\infty)}{\kappa}}.$$

Finally, $F = F(\infty)$, where

$$(9.126) \qquad \frac{dF}{dx} = u(0)kx\bar{n}.$$

It is useful to introduce the dimensionless variable $\xi = \kappa x$ (assuming $\kappa > 0$, and see Exercise 9.25 for the case where $\kappa = 0$) in terms of which we find the differential equations

$$(9.127) \qquad \frac{d\bar{n}}{d\xi} = -\frac{1}{\upsilon}\exp(\xi)\bar{n},$$

$$(9.128) \qquad \frac{dN}{d\xi} = \bar{n},$$

$$(9.129) \qquad \frac{df}{d\xi} = \xi\bar{n},$$

with $\bar{n}(0) = 1$, $N(0) = 0$, and $f(0) = 0$, and then

$$(9.130) \qquad F = \frac{kN_T}{\kappa}\frac{f(\infty)}{K_d\upsilon + N(\infty)},$$

where $\upsilon = \frac{\kappa V}{\beta}$, $K_d = \frac{\beta}{\alpha}$. The ratio $K_d = \frac{\beta}{\alpha}$ is an equilibrium constant for binding and is a measure of stickiness, smaller for stickier proteins. It is straightforward to solve these equations using the Matlab code sliding_friction.m.

In Figure 9.12 is shown a plot of the dimensionless force $\frac{\kappa F}{kN_T}$ as a function of dimensionless velocity $\upsilon = \frac{\kappa V}{\beta}$ for stickiness parameter $K_d = \frac{\beta}{\alpha} = 0.5, 1.0, 2.0$. The noteworthy feature of this plot is that it is biphasic, with $F = 0$ at $\upsilon = 0$, and $F \to 0$ as $\upsilon \to \infty$. The largest value that F can have is a decreasing function of K_d.

Now let's consider the case of a cell being pushed along a wall by a moving fluid. In this case, the velocity satisfies the differential equation (9.118), where η is the drag coefficient for the fluid. For this differential equation, we can easily find the equilibria by examining the curve

$$(9.131) \qquad V_f = V + \frac{F}{\eta},$$

plotted as a function of V, and then reverse the axes. In dimensionless terms, this equation is

$$(9.132) \qquad \upsilon_f = \upsilon + \frac{1}{\rho}\frac{\kappa F}{kN_T},$$

where $\rho = \frac{\beta\eta}{kN_T}$ is the dimensionless drag coefficient.

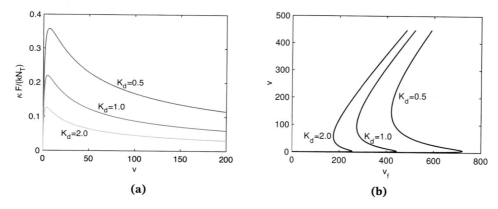

Figure 9.12. (a) Plot of dimensionless force $\frac{\kappa F}{kN_T}$ as a function of dimensionless velocity $v = \frac{\kappa V}{\beta}$. (b) Dimensionless velocity v as a function of dimensionless driving fluid velocity v_f for stickiness parameters $K_d = 0.5, 1.0, 2.0$.

Plots of the equilibria for $\rho = 0.0005$ are shown in Figure 9.12(a). What is seen here is that the velocity of sliding is a hysteretic function of the forcing velocity v_f. The differential equation (9.118) has one or two stable steady states, one for which v is very small, which exists for all v_f below a critical value v_f^l, and one which is close to v_f, which exists for v_f larger than a critical value v_f^u. There is a range $v_f^u \leq v_f \leq v_f^l$ for which the two stable steady state solutions coexist.

What we find here is an explanation for the difference between static friction and dynamic friction. Static friction is that force on an object that prevents it from sliding (or at least it slides only extremely slightly) and dynamic friction is that force which prevents a moving object from accelerating indefinitely (i.e., determines the *terminal velocity*). The interesting feature of this analysis is that it shows that the switch from static to moving can be abrupt, not gradual. Of course, this is our common experience when trying to open a sealed jar or watching a box slide off an inclined plane (see Exercise 9.26).

9.6.3. Muscle Contraction. The contraction of muscle is made possible by the interaction of the proteins actin (called thin filaments) and myosin (called thick filaments) which are arranged into bundled parallel structures, called sarcomeres. The actin and myosin fibers can slide relative to each other because of myosin crossbridges that attach to and detach from the actin.

One of the earliest quantitative studies of muscle is due to A.V. Hill [28] and was conducted before the details of the sarcomere anatomy were known. Hill observed that when a muscle contracts against a constant load (an *isotonic* contraction), the relationship between the constant rate of shortening V and the load p is well described by the *load-velocity* relationship

(9.133) $$(p + a)V = b(p_0 - p),$$

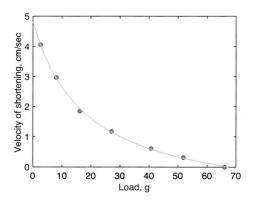

Figure 9.13. The relationship between the load on a muscle and the velocity of contraction (data reproduced from Hill, 1938; Figure 12). The symbols are the data points, while the smooth curve is calculated from (9.133) using the parameter values $a = 17.8$ grams (cm/s), $p_0 = 67.4$ grams, $b = 1.27$ cm/s.

where a and b are constants that are determined by fitting to experimental data. A typical load-velocity curve is plotted in Figure 9.13. When $V = 0$, then $p = p_0$, and thus p_0 represents the force generated by the muscle when the length is held fixed; i.e., p_0 is the *isometric* force. When $p = 0$, $V = bp_0/a$, which is the maximum speed at which a muscle is able to shorten.

It is now known that contraction takes place when the protein crossbridges bind and generate a force causing the thin filaments to slide along the thick filaments. A schematic diagram of the crossbridge cycle is given in Figure 9.14. Before binding and contraction, the crossbridge protein is in a position extended away from its myosin base. When possible, the crossbridge binds to an actin binding site. This binding triggers a change in the preferred configuration of the crossbridge, making it so that it prefers to be contracted and not extended, with neutral force at the myosin base. The movement of the crossbridge to its newly preferred configuration is called the *power stroke*. Upon reaching the neutral position, the crossbridge unbinds from the actin binding site and then is subsequently reset to its extended and unbound position, where it awaits the arrival of the next actin binding site.

To formulate a mathematical model describing crossbridge interactions in a sarcomere, we suppose that a crossbridge can bind to an actin binding site at position x, where x measures the distance along the thin filament to a binding site from the crossbridge, and $x = 0$ corresponds to the position in which the bound crossbridge exerts no force during the power stroke on the thin filament (i.e., its equilibrium position). Referring to Figure 9.14, x is positive if the actin binding site is to the right of the crossbridge base, and negative if it is to the left. Crossbridges can be bound to a binding site with $x > 0$, in which case they exert a contractile force, or they can be bound to a site with $x < 0$, in which case they exert a force that opposes contraction. A crossbridge bound to a binding site at x is said to have displacement x. We make the assumption that the actin binding sites are sufficiently far apart so that each crossbridge could be

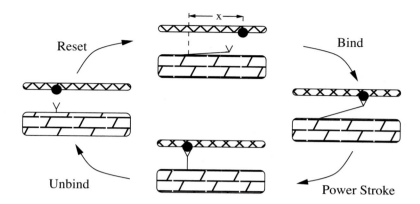

Figure 9.14. Major steps in the actin-myosin crossbridge cycle. Step 1: (Top Center) Crossbridge is set (like a mouse trap). Step 2: (Right) Crossbridge binds to binding site on thin fiber (actin). Step 3: (Bottom center) Crossbridge contracts to its neutral position. Step 4: (Left) Crossbridge unbinds from actin binding site, followed by Step 1: Crossbridge is reset, awaiting next actin binding site.

bound with one and only one binding site. With this assumption, each crossbridge, whether bound or not, can be associated with a unique value of x.

Let ρ denote the total number of crossbridges (bound or unbound) with displacement x. We assume that binding is restricted to occur in some bounded interval, $-x_0 < x < x_0$, and that ρ is a constant independent of x on that interval. In other words, for each displacement x, the total number of crossbridges with that displacement is ρ. We define $n(x, t)$ to be the fraction of crossbridges with displacement x that are bound.

Next, we assume that a crossbridge can be in one of two states, namely either unbound (U), or bound (B) and thereby generating a force. We suppose further that the binding and unbinding of crossbridges is described by the simple reaction scheme

$$\mathrm{U} \underset{g(x)}{\overset{f(x)}{\rightleftharpoons}} \mathrm{B},$$

where the rate constants are functions of the displacement x.

The conservation law for the fraction of bound crossbridges is by now standard fare. We suppose that $V(t)$ is the velocity of the actin filament relative to the myosin filament. For notational consistency, we assume that $V > 0$ denotes muscle contraction leading to a decrease in displacement x, with the actin filament moving to the left, in Figure 9.14. Since x is a structure variable, the flux of $n(x, t)$ is $J = -Vn(x, t)$. It follows that the conservation equation for $n(x, t)$ is

$$(9.134) \qquad \frac{\partial n}{\partial t} = V(t)\frac{\partial n}{\partial x} + f(x)(1 - n) - g(x)n.$$

We also suppose that a bound crossbridge is like a flexible spring, generating a restoring force kx related to its displacement. Hence, the total force exerted by the muscle is

(9.135)
$$F = \rho \int_{-\infty}^{\infty} kxn(x,t)\,dx.$$

Note that the force generated by the muscle is the same as the load the muscle is able to move. Hence, load and force are used interchangeably in this discussion.

To find the force-velocity relationship for muscle, we assume that the fiber moves with constant velocity, and that $n(x,t)$ is equilibrated so that $\partial n/\partial t = 0$. Then, the steady distribution $n(x)$ is given by the solution of the first-order differential equation

(9.136)
$$V\frac{dn}{dx} = -f(x)(1-n) + g(x)n.$$

To obtain quantitative formulas, one must make some reasonable guesses for the functions $f(x)$ and $g(x)$, and then calculate $n(x)$ and F numerically or analytically. We expect $f(x)$ and $g(x)$ to have the following features. First, binding is most likely when x is in the vicinity of the reset, extended crossbridge, and $f(x) = 0$ when x is too large or negative. Second, unbinding is not likely if $x > 0$ but is highly likely if $x < 0$.

Although numerical solutions can always be obtained, there are several choices of $f(x)$ and $g(x)$ for which analytical solutions are possible. The functions that Huxley [32] chose are illustrated in Figure 9.15 and have the form

(9.137)
$$f(x) \;=\; \begin{cases} 0, & x < 0, \\ f_1 x/h, & 0 \le x \le h, \\ 0, & x > h, \end{cases}$$

(9.138)
$$g(x) \;=\; \begin{cases} g_2, & x \le 0, \\ g_1 x/h, & x > 0. \end{cases}$$

In this model, the rate of crossbridge dissociation, g, is low when the crossbridge exerts a contractile force, but when x is negative, the crossbridge opposes contraction, and g increases. Similarly, crossbridges do not attach at a negative x ($f = 0$ when $x < 0$), and as x increases, the rate of crossbridge attachment increases as well. This ensures that crossbridge attachment contributes an overall contractile force. At some value h, the

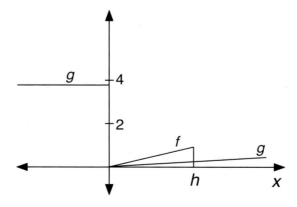

Figure 9.15. The attachment and detachment functions, $f(x)$ (9.137) and $g(x)$ (9.138), in the Huxley model [32].

rate of crossbridge attachment falls to zero, as it is assumed that crossbridges cannot bind to a binding site that is too far away.

The steady-state solution for $n(x)$ is easily obtained by direct piecewise solutions of the differential equation. Let n_I, n_{II}, and n_{III} denote, respectively, the steady-state solutions in the regions $x \leq 0$, $0 < x \leq h$, and $x > h$. Then n_I is the solution of the equation

$$(9.139) \qquad -V\frac{dn_I}{dx} = -g_2 n,$$

and thus

$$(9.140) \qquad n_I = A e^{g_2 x/V},$$

for some constant A yet to be determined. Note that this solution is bounded as $x \to -\infty$ as it should be.

Next we solve for n_{II}, which satisfies the equation

$$(9.141) \qquad -V\frac{dn_{II}}{dx} + n_{II}\left(\frac{f_1 x}{h} + \frac{g_1 x}{h}\right) = \frac{f_1 x}{h},$$

which has solution

$$(9.142) \qquad n_{II} = \frac{f_1}{f_1 + g_1} + B\exp\left(\frac{x^2(f_1 + g_1)}{2Vh}\right),$$

for some constant B, also to be determined.

The only bounded solution of the equation for n_{III},

$$(9.143) \qquad -V\frac{dn_{III}}{dt} = g_1 \frac{x}{h} n_{III},$$

is identically zero. This makes physical sense as well, since crossbridges can never be attached for $x > h$, if $V > 0$. Now, to find the unknown constants A and B we require that the solution be continuous at $x = 0$ and $x = h$, and thus

$$(9.144) \qquad n_I(0) = n_{II}(0), \qquad n_{II}(h) = 0.$$

It follows that

$$(9.145) \qquad B = -\frac{f_1}{f_1 + g_1} e^{-\frac{1}{v}},$$

$$(9.146) \qquad A = \frac{f_1}{f_1 + g_1} + B = \frac{f_1}{f_1 + g_1}(1 - e^{-\frac{1}{v}}),$$

and thus

$$(9.147) \qquad n(x) = \begin{cases} F_1\left[1 - e^{-\frac{1}{v}}\right]e^{\frac{x}{2h}G_2\frac{1}{v}}, & x < 0, \\ F_1\left\{1 - \exp\left[\left(\frac{x^2}{h^2} - 1\right)\frac{1}{v}\right]\right\}, & 0 < x < h, \\ 0, & x > h, \end{cases}$$

where $v = \frac{V}{\phi}$, $\phi = (f_1 + g_1)h/2$ has units of velocity, and $F_1 = \frac{f_1}{f_1 + g_1}$ and $G_2 = \frac{g_2}{f_1 + g_1}$ are dimensionless. This steady solution $n(x)$ is plotted in Figure 9.16(a) for four values of V. Notice the unphysiological implication of this solution, that $n > 0$ for all $x < 0$. However, only a negligible number of crossbridges are bound at unphysiological displacements, so that these have little effect on the behavior of the model. Assuming

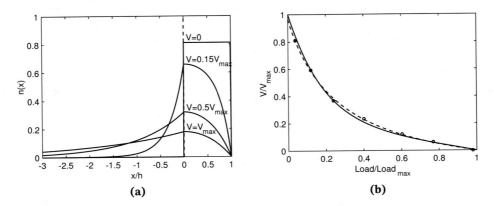

Figure 9.16. (a) Steady-state distributions of $n(x)$ in the Huxley model, for different values of V, plotted as a function of dimensionless space $\frac{x}{h}$. The parameter values for figures were chosen by Huxley by trial and error to obtain a good fit with experimental data. The values are $F_1 = f_1/(g_1 + f_1) = 13/16$, $G_2 = g_2/(f_1 + g_1) = 3.919$. (b) The load-velocity curve of the Huxley model (9.148) (solid curve) compared to Hill's data (open circles) and the fit to Hill's data from (9.133) (dashed curve). Plots made with Matlab code muscle_load_velocity.m.

that the crossbridge acts like a linear spring, the force generated by the muscle (defined by (9.135)) can be calculated as a function of the velocity of contraction, and the result compared to the Hill load-velocity equation (9.133). The force-velocity equation calculated from the Huxley model is

$$(9.148) \qquad F = \rho k F_1 \frac{h^2}{2} \left\{ 1 - v(1 - e^{-\frac{1}{v}}) \left(1 + \frac{v}{2G_2^2} \right) \right\}.$$

Huxley chose model parameters by a process of trial and error to get a good fit with experimental data. A good fit is obtained by choosing $F_1 = \frac{f_1}{f_1+g_1} = 13/16$ and $G_2 = \frac{g_2}{f_1+g_1} = 3.919$, as shown in Figure 9.16(b).

Exercises

9.1. Suppose a population of animals has a death rate that is independent of age, $\mu = 0.5/\text{year}$, and can reproduce only after the age of one year. What must the birth rate β be in order for the population to survive? (Track the number of females and assume that the birth rates of males and females are the same.)

9.2. The death rate for a population of organisms is a constant μ while the birth rate is $\beta(a) = B \exp(\kappa a)$, with $\kappa < 0$. For what values of parameters μ, B, and κ is the population sustainable?

9.3. Suppose that the probability that an organism is alive at age a is

$$P_S(a) = \frac{1}{1 + a^2}.$$

(a) Write an equation relating $P_S(a)$ to the death rate $\mu(a)$.

(b) Find $\mu(a)$.

(c) Suppose the birth rate is the constant β. Find the smallest value of β for which the population is sustainable.

(d) What is the age distribution for this minimally sustainable population?

9.4. Consider a population with the age and density dependent birth rate

$$\beta(a, N) = Ba(1 - \frac{N}{K}),$$

where N is the total population size. Suppose the death rate is constant μ. Find the equilibrium population size.

9.5. Use the method of characteristics to solve the equation $\frac{\partial u}{\partial t} - x\frac{\partial u}{\partial x} = -u$ subject to initial condition $u(x, 0) = x$.

9.6. Use the method of characteristics to solve the equation $\frac{\partial u}{\partial t} + x\frac{\partial u}{\partial x} = -u$ subject to initial condition $u(x, 0) = x$.

9.7. Use the method of characteristics to solve the equation $\frac{\partial u}{\partial t} + x^2\frac{\partial u}{\partial x} = -u$ subject to initial condition $u(x, 0) = x$ for all $x > 0$.

9.8. For the death process

$$S \xrightarrow{\alpha} \emptyset,$$

the probability that k individuals have not decayed at time t is given by $p_k(t)$ where $p_k(t)$ satisfies (1.123) with $\beta = 0$.

(a) Define the *moment generating function* $g(z, t) = \sum_{k=0}^{\infty} z^k p_k(t)$. Find a partial differential equation describing the evolution of $g(z, t)$.

Hint. Multiply the equation for $p_k(t)$ by z^k and sum over all k. Use the fact that $\frac{\partial g}{\partial z} = \sum_{k=0}^{\infty} kz^{k-1}p_k(t)$.

(b) Solve this partial differential equation subject to initial data $p_k(0) = \delta_{kN}$, so that $g(z, 0) = z^N$, using the method of characteristics.

(c) Use the binomial theorem to find $p_k(t)$. *Reminder.* The binomial theorem states that

$$(x + y)^N = \sum_{k=0}^{N} \binom{N}{k} x^k y^{N-k}.$$

9.9. Suppose that a conservation biologist wishes to re-establish a population of animals in an area where they once lived but are now absent. The question of interest is how many of the animals to release so that the population will be re-established. For simplicity, assume that the animals reproduce or die following the chemical reactions (1.119)

$$S \xrightarrow{\beta} 2S, \quad S \xrightarrow{\alpha} \emptyset,$$

and therefore the probability that k animals are alive at time t is given by $p_k(t)$ where $p_k(t)$ satisfies (1.123).

(a) Define the *moment generating function* $g(z, t) = \sum_{k=0}^{\infty} z^k p_k(t)$. Find a partial differential equation describing the evolution of $g(z, t)$.

Hint. Multiply the equation for $p_k(t)$ by z^k and sum over all k. Use the fact that $\frac{\partial g}{\partial z} = \sum_{k=0}^{\infty} kz^{k-1}p_k(t)$.

(b) Solve this partial differential equation subject to initial data $p_k(0) = \delta_{kN}$, so that $g(z, 0) = z^N$, using the method of characteristics.

(c) Find and plot $p_0(t) = g(0, t)$. What is the probability that the population will go extinct if $\alpha > \beta$ and if $\alpha < \beta$?

9.10. Suppose $\alpha = \beta$ in Exercise 9.9. Find $p_0(t) = g(z = 0, t)$ where $\frac{\partial g}{\partial t} - \alpha(z-1)^2 \frac{\partial g}{\partial z} = 0$ and $g(z, 0) = z^N$.

9.11. Use the method of characteristics to solve the equation $\frac{\partial u}{\partial t} = \frac{\partial}{\partial x}(kxu) - \lambda u$, with initial data $u(x, 0) = u_0(x)$.

9.12. Suppose a boat is traveling upstream at velocity v_b in a stream with water flow velocity v_s. The boat leaks a toxic chemical so that the concentration of chemical in the water at the location of the boat is u_0, independent of time, and the toxic chemical degrades at rate λ. At time $t = 0$ the boat leaves a dock at $x = 0$ at which time the concentration of chemical in the stream is everywhere zero. Determine the concentration of chemical at the dock for all later times.

   Hint. Use the method of characteristics.

9.13. Simulate the equations (9.38)–(9.39) with $f(U) = \frac{A}{1+U^7}$ for several parameter values A, X, and d. Verify that the steady state solution of these equations is stable for parameter values below the curve shown in Figure 9.2(a), and unstable for parameter values above this curve.

9.14. Simulate the delay differential equation

$$\frac{dU}{dt} = -\beta U + f(U(t - d)).$$

(known as the Mackey–Glass equation) with $f(U) = \frac{A}{1+U^7}$ for several values of A, β, and d. Find values of the parameters for which the steady solution is stable and for which the steady solution is unstable but there is a stable periodic solution.

   Hint. Simulation of this equation is similar to that of the equations (9.38)–(9.39). Use that $U(t - x)$ satisfies the partial differential equation (9.59). So, discretize the function $U(t - x)$ for discrete values of $x = j\Delta x$, $j = 0, 1, \ldots, N$, setting $U_j(t) = U(t - j\Delta x)$. If N is such that $d = N\Delta x$, then the Mackey–Glass equation can be written as

$$\frac{dU_0}{dt} = -\beta U_0 + f(U_N).$$

and for all other values of j, $j = 1, \ldots, N$,

$$\frac{dU_j}{dt} = \frac{1}{\Delta x}(U_{j-1} - U_j).$$

This system constitutes a *method of lines* approximation for the delay differential equation, and can readily be simulated using one's favorite differential equation solution technique.

9.15. Find an equation for the curve in $z - t$ space for which the two polynomials in (9.95) have simultaneous zeros, for $k = 4$ and $k = 5$. Find the gel time, i.e., the value of t for which the curve has $z = 1$.

9.16. Suppose that a reactive monomer with k binding sites is produced at a constant rate S_1 and added to a solution that initially had no monomer. The purpose of this exercise is to find the gel time for this process.

(a) Derive the appropriate modification of Burgers' equation to account for this monomer source to describe the production of polymer and gelation.

(b) Use the method of characteristics to determine the differential equations describing the characteristic curves $W = W(t)$, $z = Z(t)$ for this equation.

(c) Provide a phase plane analysis of the characteristic curves. Define $T(z_0)$ to be the time it takes for the characteristic curve with $W(0) = 0$ and $Z(0) = z_0$ to reach $Z = 1$. What is the smallest possible value of $T(z_0)$? This is the gel time for this process.

9.17. Solve Burgers' equation $W_t = WW_x$ using the method of characteristics, with initial data $W(x, 0) = -x$.

9.18. Solve the equation $\frac{\partial u}{\partial t} = \frac{1}{2}(\frac{\partial u}{\partial x})^2$, subject to initial condition $u(x, 0) = -x^2$.

   Hint. Set $w = \frac{\partial u}{\partial x}$, solve the equation for w by the method of characteristics, and integrate w to find u.

9.19. Solve the differential equation

$$\frac{\partial u}{\partial t} + \frac{\partial}{\partial x}(u^2) = 0,$$

on the interval $-5 < x < 5$, starting from initial data $u(x, 0) = \frac{1}{1+x^2}$, using two methods:

(a) the method of lines with upwinding; and

(b) the method of characteristics.

(c) Find (and plot) the boundary of the region in $x - t$ space for which the solution is multivalued.

9.20. The equation

$$\frac{\partial u}{\partial t} + u\frac{\partial u}{\partial x} = \epsilon\frac{\partial^2 u}{\partial x^2}$$

is often referred to as the viscous Burgers' equation. Suppose $\lim_{x\to-\infty} u(x, t) = \alpha > \lim_{x\to\infty} u(x, t) = \beta$. Show that the viscous Burgers' equation has a traveling wave solution and find the wave speed in terms of α and β. What happens if $\alpha < \beta$?

   Hint. Find the ordinary differential equation for traveling wave solutions and look for a trajectory that connects α and β.

9.21. Solve the differential equations (the steady state versions of (9.103)–(9.104))

$$\frac{dc_1}{dx} = d(c_2 - c_1), \quad \frac{dc_2}{dx} = d(c_1 - c_2)$$

on the interval $0 < x < L$, with $c_1(0) = c_1^0$, $v_1 > 0$ and the following.

(a) $v_2 > 0$, $c_2(0) = 0$. Find $c_2(L)$ and verify (9.108).

(b) $v_2 < 0$, $v_1 + v_2 \neq 0$, $c_2(L) = 0$. Find $c_2(0)$ and verify (9.109).

(c) $v_2 = -v_1$, $c_2(L) = 0$. Find $c_2(0)$ and verify (9.110).

9.22. Make a (one-dimensional) model of oxygen transport and metabolism by tissue. Suppose that oxygen is supplied by advection through a vessel (a capillary or arteriole) at velocity v and input concentration c_0, and that it diffuses across a membrane into a (one-dimensional) tissue with the same cross-sectional area as the vessel, where it is consumed at each position in the tissue at the metabolic rate m.

(a) Find the concentration of oxygen in the vessel as a function of distance along the vessel in steady state. At what distance along the vessel does the tissue go into oxygen debt (i.e., concentration in the tissue is zero?)

(b) Suppose that oxygen is also supplied as oxymyoglobin, which is in steady state with the inflow concentration of free oxygen. (The assumption here is that the oxygen carrier is myoglobin, so you need not be concerned with the more complicated details of hemoglobin binding of oxygen.) Make a model of oxygen supply to tissue that includes both free and bound oxygen in the blood, taking into account that oxymyoglobin does not diffuse across the membrane wall. Find the concentration of oxygen in the vessel as a function of distance along the vessel in steady state. At what distance along the vessel does the tissue go into oxygen debt (i.e., concentration in the tissue is zero?)

Important Help. Make the simplifying assumption that the binding and unbinding of oxygen to myoglobin is fast compared to all other processes, so that the reaction is in quasi-steady state. There is a nondimensionalization argument that makes this reasonable, but you are not asked to produce this argument here.

9.23. Make a (one-dimensional) model of oxygen transport and metabolism by tissue. Suppose that oxygen is supplied by advection through a vessel at velocity v and input concentration c_0, and that it diffuses across a membrane into a (one-dimensional) tissue where it is consumed at each position in the tissue at the rate $\frac{Vc}{K+c}$. Find the concentration of oxygen in the vessel as a function of distance along the vessel. (That is, how much of the supplied oxygen is consumed by the tissue along the vessel distance?) Compare this profile with the profile of Exercise 9.22.

9.24. Make a (one-dimensional) model of carbon dioxide production in tissue and removal by a vessel. Suppose that carbon dioxide is produced in the (one-dimensional) tissue at a constant rate m, diffuses across a membrane into the vessel where it is transported away at velocity v. Assume that the concentration of carbon dioxide at the input end of the vessel is zero. Find the concentration of carbon dioxide as a function of distance along the tissue and in the vessel. (For simplicity, assume that the cross-sectional areas of the vessel and tissue are the same.)

9.25. Show that the relationship between F and V determined by (9.117) and (9.119) when $\kappa = 0$ is linear.

Hint. Show that

$$F = kn(0)f(\infty),$$

where

$$\frac{df}{dx} = x\bar{n},$$

$$\frac{d\bar{n}}{dx} = \frac{\beta}{V}\bar{n},$$

$$\frac{dN}{dt} = \bar{n},$$

with $f(0) = 0$, $\bar{n}(0) = 1$, $N(0) = 0$, and

$$n(0) = \frac{\alpha N_T}{V + \alpha N(\infty)}.$$

9.26. Suppose a "cell" with mass m slides on an inclined plane with incline angle θ. Assume that the forces on the cell are gravity and the protein binding force F from (9.130).

    (a) Find the equation of motion for the velocity V of the cell sliding along the inclined plane.

    (b) Use the plots of F in Figure 9.12 to show that if θ is sufficiently small, the differential equation for the velocity has two steady state solutions, one stable and one unstable.

    (c) Suppose $F_m = \max_V F(V)$. Find a condition on θ, say $\theta > \theta^*$ for which there are no steady solutions. How does θ^* depend on the stickiness parameter $K_d = \frac{\beta}{\alpha}$?

9.27. Find the load-velocity curve for muscle contraction for which the binding rate $f(x) = \alpha\delta(x - h)$ with $h > 0$ and unbinding rate is $g(x) = \beta H(-x)$, where $H(x)$ is the Heaviside function. Does the shape of this load-velocity curve match the Hill data?

    Hint. To solve an equation of the form $\frac{dn}{dx} = a\delta(x - h)(n - 1)$, use that this equation is separable to write $\frac{dn}{n-1} = a\delta(x - h)dx$.

9.28. Find the load-velocity relationship for the Huxley crossbridge model for $V > 0$ with

$$f(x) = \begin{cases} f_{\max}e^{(x-h)/\lambda}, & x < h, \\ 0, & x > h, \end{cases}$$

$$g(x) = f_{\max}\left(1 - e^{(x-h)/\lambda}\right),$$

and force generated by an exponential spring

$$F = \rho \int_{-\infty}^{\infty} r(x)n(x, t)\,dx,$$

where $r(x) = r_{\max}\frac{e^{(x-h)/\lambda} - \alpha}{1 - \alpha}$.

    Remark. This model reproduces the Hill load-velocity curve exactly.

Chapter 10

Advection with Diffusion

Now let's consider the situation where particles are both advecting and diffusing. We begin with some examples.

10.1. A Biased Random Walk

Let's begin our discussion with a simple example where a particle takes a step of length Δx by an exponential process with rate λ. If $p_n(t)$ is the probability of being at position $x = n\Delta x$ at time t, then

$$(10.1) \qquad \frac{dp_n}{dt} = -\lambda p_n + \lambda p_{n-1}.$$

Taking $p_n(t) = p(n\Delta x, t)$, and using Taylor's theorem, it follows that, keeping only two terms,

$$(10.2) \qquad \frac{\partial p}{\partial t} = -\lambda\Delta x \frac{\partial p}{\partial x} + \frac{1}{2}\lambda\Delta x^2 \frac{\partial^2 p}{\partial x^2}.$$

This is an equation, an *advection-diffusion equation*, where $\lambda\Delta x$, is the effective advection velocity and $D_e = \frac{1}{2}\lambda\Delta x^2$ is the effective diffusion coefficient.

10.2. Transport with Switching

Suppose there are objects (for example, bacteria) that move in one of two directions along a one-dimensional path, and they randomly switch their direction of motion via the process

$$(10.3) \qquad L \underset{k^-}{\overset{k^+}{\rightleftharpoons}} R,$$

where L and R refer to the left-moving and right-moving states, respectively. In Chapter 4, this was identified as a run and tumble process, and using simulations, we could

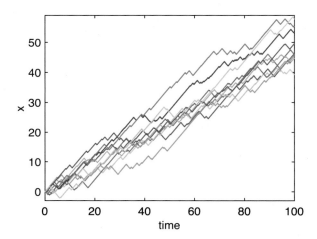

Figure 10.1. Sample trajectories of the biased run and tumble process, where $k^- = 0.5$, $k^+ = 1.5$, and $v = 1$.

establish that if $k^+ = k^- = k$, then this is equivalent to a diffusion process with effective diffusion coefficient $D_{\text{eff}} = \frac{v^2}{2k}$. But what happens if $k^+ \neq k^-$?

The first step to answer this question is to simulate this process. Examples of trajectories of this process are shown in Figure 10.1 (computed using the Matlab code one_d_direction_switcher_w_drift.m). If you do Exercise 10.1, you will observe that there is a linear net drift that is related to the difference $k^+ - k^-$, and that the variance grows linearly, also with a slope that is related to both k^+ and k^-.

To get an analytical understanding of this process, we write the corresponding conservation equations. Setting u_L and u_R to be the population density of left and right-moving bacteria, respectively, we write the conservation equations as

$$(10.4) \qquad \frac{\partial u_L}{\partial t} = -k^+ u_L + k^- u_R + \frac{\partial (v u_L)}{\partial x},$$

$$(10.5) \qquad \frac{\partial u_R}{\partial t} = k^+ u_L - k^- u_R - \frac{\partial (v u_R)}{\partial x}.$$

The total flux of bacteria is given by

$$(10.6) \qquad J = v u_R - v u_L.$$

Differentiate the flux J with respect to time and find, using (10.4) and (10.5),

$$(10.7) \qquad \frac{\partial J}{\partial t} - \frac{J}{v} \frac{\partial v}{\partial t} = -J(k^- + k^+) + vu(k^+ - k^-) - v \frac{\partial (vu)}{\partial x},$$

where $u = u_L + u_R$. At steady state (set $\frac{\partial J}{\partial t} = \frac{\partial v}{\partial t} = 0$) we find

$$(10.8) \qquad J = -\frac{v^2}{k^- + k^+} \frac{\partial u}{\partial x} + v \frac{k^+ - k^-}{k^- + k^+} u - \frac{v}{k^- + k^+} \frac{\partial v}{\partial x} u.$$

Here we see that the flux J comprises three terms. The first, $-\frac{v^2}{k^- + k^+} \frac{\partial u}{\partial x}$, being proportional to the gradient of u, is Fickian in nature and therefore represents a diffusive motion with diffusion coefficient $D = \frac{v^2}{k^- + k^+}$. The second term, $v \frac{k^+ - k^-}{k^- + k^+} u$, represents advection with velocity $v_e = v\frac{k^+ - k^-}{k^- + k^+}$. If the two switching rates are equal, this has zero velocity, but if, for example, $k^+ > k^-$, then the advective velocity is positive, since bacteria spend more time in the right-moving state than in the left moving state. The third term is an advective term that is nonzero only when the velocity v varies with position, a situation which we do not consider further here.

As a check, notice in Figure 10.1 that the advective velocity $v\frac{k^+ - k^-}{k^- + k^+}$ is 0.5 and indeed the average slope of the trajectories is about 0.5.

With the flux J given by (10.8), we can write the conservation equation for u as

$$(10.9) \qquad \frac{\partial u}{\partial t} = -v_e \frac{\partial u}{\partial x} + D \frac{\partial^2 u}{\partial x^2},$$

an advection-diffusion equation.

There are several ways that we might proceed to find solutions of the advection-diffusion equations. The first is to make a change of variables into a uniformly moving coordinate system by setting

$$(10.10) \qquad y = x - v_e t, \qquad s = t.$$

In these new variables, the equation (10.9) is

$$(10.11) \qquad \frac{\partial p}{\partial s} = D_e \frac{\partial^2 p}{\partial y^2},$$

and, of course, this is the diffusion equation. It follows that if $U(t, s)$ is a solution of the diffusion equation equation, then

$$(10.12) \qquad u(x, t) = U(x - v_e t, t)$$

is a solution of the advection-diffusion equation (10.9).

The second way is, of course, numerical, and while we do not give it much attention here, this will be important in Chapter 12.

10.3. Ornstein–Uhlenbeck Process

Now consider a particle that diffuses, but is also constrained by a restoring force, like a spring, that pulls it back to its zero position. For example, in Chapter 9 (see Figure 9.11), we described a cell that had a number of protein binders that were attached to the cell wall by a spring.

To find the equation of motion for this particle, we first consider the differential equation for the particle if it were not diffusing. In this case, we have a simple mass-spring system for which the governing equation is

$$(10.13) \qquad m\frac{dv}{dt} + \mu v + kx = 0,$$

where $v = \frac{dx}{dt}$ is the particle's velocity and x is the particle's position. This is a statement of Newton's second law ($F = ma$), where μv is the force due to viscosity. If we make the approximation that this is a viscosity dominated process (inertia is negligible compared to viscosity), then

$$(10.14) \qquad v = -\frac{k}{\mu}x = -\kappa x$$

specifies the rate of advection. Now, we can write an equation for the probability that the particle is at position x at time t by including both the advection (velocity) term and the diffusive term

$$(10.15) \qquad \frac{\partial p}{\partial t} = \frac{\partial}{\partial x}(\kappa x p) + D\frac{\partial^2 p}{\partial x^2}.$$

The process described here is called an *Ornstein–Uhlenbeck process*.

How might one simulate this process? The answer is straightforward. Since the motion consists of two parts, we take steps dx determined by

$$(10.16) \qquad dx = v dt + \sqrt{2D dt}\mathcal{N}(0,1) = -\kappa x dt + \sqrt{2D dt}\mathcal{N}(0,1).$$

This simulation is carried out in the Matlab code single_particle_diffusion.m used in Chapter 3 to simulate diffusion alone, but here it is modified to include the drift due to the deterministic velocity (10.14). The result of the simulation is shown in Figure 10.2, where sample paths and the variance (mean squared displacement), are shown.

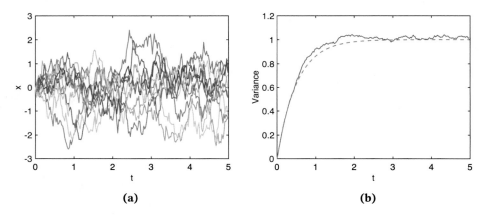

(a)   **(b)**

Figure 10.2. (a) Ten examples of sample paths for an Ornstein–Uhlenbeck process. (b) Variance for 1000 particles as a function of time compared with the curve $\sigma^2 = (\frac{D}{\kappa})(1 - \exp(-4\kappa D t))$ (dashed line), both for $D = 1, \kappa = 1$.

Now let's get an analytical understanding of this process. First, to make things a bit easier, notice (see Exercise 10.3) that by rescaling space and time, equation (10.15) can be transformed into the dimensionless form

$$(10.17) \qquad \frac{\partial p}{\partial \tau} = \frac{\partial}{\partial \xi}(\xi p) + \frac{\partial^2 p}{\partial \xi^2},$$

an equation with no free parameters. There are several things to notice about this process. First, the total integral of $p(\xi, \tau)$ is constant (and equal to 1). Second, if there were no diffusion, the equation would be an advection equation with solutions (which can be found by the method of characteristics, see Exercise 9.11) that move along characteristics $\xi = Y(\tau)$ that satisfy the differential equation

$$(10.18) \qquad \frac{dY}{d\tau} = -Y,$$

which has a solution $Y(t) = y_0 \exp(-\tau)$.

To get more information about the solution, we calculate the expected value of ξ,

$$\frac{dE(\xi)}{d\tau} = \frac{d}{d\tau}\int_{-\infty}^{\infty}\xi p\,d\xi = \int_{-\infty}^{\infty}\xi\left(\frac{\partial}{\partial\xi}(\xi p) + \frac{\partial^2 p}{\partial\xi^2}\right)d\xi$$

(10.19)
$$= -E(\xi),$$

after integration by parts, and the expected value of ξ^2 satisfies

$$\frac{dE(\xi^2)}{d\tau} = \frac{d}{d\tau}\int_{-\infty}^{\infty}\xi^2 p\,d\xi = \int_{-\infty}^{\infty}\xi^2\left(\frac{\partial}{\partial\xi}(\xi p) + \frac{\partial^2 p}{\partial\xi^2}\right)d\xi$$

(10.20)
$$= -2E(\xi^2) + 2,$$

also, after integration by parts. Consequently, the variance $\text{var} = \sigma^2 = E(\xi^2) - (E(\xi))^2$ satisfies

$$\frac{d(\text{var})}{d\tau} = \frac{dE(\xi^2)}{d\tau} - 2E(\xi)\frac{dE(\xi)}{d\tau}$$

(10.21)
$$= 2 - 2\,\text{var}.$$

These two equations tell us that no matter how initial data are chosen, the distribution approaches a distribution with mean zero and variance 1.

Let's try to find that steady distribution. Set $\frac{\partial p}{\partial\tau} = 0$ and integrate once to find

(10.22)
$$\xi p + \frac{dp}{d\xi} = 0,$$

with constant of integration zero so that p vanishes as $\xi \to \pm\infty$. This first order differential equation is separable and so yields

(10.23)
$$\ln\frac{p}{p_0} = -\frac{\xi^2}{2}$$

or

(10.24)
$$p(\xi) = p_0\exp(-\frac{\xi^2}{2}),$$

which is, as expected, a Gaussian distribution, and $p_0 = \frac{1}{\sqrt{2\pi}}$ so that the total integral of p is one.

This suggests that we should look for a solution of (10.15) which is a Gaussian distribution of the form

(10.25)
$$p(\xi,\tau) = \frac{1}{\sqrt{2b(\tau)\pi}}\exp\left(-\frac{(\xi - c(\tau))^2}{2b(\tau)}\right).$$

Substituting this into the governing equation, we find that we must require
(10.26)
$$(2b + \frac{db}{d\tau} - 2)\xi^2 + (-2bc + 2b\frac{dc}{d\tau} - 2c\frac{db}{d\tau} + 4c)\xi - 2bc\frac{dc}{d\tau} + c^2\frac{db}{d\tau} - 2b^2 - b\frac{db}{d\tau} - 2c^2 + 2b = 0.$$

Notice that (10.26) is a quadratic equation in ξ, and as such each of the three coefficients of the powers of ξ must individually be zero, leading to the three differential

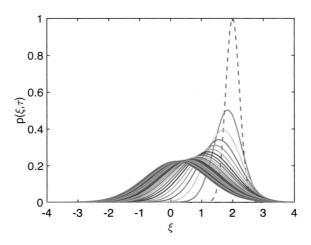

Figure 10.3. Simulation of the Ornstein–Uhlenbeck equation (10.17). Initial data shown as dashed curve.

equations for the quantities b and c. Fortunately, only two of these are independent, requiring

$$\text{(10.27)} \qquad \frac{db}{d\tau} = 2 - 2b,$$

$$\text{(10.28)} \qquad \frac{dc}{d\tau} = -c.$$

The solutions of these are also easy to find, being

$$\text{(10.29)} \qquad b(\tau) = 1 - \exp(-2\tau),$$

$$\text{(10.30)} \qquad c(\tau) = y_0 \exp(-\tau).$$

The equation for $c(\tau)$ is exactly as we expected from the deterministic equation of motion, and $b(\tau)$ is the variance, also as expected. A numerical simulation of this equation is shown in Figure 10.3, and the Matlab code for this simulation is titled OU_process.m. The Matlab code uses upwinding for the advective part and Crank–Nicolson for the diffusive part of this equation.

What we see from both the simulation and the exact solution is that diffusion causes that solution to spread out, but the nonconstant advection focuses the solution toward the origin. Ultimately, in the limit $t \to \infty$, the solution converges to the steady Gaussian profile $\mathcal{N}(0,1)$.

10.4. Spread of an Ornstein–Uhlenbeck Epidemic

In Chapter 6, we discussed the spread of the epidemic described by the reaction

$$\text{(10.31)} \qquad S + I \xrightarrow{\alpha} 2I,$$

where the individuals moved by diffusion. We found that the disease spread with velocity $c = \sqrt{D_i \alpha S_0}$, where D_i is the diffusion coefficient for both S and I individuals.

Of course, the use of diffusion to describe the motion of people is a crude approximation at best. So let's investigate what happens if we make a different approximation for how individuals move. Let's suppose that individuals each move by an Ornstein–Uhlenbeck process with diffusion coefficient D and restoring rate κ, tethered to their homes along a street in a neighborhood, and the disease is passed from person to person only by nearest neighbor interactions. The rate of infection in the ordinary differential equation SI model given by

$$(10.32) \qquad \frac{di}{dt} = \alpha s i$$

has s in units of concentration, so the rate at which a single uninfected individual becomes infected from contact with another infected individual is $\alpha_v = \frac{\alpha}{\text{vol}}$, where vol is the volume conversion factor between concentration and number. But this rate of infection is assuming full contact between the two individuals, and since they are each moving via an Ornstein–Uhlenbeck process, their contact is only partial. So, let's assume that their location is given by a steady state Ornstein–Uhlenbeck process, in nondimensional units, centered at $\xi = 0$ and $\xi = \xi_0$, respectively, denoted by $p(\xi) = \mathcal{N}(0,1)$ and $p(\xi - \xi_0) = \mathcal{N}(\xi_0, 1)$, respectively. Then, the fraction of time that they are in close proximity, say, within distance ϵ is

$$(10.33) \qquad \rho(\epsilon, \xi_0) = \int_{-\infty}^{\infty} \int_{\xi-\epsilon}^{\xi+\epsilon} p(\xi) p(\eta - \xi_0) d\eta\, d\xi.$$

Assuming $\epsilon \ll 1$,

$$\rho(\epsilon, \xi_0) = \frac{1}{2\pi} \int_{-\infty}^{\infty} \int_{\xi-\xi_0-\epsilon}^{\xi-\xi_0+\epsilon} \exp\left(-\frac{\xi^2}{2} - \frac{\eta^2}{2}\right) d\eta\, d\xi$$

$$\approx 2\epsilon \frac{1}{2\pi} \int_{-\infty}^{\infty} \exp\left(-\frac{\xi^2}{2} - \frac{(\xi - \xi_0)^2}{2}\right) d\xi$$

$$(10.34) \qquad = \frac{\epsilon}{\sqrt{\pi}} \exp\left(-\frac{\xi_0^2}{4}\right).$$

In dimensional units this is

$$(10.35) \qquad \rho = \frac{\delta}{\sqrt{\pi}} \sqrt{\frac{\kappa}{D}} \exp\left(-\frac{\kappa}{4D} \Delta x^2\right),$$

where δ is the length of close interaction, and Δx is the separation between houses. It follows that the rate of spread from individual to individual is

$$\lambda = \alpha_v \rho = \alpha_v \frac{\delta}{\sqrt{\pi}} \sqrt{\frac{\kappa}{D}} \exp\left(-\frac{\kappa}{4D} \Delta x^2\right),$$

$$(10.36) \qquad = \alpha_v \frac{2\delta}{\sqrt{\pi}\Delta x} \sqrt{\Lambda} \exp(-\Lambda),$$

where $\Lambda = \frac{\kappa \Delta x^2}{4D}$. It follows from (10.2) that the infection spreads as an advection diffusion process with velocity $\lambda \Delta x$ and diffusion $\frac{1}{2}\lambda \Delta x^2$, with λ given by (10.36). Interestingly, the effect of the tethering rate κ on this velocity is not monotone, but there is a sweetspot for the spread, at $\Lambda = \frac{1}{2}$, at which the spread is fastest. This makes sense in that if Λ is large, the individuals stay close to home and never interact with neighbors, whereas if Λ is small, individuals are quite spread apart and therefore are rarely in the same place as their neighbors. A plot of the function $f(\Lambda) = \sqrt{\Lambda}\exp(-\Lambda)$ is shown in Figure 10.4.

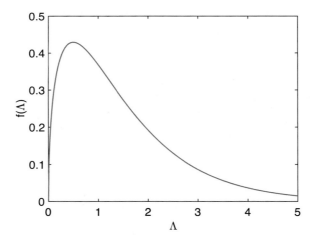

Figure 10.4. Plot of the function $f(\Lambda) = \sqrt{\Lambda}\exp(-\Lambda)$ as a function of Λ.

Exercises

10.1. Modify the Matlab code one_d_direction_switcher.m to simulate the motion of run and tumble bacteria with unequal switching rates $k^- \neq k^+$. Both the mean drift and variance of the population are linear functions of time. Estimate the rate of drift and the effective diffusion coefficient as functions of the three parameters v, k^-, and k^+.

10.2. The population of zooplankton in a deep lake varies as a function of the depth. Zooplankton diffuse vertically with diffusion constant D and advect toward the surface with constant velocity v (because of their buoyancy).
   (a) Find the partial differential equation model (in one spatial dimension) for the population density of zooplankton in the lake, ignoring birth and death.
   (b) Find a nondimensionalization of the problem that eliminates all parameters from the governing equation.
   (c) Find the steady state population density for zooplankton as a function of depth, assuming a known density at the surface.

10.3. Show that with an appropriate change of time and space scales, the Ornstein–Uhlenbeck equation (10.15) can be written as (10.17).

10.4. Find the differential equation for the expected value and the variance of the solution of the modified Ornstein–Uhlenbeck equation

$$\frac{\partial p}{\partial t} = \frac{\partial}{\partial x}\left((x - y(t))p\right) + D\frac{\partial^2 p}{\partial x^2},$$

where $y(t)$ is an arbitrary function of time.

Use the Matlab code OU_process.m to numerically verify these differential equations.

10.5. Add advection to the fire-diffuse-fire model (8.70) to determine the effect of a prevailing wind on the progress of a traveling wave.

10.6. **An Ornstein–Uhlenbeck Epidemic.** In Chapter 6, we did an agent-based simulation of the spread of an SI epidemic represented by the reaction

(10.37) $$S + I \xrightarrow{\alpha} 2I,$$

where both S and I diffuse with equal diffusion coefficients. (Recall Matlab codes agent_SIR_one_d.m and agent_SIR_2d.m.) Suppose instead that individuals do not diffuse freely but rather move by an Ornstein–Uhlenbeck process tethered to their individual homes, which are uniformly and regularly (not randomly) distributed throughout their neighborhood. Modify the codes agent_SIR_one_d.m to study the spread of the disease through a neighborhood. How is the spread of the disease affected by the restoring force constant κ?

10.7. Why is it reasonable to assume that for the Ornstein–Uhlenbeck epidemic the spread is only between nearest neighbors? What is the spread rate to the second neighbor, and how does it compare to the rate of spread to the nearest neighbor?

10.8. Suppose a diffusing particle is tethered to a point $x = 0$ with a restorative velocity $v = \kappa(1 - 2H(x))$, where $H(x)$ is the Heaviside function. What is the equation governing the probability of finding it at position x at time t? Find the steady state distribution for this particle. What is the variance of this distribution?

Chapter 11

Chemotaxis

The ability to signal and respond to signals in the environment is an obviously important ability required for the survival of living organisms. Chemotaxis refers to the ability of cells or organisms to have directed motion in response to chemical gradients. This motion could be away from a source if the chemical is toxic or toward the source if the chemical is a nutrient or another attractant such as a pheromone.

According to Wikipedia (http://en.wikipedia.org/wiki/Chemotaxis), the description of chemotaxis was first made by T. W. Engelmann (1881) and W. F. Pfeffer (1884) in bacteria and by H. S. Jennings (1906) in ciliates. An understanding of the biochemical basis for chemotaxis in *E. coli* is attributed to J. S. Adler [1] who found that flagellar rotation was regulated by its chemoreceptors. *E. coli* have several rotary flagellar motors which can rotate either clockwise or counterclockwise. When they rotate counterclockwise, the flagella come together to form a bundle which acts as a propeller to move the bacteria along a straight line. However, if one or more of the flagella rotate in the clockwise direction, the bundle is broken and the bacteria can only tumble in place. Adler discovered that in the presence of increasing attractant, bacteria swim more smoothly due to a continuous counterclockwise rotation of their flagella. In contrast, a gradient of decreasing attractant resulted in an increase in the frequency of bacterial tumbling, produced by a clockwise flagellar rotation.

Two questions naturally arise. First, is it correct that, by modifying the frequency of tumbling in response to the gradient of a chemoattractant, a bacterium can successfully swim up the gradient of a food source? Second, how can this be modeled mathematically, and what can be learned from such a model?

To address the first question, let's do a particle-based simulation. After doing Exercise 4.16, you now have the Matlab code for an agent-based simulation of a run and tumble process, because that is where we begin this simulation. As a reminder, a run and tumble process is described as follows: Suppose that a particle (a swimming bacterium) is in one of two states, swimming in two dimensions or tumbling. It changes state with rates k_{on} and k_{off} to swim or tumble, respectively. In the swimming state it moves with constant velocity v in the direction θ, i.e., $\frac{dx}{dt} = v\cos\theta$, $\frac{dy}{dt} = v\sin\theta$. In the tumbling state, it does not change its position, but θ changes to a new angle with uniform probability.

How can a bacterium measure a spatial gradient? Because a bacterium is so small, it cannot detect differences in concentration along its length. So, to measure gradients it must move, and then using a complicated signaling network, it can measure the rate of change of the surrounding concentration. So, for our simulation, we assume that the rate of switching to tumbling, k_{off}, is a function of $\frac{\partial c}{\partial t}$, specifically, $k_{\text{off}} = k_0 - \chi\frac{\partial c}{\partial t}$ where c is the external chemoattractant (or repellant) concentration. Notice that $\chi > 0$ for an attractant, since a decrease of c should make the switch to tumbling occur sooner. There is one minor problem with this definition, which is that it is possible, if the gradient is large and positive, that k_{off} will be negative. However, if that is the case, it simply means that a switch to the tumbling state cannot occur.

The simulation is done using the Matlab code chemotax_agents.m. With that code, two cases are considered, namely $\chi = 0$ and $\chi = 0.1$. The case $\chi = 0$ is exactly the same as Exercise 4.16, for which there is no response to the external concentration. Here, the external concentration is taken to be $c(x, y) = -(x - L_x)^2 - (y - L_y)^2$, $L_x = L_y = 5$, which, because it can be negative, is not a physically realistic concentration profile, but it is nonetheless useful, as we will see below.

The results of the simulations can be seen in Figure 11.1. On the left in Figure 11.1(a) is shown the position of the $N = 1000$ particles at the end of the simulation, all of which started at time $t = 0$ at the origin, $x = y = 0$. On the right in Fig 11.1(b) is shown the variance of the positions, plotted as a function of time. The blue color indicates $\chi = 0$ and the red color indicates $\chi = 0.1$. What we see is quite interesting. When $\chi = 0$, the particles spread by a diffusion process, as documented by the linear

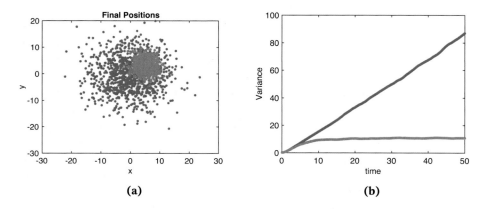

Figure 11.1. Results of agent-based simulation with ($\chi = 0.1$ red) and without ($\chi = 0$ blue) chemotaxis with attractant distribution $c(x, y) = -(x - L_x)^2 - (y - L_y)^2$, $L_x = 5$, $L_y = 3$. (a) shows the final positions of $N = 1000$ particles, and (b) shows the variance as a function of time. The particles with $\chi = 0$ are spreading with variance that is linear in time, while the particles with $\chi = 0.1$ have reached a fixed variance at the end of the simulation.

growth of the variance, with effective diffusion $D = 0.9$. In contrast, when $\chi = 0.1$, the particles migrate and aggregate around the location of the maximal concentration, with variance that is bounded.

Let's figure out how to put this into mathematical terms. For simplicity, we suppose that the bacterium is moving along a one dimensional line with velocity v, and switching between leftward and rightward movement by the exponential process

$$(11.1) \qquad L \underset{k^-}{\overset{k^+}{\rightleftharpoons}} R.$$

In Chapter 10, we found that the flux of bacteria for this process is given by

$$(11.2) \qquad J = -\frac{v^2}{k^- + k^+}\frac{\partial u}{\partial x} + v\frac{k^+ - k^-}{k^- + k^+}u - \frac{v}{k^- + k^+}\frac{\partial v}{\partial x}u.$$

Now, to take into account the effect of the environment on the switching rates, we take

$$(11.3) \qquad k^\pm = k_0 - \chi\frac{dc}{dt},$$

as we did for the agent-based simulation. However, the bacteria can measure $\frac{\partial c}{\partial t}$ only because they are moving, and so

$$(11.4) \qquad \frac{\partial c}{\partial t} = \pm v\frac{\partial c}{\partial x}$$

with the plus sign when moving to the right and the minus sign when moving to the left. It follows that

$$(11.5) \qquad k^\pm = k_0 \pm \chi v\frac{\partial c}{\partial x}.$$

Now we substitute this into (11.2), and find

$$(11.6) \qquad J = -\frac{v^2}{2k_0}\frac{\partial u}{\partial x} + \frac{v^2}{k_0}\chi u\frac{\partial c}{\partial x}.$$

Here we find what we were looking for, a description of flux that responds to the gradient of the chemoattractant c. In fact, the flux J consists of two terms, a diffusive term and an advective term, where the advective velocity is directly proportional to $\frac{\partial c}{\partial x}$.

The steady state distribution of bacteria is found when $J = 0$. For this it follows that

$$(11.7) \qquad u = u_0 \exp(2\chi c),$$

a profile that is maximal at the maxima of c, if $\chi > 0$, and the opposite if $\chi < 0$. Notice that this is exactly an Ornstein–Uhlenbeck process if $\frac{\partial c}{\partial x}$ is a linear decreasing function of x.

11.1. Amoeba Aggregation

Dictyostelium discoideum is a species of soil-living amoebae (commonly referred to as slime mold), that transitions from a collection of unicellular amoebae into a multicellular slug and then into a fruiting body within its lifetime. Its unique lifecycle consists

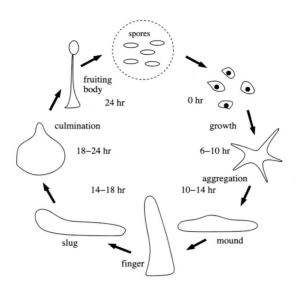

Figure 11.2. *D. discoideum* life cycle

of four stages: vegetative, aggregation, migration, and culmination. In the wild, *D. discoideum* can be found in soil and moist leaf litter. Its primary diet consists of bacteria, such as *E. coli*, found in the soil and decaying organic matter.

The lifecycle of the amoebae *D. discoideum* begins when spores are released from a mature fruiting body. Myxamoebae hatch from the spores under warm and moist conditions. During their vegetative stage, the myxamoebae divide by mitosis as they feed on bacteria. The bacteria secrete folic acid, attracting the myxamoebae. When the supply of bacteria is depleted, the myxamoebae enter the aggregation stage.

During aggregation, starvation initiates the creation of a biochemical machinery that includes cyclic AMP (cAMP). Cyclic AMP is secreted by the amoebae to attract neighboring cells to a central location. As they move toward the signal, they bump into each other and stick together to form a tight aggregate, known as a slug.

The migration stage begins once the slug is formed and it moves toward attractants such as light, heat, and humidity. Simultaneously, the slug cells differentiate into prestalk and prespore cells that move to the anterior and posterior ends of the slug, respectively. Once the slug has found a suitable environment, the anterior end of the slug forms the stalk of the fruiting body and the posterior end forms the spores of the fruiting body. After the slug settles into one spot, the posterior end spreads out with the anterior end raised in the air, forming what is called the "Mexican hat", and the culmination stage begins.

During the culmination stage, the prestalk cells and prespore cells switch positions to form the mature fruiting body. This fruiting body is 1–2 mm tall and is able to start the entire cycle over again by releasing the spores that become myxamoebae.

Here we focus on the aggregation stage of the life cycle. A simple model of this aggregation process includes secretion of cAMP by amoebae, degradation of cAMP, chemoattraction of amoebae to cAMP, and diffusion of both amoebae and cAMP. A one dimensional spatial model with these ingredients is given by

$$(11.8) \qquad \frac{\partial u}{\partial t} = -\frac{\partial}{\partial x}\left(\chi u \frac{\partial c}{\partial x} - \mu \frac{\partial u}{\partial x}\right),$$

$$(11.9) \qquad \frac{\partial c}{\partial t} = \rho u - kc + D\frac{\partial^2 c}{\partial x^2},$$

where u and c represent the concentrations of amoebae and cAMP, respectively. Do you understand the meaning of all of these terms? The assumption is that the amoebae u diffuse and move chemotactically following the gradient of cAMP c. Further, cAMP is produced at a linear rate by amoebae, and it degrades at rate k and diffuses with diffusion coefficient D. Here, we assume that the one-dimensional domain has length L and that there are no-flux boundary conditions for both c and u. Consequently, since there is no birth, death, or escape for amoebae, the total amount of amoebae u is conserved, stated as

$$(11.10) \qquad \int_0^L u(x,t)dx = u^*L.$$

The (numerical) solution of these equations is shown in Figure 11.3 (the Matlab code for this simulation is CN_upwind_chemotax.m). Here we see the time-dependent formation of an amoebae aggregate starting from a nearly uniform initial distribution of amoebae. A relevant question to ask is when, i.e., under what conditions does an aggregate form?

To address this question, we ask when a spatially homogeneous solution is stable or unstable. Notice that the homogeneous steady state solutions u^* and c^* satisfy $\rho u^* - kc^* = 0$. We linearize the governing equations about the steady solution, setting $u =$

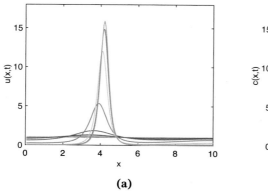
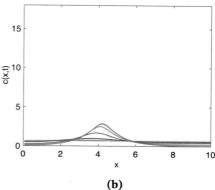

(a)   (b)

Figure 11.3. Numerical solution of (11.8)–(11.9) for (a) chemotactic amoebae $u(x,t)$ and (b) chemoattractant $c(x,t)$ for several values of t, with parameter values $L = 10$, $D = 0.25$, $\mu = 0.07$, $\rho = 0.2$, $k = 0.3$, $\chi = 0.2$.

$u^* + \delta u$, $c = c^* + \delta c$, and finding

(11.11)
$$\frac{\partial \delta u}{\partial t} = -\frac{\partial}{\partial x}\left(u^* \chi \frac{\partial \delta c}{\partial x} - \mu \frac{\partial \delta u}{\partial x}\right),$$

(11.12)
$$\frac{\partial \delta c}{\partial t} = \rho \delta u - k \delta c + D \frac{\partial^2 \delta c}{\partial x^2}.$$

Now, we look for solutions of the linearized equations of the form

(11.13)
$$\delta u = A \exp(\lambda t + i\omega x), \qquad \delta c = C \exp(\lambda t + i\omega x),$$

and upon substitution we find the linear system of equations

(11.14)
$$\lambda \begin{pmatrix} A \\ C \end{pmatrix} = \begin{pmatrix} -\mu\omega^2 & u^* \chi \omega^2 \\ \rho & -k - \omega^2 D \end{pmatrix} \begin{pmatrix} A \\ C \end{pmatrix}.$$

The characteristic equation for this system is

(11.15)
$$\lambda^2 - \text{Tr}\lambda + \det = 0,$$

where $\text{Tr} = -k - \omega^2 D - \mu\omega^2$, and $\det = \mu\omega^2(\omega^2 D + k) - \omega^2 \rho\chi u^*$. Since $\text{Tr} < 0$, the only way that the homogeneous steady solution can be unstable is if $\det < 0$, so neutral stability occurs wherever $\det = 0$. It follows that the homogeneous steady solution is unstable if

(11.16)
$$\mu\omega^2 D < \rho\chi u^* - \mu k.$$

Obviously, if $\rho\chi u^* - \mu k < 0$, the homogeneous steady solution is stable. However, if $\rho\chi u^* - \mu k > 0$, then the homogeneous solution is unstable if the domain size L is large enough,

(11.17)
$$L^2 > \frac{\pi^2 \mu D}{\rho\chi u^* - \mu k}.$$

This follows since, for a bounded domain with no-flux boundary conditions, $\omega L = \pi$.

There are a few observations to make here. First, if $\chi < 0$, (for a chemorepellant) the homogeneous solution is always stable. However, if $\chi > 0$ (for a chemoattractant) and if u^* is large enough, the homogeneous solution is unstable, suggesting that an aggregated pattern forms if the domain and the population are sufficiently large.

Now, we look for steady, inhomogeneous solutions of the governing equations. That is, set time derivatives $\frac{\partial u}{\partial t}$ and $\frac{\partial c}{\partial t}$ in equations (11.8)–(11.9) to zero, to learn that

(11.18)
$$\chi u \frac{\partial c}{\partial x} - \mu \frac{\partial u}{\partial x} = 0,$$

so that

(11.19)
$$\frac{\chi}{\mu}(c - K) = \ln \frac{u}{u^*}.$$

The homogeneous steady state must satisfy $\rho u^* - kc^* = 0$, so that $K = c^* = \frac{\rho u^*}{k}$. Solving for u, we find the single equation for c,

(11.20)
$$\rho u^* \exp\left(\frac{\chi}{\mu}\left(c - \frac{\rho u^*}{k}\right)\right) - kc + D \frac{\partial^2 c}{\partial x^2} = 0.$$

Before proceeding any further, it is useful to rescale the problem. We set $\xi = x\sqrt{\frac{k}{D}}$ and $v = \frac{kc}{\rho u^*}$ (not to be confused with velocity from the previous section), in terms of which the governing equation (11.20) becomes

$$(11.21) \qquad \frac{d^2v}{d\xi^2} + f(v) = 0,$$

where $f(v) = \exp(\kappa(v-1)) - v$, $\kappa = \frac{\chi}{\mu}\frac{\rho u^*}{k}$.

Since we have seen problems like this before, what to do next should be clear. (*Answer.* Phase plane analysis.)

Notice that $f(0) > 0$, and $f'(0) = \kappa\exp(-\kappa)-1 < 0$ for all positive κ. Furthermore, $f'(v) > 0$ for v sufficiently large, $f''(v) > 0$ for all $v > 0$, and $f(1) = 0$. Hence, since $f(v)$ is concave up, the equation $f(v) = 0$ has exactly two positive roots, one of which is $v = 1$. Since $f'(1) = \kappa - 1$, the root at $v = 1$ is the smaller of the two roots if $\kappa < 1$ and is the larger of the two roots if $\kappa > 1$.

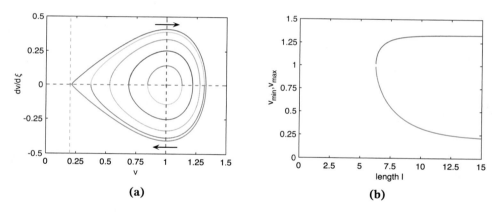

(a)   **(b)**

Figure 11.4. (a) Phase portrait for solutions of the equation (11.21). (b) Plot of the maximum and minimum of the solution plotted as a function of the nondimensional length $l = L\sqrt{\frac{k}{D}}$ in the case $\kappa = 2.0$.

The phase portrait analysis for this equation is straightforward (and has been done several times before in this text). The larger of the two critical points is a center, and the smaller of the two critical points is a saddle point. Consequently, there is a family of closed orbits surrounding the center, expanding out to the closed saddle-saddle homoclinic trajectory.

The solutions of interest here are when $v = 1$ is the larger of the two roots, which is when $\kappa > 1$. In that case, the family of closed orbits exists and satisfies no-flux boundary conditions provided $l \equiv L\sqrt{\frac{k}{D}} > \frac{\pi}{\sqrt{\kappa-1}}$. The phase portrait and bifurcation diagram depicting this result are shown in Figure 11.4, and an example of a solution profile is shown in Figure 11.5 (produced using Matlab code dd_chemotax_ss_pp.m).

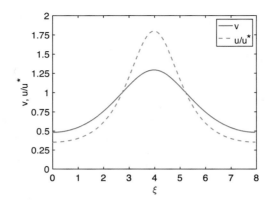

Figure 11.5. Typical profile for solutions of the equation (11.21) for v (solid line) and $\frac{u}{u^*}$ (dashed line) for $\kappa = 2.0$.

What we learn from this analysis is that if the amoebae population and cAMP production rate are large enough, while the diffusion coefficient and degradation rate of cAMP are small enough, then an aggregate of amoebae will form. This helps to tell the story of how the colony switches between different stages in its life cycle. As long as there is nutrient available, the colony continues to grow. However, when nutrient is depleted, the individual amoeba start to secrete cyclic AMP. This combination of large population size and cyclic AMP production initiates the formation of the slug which ultimately leads to dissemination of spores.

This concludes our introduction to the fascinating topic of chemotactic pattern formation. The model presented here is a simple version of a Keller–Segel model [**38**], [**63**], which forms the basis for a large body of work on this topic. For a very nice review of chemotaxis models, see [**29**].

Exercises

11.1. Suppose two populations of bacteria each secrete a chemical that is toxic to the other and is a chemorepellant. Under what conditions is a homogeneous population mixture stable or unstable?

Hint. Assuming the chemical concentrations are directly proportional to that of their secreter, model the two populations with the equations

$$
\begin{aligned}
\frac{\partial u}{\partial t} &= D_u \frac{\partial^2 u}{\partial x^2} + \chi_u \frac{\partial}{\partial x}\left(u \frac{\partial v}{\partial x}\right) \\
\frac{\partial v}{\partial t} &= D_v \frac{\partial^2 v}{\partial x^2} + \chi_v \frac{\partial}{\partial x}\left(v \frac{\partial u}{\partial x}\right).
\end{aligned}
$$

Determine the stability of a homogeneous steady state solution $u = u^*$, $v = v^*$.

11.2. In Chapter 6, we discussed the problem of resource consumption by bacteria and found that there were traveling wave solutions. Modify the Matlab code used in that section CN_diffusion_gluc_micro_X.m to simulate the resource consumption equations

$$\frac{\partial u}{\partial t} = D_u \frac{\partial^2 u}{\partial x^2} + \chi \frac{\partial}{\partial x}(u \frac{\partial g}{\partial x}) + \alpha u g,$$

$$\frac{\partial g}{\partial t} = D_g \frac{\partial^2 g}{\partial x^2} - \alpha u g.$$

which are the equations (6.80)–(6.81) modified to include chemotaxis of the bacteria for the resource. What is the effect of chemotaxis on the rate of growth of the population and rate of resource consumption? What happens if the resource is a chemorepellant?

Hint. Use the Matlab code CN_upwind_chemotax.m as a template for how to add chemotaxis to your simulation.

Chapter 12

Spatial Patterns

It is impossible to observe biological organisms and not be astounded at the incredible array of shapes and patterns that one sees. And the realization that each multicellular organism emerged from a single cell, in which none of these shapes and patterns were evident makes this even more astounding. What one realizes after a bit of reflection is that these shapes and patterns are *emergent features* of the underlying chemistry, since it is unlikely, perhaps impossible, that every detail of structure is encoded in the DNA. To the best of our knowledge, all that is encoded in the DNA is what proteins to make and when to make them. Structures and patterns result when different cells do different things and manage to self-organize into a large macrocellular structure, or within a single cell different proteins manage to self-organize into a particular macromolecular structure. For the most part, the underlying mechanisms behind this self-organization is unknown,

What is a pattern? In its simplest terms, it is a collection of objects, like cells or proteins, that is not homogeneously mixed but has managed to form spatially inhomogeneous aggregates. Immediately, we see the challenge, because we know that natural processes (i.e., diffusion) *always* move things down gradients and *always* oppose aggregation. So, if there is an aggregate, it must have somehow overcome the tendency of things to spread out, and energy must have been expended to create and maintain the aggregate.

 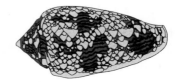

Zebra fish   Zebra stripes   Conus shell patterns

Image credit: Johanna Bossart.

12.1. The Turing Mechanism

We are a long way from understanding biological pattern formation and development. However, one of the best known ideas for how biological patterns form is known as the Turing mechanism. Alan Turing (1912–1954) is more famous for his work in cryptography and computer science, being identified with a *Turing machine*, the *Turing test*, and the breaking of the Enigma code in World War II. However, the Turing mechanism was suggested by Turing in a paper in 1952 [**69**] and has since been the subject of thousands of publications.

There are many chemical and biological systems that might be modeled as reaction-diffusion systems of the form

$$\frac{\partial u}{\partial t} = D_u \nabla^2 u + f(u, v), \tag{12.1}$$

$$\frac{\partial v}{\partial t} = D_v \nabla^2 v + g(u, v), \tag{12.2}$$

where the chemical reaction kinetics have a *stable* steady state solution $u = u_0$, $v = v_0$. Turing's idea was to determine if this spatially homogeneous stable steady state can be rendered unstable when spatial variations are allowed.

Before we consider this problem, let's remind ourselves about what happens with only one species. In this case we have the diffusion reaction equation

$$\frac{\partial u}{\partial t} = D_u \nabla^2 u + f(u), \tag{12.3}$$

where $f(u_0) = 0$. We linearize this equation around $u = u_0$, setting $u = u_0 + \epsilon U$, substituting into the governing equations, differentiating with respect to ϵ, and then setting $\epsilon = 0$, to find

$$\frac{\partial U}{\partial t} = D_u \nabla^2 U + f'(u_0)U. \tag{12.4}$$

We know from Section 6.1 that the solution of this problem is given by

$$U(x, t) = \exp(f'(u_0)t)v(x, t), \tag{12.5}$$

where $v(x, t)$ satisfies the diffusion equation. Obviously, if $f'(u_0) < 0$, this solution is linearly stable. In other words, the spatially inhomogeneous solution has the same stability characteristic as the homogeneous (space-independent) solution.

Now, for the two-variable system (12.1)–(12.2), we perform a linear stability analysis. That is, we let $u = u_0 + \epsilon U$, $v = v_0 + \epsilon V$, substitute into the governing equations, differentiate with respect to ϵ, and then set $\epsilon = 0$. The consequence of this procedure is the linear system of equations

$$\frac{\partial U}{\partial t} = D_u \nabla^2 U + \frac{\partial f^0}{\partial u}U + \frac{\partial f^0}{\partial v}V, \tag{12.6}$$

$$\frac{\partial V}{\partial t} = D_v \nabla^2 V + \frac{\partial g^0}{\partial u}U + \frac{\partial g^0}{\partial v}V, \tag{12.7}$$

where the superscript "0" refers to evaluation at the steady state solution $u = u_0$, $v = v_0$.

The assumption that this steady state solution is a stable solution of the ordinary differential equation system implies that $\text{Tr} \equiv \frac{\partial f^0}{\partial u} + \frac{\partial g^0}{\partial v} < 0$ and $\det \equiv \frac{\partial f^0}{\partial u}\frac{\partial g^0}{\partial v} - \frac{\partial f^0}{\partial v}\frac{\partial g^0}{\partial u} > 0$. To be specific, we assume that $\frac{\partial f^0}{\partial u} < 0$.

The stability of the system (12.6)–(12.7) is determined by setting

$$(12.8) \qquad \begin{pmatrix} U \\ V \end{pmatrix} = \begin{pmatrix} \alpha \\ \beta \end{pmatrix} \exp(\lambda t) \cos(\omega x),$$

and consequently requiring

$$(12.9) \qquad \begin{pmatrix} \frac{\partial f^0}{\partial u} - \omega^2 D_u & \frac{\partial f^0}{\partial v} \\ \frac{\partial g^0}{\partial u} & \frac{\partial g^0}{\partial v} - \omega^2 D_v \end{pmatrix} \begin{pmatrix} \alpha \\ \beta \end{pmatrix} = \lambda \begin{pmatrix} \alpha \\ \beta \end{pmatrix}.$$

This implies that λ is a solution of the quadratic equation

$$(12.10) \qquad \lambda^2 - (\text{Tr} - \omega^2 D_u - \omega^2 D_v)\lambda + D_\omega = 0,$$

where $D_\omega = \det - \omega^2 D_u \frac{\partial g^0}{\partial v} - \omega^2 D_v \frac{\partial f^0}{\partial u} + \omega^4 D_u D_v$. Stability is determined by the sign of the real part of the roots of this polynomial, and since

$$(12.11) \qquad \text{Tr} - \omega^2 D_u - \omega^2 D_v < 0,$$

the solution is stable if $D_\omega > 0$ and unstable if $D_\omega < 0$. Consequently, the only way that there can be a change of stability is if $D_\omega = 0$.

There are two immediate observations to make. First, since we have assumed that $\det > 0$ and $\frac{\partial f^0}{\partial u} < 0$, instability is impossible unless $\frac{\partial g^0}{\partial v} > 0$, and second, since $\frac{\partial f^0}{\partial u} + \frac{\partial g^0}{\partial v} < 0$, instability is not possible if $D_v > D_u$. Notice also that since $\frac{\partial g^0}{\partial v}$ and $\frac{\partial f^0}{\partial u}$ are of opposite sign, $\frac{\partial g^0}{\partial u}$ and $\frac{\partial f^0}{\partial v}$ must also be of opposite sign.

A convenient way to understand this condition is to express the neutral stability curve as

$$(12.12) \qquad \omega^2 D_u = \frac{\det - \omega^2 D_v \frac{\partial f^0}{\partial u}}{\frac{\partial g^0}{\partial v} - \omega^2 D_v}.$$

A plot of this curve (made using the Matlab code Gray_Scott_Turing_via_MOL.m) is shown in Figure 12.1. If parameters are such that one is above this curve for $\omega = \frac{n\pi}{L}$, then the nth mode is unstable, suggesting that a pattern with the shape of $\cos(\frac{n\pi x}{L})$ will emerge from the evolution of the equations. Of course, this is only a suggestion, and if more than one mode is unstable, it is unclear what the shape of the emergent pattern will be. Furthermore, there is no indication from this analysis if the pattern that emerges will be stable or not. This needs to be determined from other considerations, such as numerical simulation.

It is also apparent that if all points on the straight line $\frac{D_u}{D_v} = $ constant lie below this curve, then there is no domain size for which the homogenous steady solution is unstable. On the other hand, if the straight line $\frac{D_u}{D_v} = $ constant intersects this curve, it does so twice, indicating that for L sufficiently small, the solution is stable, but for larger

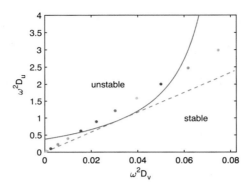

Figure 12.1. Neutral stability curve for the diffusion reaction system (12.6)–(12.7) with det = 0.0311, $\frac{\partial f^0}{\partial u} = -0.5025$, $\frac{\partial g^0}{\partial v} = 0.0825$. Dots show the points $\omega_n^2 D_u$ and $\omega_n^2 D_v$ plotted for $D_u = 1.0$, $D_v = 0.025$, with $\omega_n = \frac{n\pi}{L}$ and $L = 20$.

values of L, there are guaranteed to be some modes that are unstable. The dividing line between these two cases is the straight line $\frac{D_u}{D_v} = \alpha$, where

$$(12.13) \qquad \text{Disc} \equiv \alpha^2 \left(\frac{\partial g^0}{\partial v} \right)^2 + 2\alpha \frac{\partial f^0}{\partial u} \frac{\partial g^0}{\partial v} - 4\alpha \det + \left(\frac{\partial f^0}{\partial u} \right)^2 = 0.$$

This is the line shown dashed in Figure 12.1.

Notice also that any specific mode can be unstable if the diffusion coefficient D_u is sufficiently large and D_v is sufficiently small. This instability is called a *diffusion-driven instability*, or simply a diffusive instability. It is also called the Turing instability, in recognition of its discovery by A. Turing in 1952 [**69**].

Let's think for a moment about what all these conditions mean. The condition $\frac{\partial f^0}{\partial u} < 0$ means that by itself, without any contribution from v, the steady solution u^* is stable, whereas the condition $\frac{\partial g^0}{\partial v} > 0$ means that by itself, without any influence from u, the steady solution v^* is unstable. The fact that together, the ordinary differential equation system is stable implies that u is a stabilizer of v, that is, the influence of u on v is such that the growth of v is held in check by u. With this in mind, the species v is often called an *activator*, and the species u is called an *inhibitor*.

Now, if an instability arises, it is only because $D_u > D_v$. In other words, only because the inhibitor diffuses faster than the activator, and it is therefore unable to control the growth of species v; it diffuses away too fast.

12.1.1. A Specific Example. To get a better understanding of how this works, let's consider the specific example with reaction dynamics

$$(12.14) \qquad f(u, v) = -uv^2 + \rho(1 - u),$$

$$(12.15) \qquad g(u, v) = uv^2 - (\rho + k)v.$$

These dynamics are referred to as the Gray–Scott model [**41**], [**56**]. The interpretation is that there are chemical species U and V with U being converted to V via the reaction

$$(12.16) \qquad U + 2V \rightarrow 3V,$$

and V being converted to a product (or degraded) at rate k. In addition, there is a constant source of U and removal of U, V, at rate ρ.

There are up to three steady state solutions. The trivial steady state solution is $v = 0$, $u = 1$, and the nontrivial steady state solutions satisfy $u(1 - u) = \frac{(\rho+k)^2}{\rho}$, $v^2 = \rho\frac{1-u}{u}$. Thus, there are two nontrivial steady states provided $\frac{(\rho+k)^2}{\rho} < \frac{1}{4}$, i.e., provided $k < \frac{1}{2}\sqrt{\rho} - \rho$ with $0 < \rho < \frac{1}{4}$. Of these two nontrivial steady states, the one with largest u is a saddle point, and the one with smallest u is a stable node. The phase portrait for these dynamics are shown in Figure 12.2. This stable steady state is a perfect candidate for a diffusive instability, since $\frac{\partial f^0}{\partial u} < 0$, $\frac{\partial g^0}{\partial v} > 0$, and Tr is negative. In fact, the stability diagram shown in Figure 12.1 is for these dynamics and parameter values.

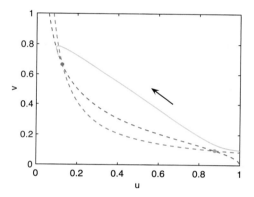

Figure 12.2. Phase portrait for the ordinary differential equation dynamics of the Gray–Scott model $\frac{du}{dt} = f(u, v)$, $\frac{dv}{dt} = g(u, v)$, with $f(u, v)$ and $g(u, v)$ given by (12.14)–(12.15). with parameter values $\rho = \frac{1}{16}$, $k = 0.02$.

To get some idea of what nontrivial patterns might form, take a closer look at Figure 12.1 and notice the dots. These correspond to the location of the points $\omega_n^2 D_u$ and $\omega_n^2 D_v$ plotted for $D_u = 1.0$, $D_v = 0.025$, with $\omega_n = \frac{n\pi}{L}$ and $L = 20$. Notice that there are five such points inside the unstable region. This means that the integration of (12.1)–(12.2) starting with initial data that are close to the unstable modes will evolve into something far from the homogeneous equilibrium. Examples of two such nontrivial steady solutions are shown in Figure 12.3 (computed using the Matlab code Gray_Scott_Turing_via_MOL.m). An intriguing question is how many different stable nontrivial patterns can emerge when there are a number of different unstable modes. For this example, we found three such patterns, corresponding to $\omega_n = \frac{n\pi}{L}$ with $n = 6, 7, 8$, two of which ($n = 6, 8$) are shown in Figure 12.3. We were not able to find stable nontrivial patterns corresponding to $n = 5, 9$, even though these correspond to unstable modes for the spatially homogeneous solution. We know of no general way to determine which stable patterns exist in these situations.

The Matlab code to perform these simulations is Gray_Scott_Turing_via_MOL.m, and it uses the method of lines to solve the coupled diffusion reaction equations.

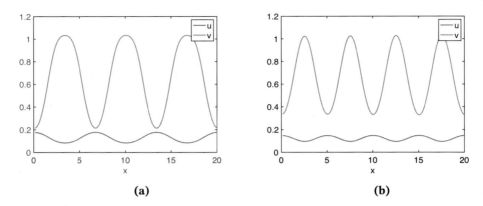

Figure 12.3. Steady solutions of the Gray–Scott model with parameter values $\rho = \frac{1}{16}$, $k = 0.02$, and $D_u = 1.0$, $D_v = 0.025$, with $L = 20$.

In one spatial dimension, the patterns seen in the Gray–Scott model are typified by those shown in Figure 12.3. In two spatial dimensions, however, there is a wide array of patterns, including stripes and spots and moving intertwined bands, which have been argued to be related to patterns seen in real biological situations. Further exploration of these pattern forming dynamics is left to the interested reader [**41**], [**56**]. You may also be interested in the discussions of the Turing pattern forming mechanism found in [**47**] (for sea shells) and [**49**] (for animal coat patterns).

12.2. Tiger Bush Stripes

The point of the Turing mechanism is that there are systems of ordinary differential equations with stable equilibria, which when the species are allowed to diffuse, produce spatially inhomogeneous patterns. The question of the relevance of this observation to biology is hotly debated, and at present there are very few naturally occurring systems for which the Turing mechanism, strictly interpreted, is known to be the underlying pattern formation mechanism. However, the idea of a diffusion-driven instability remains interesting and important. In the remainder of this chapter we describe situations for which a diffusion-driven instability is reasonably well established as the underlying pattern-forming mechanism.

Vegetation in semiarid regions is often noticeably patterned, with regular stripes on hillsides and irregular mosaics on flat ground. These vegetation stripes are typically found in remote regions, such as southwest Niger, as well as regions of Australia and Mexico. It is called *tiger bush* because the patterns resemble the stripes on the fur of a tiger (see Figure 12.4). One of the surprising features of tiger bush is that it can occur for a wide variety of different kinds of plants (e.g., grasses, shrubs, or trees) and for a wide variety of soil types (e.g., sandy, silty, or clayey). Furthermore, the pattern seems not to be induced by local heterogeneities or variations in topography, and instead typically occurs on relatively flat plateaus or very gradual slopes.

The verbal explanation given for the formation and maintenance of striped vegetation is the following. (i) Water enters the ground via rainfall and leaves by either

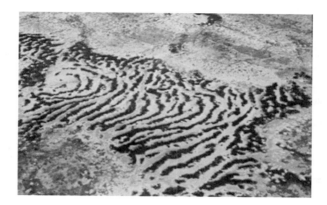

Figure 12.4. Tiger bush vegetation stripes in Niger (reprinted here from [**68**] with permission of the authors).

flowing subsurface downhill, evaporating directly, or being taken up by the roots of plants and then evaporating. (ii) Water flow is depleted by the plants in the downhill direction, leading to stripes of bare ground. (iii) The stripes slowly move uphill because colonization of bare areas can occur only at the moister uphill side of the stripe, and because plants on the downhill side of the stripe die as a result of inadequate water.

A simple model for this process [**40**] is

$$(12.17) \qquad \frac{\partial W}{\partial t} = A - EW - RWN^2 + V\frac{\partial W}{\partial x},$$

$$(12.18) \qquad \frac{\partial N}{\partial t} = RBWN^2 - MN + D\nabla^2 N,$$

where W is the concentration of water in the soil, N is the number density of plants, A is the (average) constant source of water, E is the natural evaporation rate, R is the rate at which water is taken up by plants, B is the amount of plant biomass produced per unit of water consumed, M is the rate of death of plants, V is the advected velocity of water, and D is the diffusion coefficient governing the spread of plants. Obviously, there are many simplifying assumptions made for this model. If $V > 0$ represents flow downhill, then the variable x is increasing in the uphill direction. Typical parameter values are given in Table 12.1.

The analysis of this model is in several steps. First, it is useful to introduce dimensionless variables and parameters,

$$(12.19) \qquad \tau = Et, \qquad x = \alpha\xi, \qquad N = \eta n, \qquad W = \rho w,$$

in terms of which the equations become

$$(12.20) \qquad \frac{\partial w}{\partial \tau} = a - w - wn^2 + v\frac{\partial w}{\partial \xi},$$

$$(12.21) \qquad \frac{\partial n}{\partial \tau} = wn^2 - mn + \nabla^2 n,$$

where $a = \frac{A}{\rho E}$, $m = \frac{M}{E}$, $v = \frac{V}{\sqrt{DE}}$, $\eta^2 = \frac{E}{R}$, $\alpha^2 = \frac{D}{E}$, and $\rho = \frac{E}{\eta RB}$, reducing the number of parameters to three.

Table 12.1. The definition and value of parameters for the tiger bush model.

Param	Definition	value
A	average rainfall	250-750 kg H_2O m^{-2} year^{-1}
E	evaporation rate	4 year^{-1}
V	advected water velocity	0-365 m year^{-1}
D	plant spread diffusion	1 m^2 year^{-1}
for grass		
B_{grass}	biomass production rate	0.003 kg dry mass (kg H_2O)$^{-1}$
M_{grass}	plant death rate	1.8 year^{-1}
R_{grass}	water uptake rate	100 kg H_2O m^{-2} year^{-1} (kg dry mass)$^{-2}$
for trees		
B_{tree}	biomass production rate	0.002 kg dry mass (kg H_2O)$^{-1}$
M_{tree}	plant death rate	0.18 year^{-1}
R_{tree}	water uptake rate	1.5 kg H_2O m^{-2} year^{-1} (kg dry mass)$^{-2}$

Next, we examine the dynamics of the spatially homogeneous model, the two-variable system

$$(12.22) \qquad \frac{\partial w}{\partial \tau} = a - w - wn^2,$$

$$(12.23) \qquad \frac{\partial n}{\partial \tau} = wn^2 - mn.$$

The phase portrait for this system is shown in Figure 12.5(a) (made using the Matlab code tiger_bush_pp.m). If $a > 2m$, there are three equilibria: $n = 0$, $w = a$, corresponding to no vegetation, and $n = \frac{m}{w}$, $w = \frac{1}{2}(a \pm \sqrt{a^2 - 4m^2})$. If $a < 2m$, the no vegetation state $n = 0$, $w = a$ is the only equilibrium. It is a straightforward matter to verify that the equilibrium $n = 0$, $w = a$ is always stable, and when it exists, the intermediate equilibrium $n = \frac{m}{w}$, $w = \frac{1}{2}(a + \sqrt{a^2 - 4m^2})$ is a saddle point, hence unstable. For the third equilibrium $n = \frac{m}{w}$, $w = \frac{1}{2}(a - \sqrt{a^2 - 4m^2})$, the determinant of its Jacobian is always positive, so stability is determined by the trace of its Jacobian. The trace of the Jacobian is zero along the curve $a = \frac{m^2}{\sqrt{m-1}}$, provided $m \geq 2$, plotted as a dashed curve in Figure 12.5(b). Below this dashed curve (Region II) the equilibrium is stable, and above it (Region III), the equilibrium is unstable. In the region above the dashed curve and below the solid curve (Region III) the equilibrium is an unstable spiral point.

Notice the interesting interpretation of these steady solutions. Suppose $a > 2m$ and the system resides at its stable vegetative state, but there is some gradual environmental change for which a slowly decreases (e.g., decreased rainfall) or m gradually increases (e.g., increased grazing by cattle). If a decreases enough or if m increases enough, the vegetative state will become unstable or cease to exist, and the system will collapse to the stable, nonvegetative state. However, once in the nonvegetative state, there is no environmental rescue. That is, increasing a or decreasing m will not make the system return to its original vegetative state. The collapse of the vegetative state is

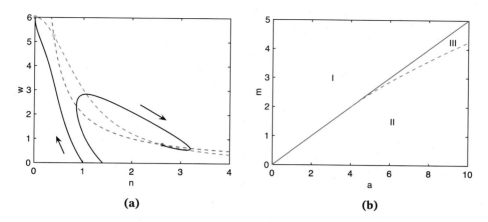

Figure 12.5. (a) Phase portrait for the system (12.22)–(12.23), with nullclines (dashed lines) and two trajectories (solid curves) shown for $a = 6$ and $m = 2$. (b) Stability diagram for the equilibria of the system (12.22)–(12.23). In Region I, the only steady state has no vegetation. In Region II, there are three steady state solutions, two of which are stable, one with no vegetation and one with vegetation. In Region III, there are three steady state solutions, but only the no vegetation state is stable.

irreversible. The only way to recover the vegetative state is to add a large perturbation (e.g., reforestation) to the system. A small perturbation of the system will not suffice to restore the vegetative state.

Now let's look for spatially inhomogeneous solutions by linearizing the system (12.20)–(12.21) about the homogeneous, vegetative equilibrium by setting

$$w = w_0 + \epsilon w_1 \exp(\lambda \tau + i\omega \xi), \qquad n = n_0 + \epsilon n_1 \exp(\lambda \tau + i\omega \xi),$$

and keeping only the terms linear in ϵ. A nontrivial solution of this system requires that λ be an eigenvalue of the Jacobian matrix,

$$(12.24) \qquad J = \begin{pmatrix} -1 - n_0^2 + iv\omega & -2m \\ n_0^2 & m - \omega^2 \end{pmatrix}.$$

There is no easy way to find λ analytically, but it is quite easy to find λ numerically using Matlab's eig command to find eigenvalues of the Jacobian matrix. Doing so for a range of ω, we are able to find and plot the largest real part of an eigenvalue as a function of ω, shown in Figure 12.6(a). This curve, called the *dispersion curve*, shows for what values of ω the solution is stable or unstable. As seen in Figure 12.6(a), with $m = 2$ and $a = 6.5$, the solution is stable for all ω, whereas, for $m = 2$ and $a = 5$, there is a range of ω for which the spatially homogeneous solution is unstable. Exploring parameter space a bit, we find that the dispersion curve is an increasing function of m; decreasing m tends to stabilize the spatially homogeneous solution by decreasing $\text{Re}(\lambda)$.

Now let's try to find the boundary in parameter space between stable and unstable solutions. It is clear from Figure 12.6(a) that the boundary between stable and unstable solutions are those parameter values for which the dispersion curve $\text{Re}(\lambda)$ has a double zero. So our challenge is to determine where in parameter space $\mathrm{Re}(\lambda)$ has a double zero when viewed as a function of ω.

Let's think for a moment about what this entails. Because we are seeking roots of a complex polynomial as a function of ω, say $P(\lambda, \omega) = 0$, we split this into real and imaginary parts, setting $\lambda = \alpha + i\beta$, and we write this as

(12.25) $$P_{\mathrm{Im}}(\alpha, \beta, \omega) = 0, \quad P_{\mathrm{Re}}(\alpha, \beta, \omega) = 0.$$

Now, realize that solutions can be viewed as functions of ω, i.e., $\alpha = \alpha(\omega)$, $\beta = \beta(\omega)$. Of course, differentiation with respect to ω yields

(12.26) $$\frac{\partial P_{\mathrm{Im}}}{\partial \alpha}\alpha' + \frac{\partial P_{\mathrm{Im}}}{\partial \beta}\beta' + \frac{\partial P_{\mathrm{Im}}}{\partial \omega} = 0, \quad \frac{\partial P_{\mathrm{Re}}}{\partial \alpha}\alpha' + \frac{\partial P_{\mathrm{Re}}}{\partial \beta}\beta' + \frac{\partial P_{\mathrm{Re}}}{\partial \omega} = 0.$$

To find a double root of $\mathrm{Re}(\lambda)$, we want $\alpha = \alpha' = 0$, ($\alpha = 0$ makes ω a root, $\alpha' = 0$ makes ω a double root) that is, we want to find β, β' and ω so that

(12.27)
$$P_{\mathrm{Im}}(0, \beta, \omega) = 0, \quad P_{\mathrm{Re}}(0, \beta, \omega) = 0, \quad \frac{\partial P_{\mathrm{Im}}}{\partial \beta}\beta' + \frac{\partial P_{\mathrm{Im}}}{\partial \omega} = 0, \quad \frac{\partial P_{\mathrm{Re}}}{\partial \beta}\beta' + \frac{\partial P_{\mathrm{Re}}}{\partial \omega} = 0.$$

But now we realize that this represents four equations in three unknowns, so the solution represents a condition on the parameters of the polynomial for which a double root exists.

For the specific problem at hand, we seek solutions of

(12.28) $$\beta(\omega^2 + b - m) + (m - \omega^2)\upsilon\omega = 0,$$

(12.29) $$2mn_0^2 - bm + b\omega^2 + \upsilon\omega\beta - \beta^2 = 0,$$

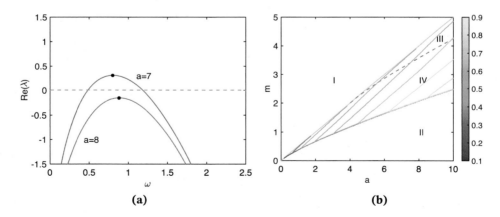

Figure 12.6. (a) Dispersion curve $\mathrm{Re}(\lambda)$ as a function of ω, shown for $m = 2$, $\upsilon = 20$, and $a = 7, 8$. (b) Stability diagram for the system (12.22)–(12.23), a modification of Figure 12.5 to include spatially inhomogeneous perturbations, with $\upsilon = 20$. In Region I, the only steady state has no vegetation. In Region II, there are three steady state solutions, two of which are stable, one with no vegetation and one with vegetation. In Region IV, the nodal steady state is unstable to spatially inhomogeneous perturbations. The colored curves in Region IV are the level surfaces of ω for the most unstable mode.

where $b = (1 + n_0^2)$, and

(12.30)
$$(b - m + \omega^2)\beta' - 3v\omega^2 + 2\beta\omega + mv = 0,$$

(12.31)
$$(v\omega - 2\beta)\beta' + 2b\omega + v\beta = 0.$$

We easily solve for and eliminate β and β' using (12.28) and (12.31) leaving us with two third order polynomials in ω^2.

At this point we would be stuck, were it not for the resultant and the wonders of Maple and Mathematica. For the two polynomials at hand, we calculate the resultant and find an expression that is far too complicated to display here (having 24 terms). However, it is an easy matter to let Matlab or Maple use it and to plot its zero level surface, and this is what is shown in Figure 12.6(b) (computed using the Matlab code tiger_bush_dispersion_critical_crv.m). In particular, in Figure 12.6(b) is shown a modification of Figure 12.5(b) to include the critical curve for instability due to spatially inhomogeneous perturbations with $v = 20$. As before, in Region I, the only steady state has no vegetation, and in Region II, there are three steady state solutions, two of which are stable, one with no vegetation and one with vegetation. The new curve divides Region II into two regions: now, in Region IV, the stable vegetative steady state is unstable to spatially inhomogeneous perturbations.

What do solutions look like in this new Region IV? We get a clue from the dispersion curve, realizing that there is a value of ω at which $\text{Re}(\lambda)$ is maximized. At this value of λ the growth is maximized and it is reasonable to expect that the solution should have features of this fastest growing mode. For example, in Figure 12.6(a), the dispersion curve for $a = 7$ is maximized at $\omega = 0.8$, with $\lambda = \alpha + i\beta = 0.3067 - 1.62i$. This means that the wavelength (the distance between the relative maxima of the solution profile) is $\Lambda = \frac{2\pi}{\omega} = 7.85$, and the wavespeed of this profile is $c = -\frac{\beta}{\omega} = 2.02$. Of course, this is only an approximation, and numerical simulation is necessary to find the full answer.

The Matlab code tiger_bush_via_MOL.m is set up to do exactly that, using, as the name suggests, the method of lines. In Figure 12.7 is shown the traveling wave solution profile, which is traveling to the right (with ξ increasing, i.e. uphill) with velocity 1.98, which is not quite the same as 2.02, but it is close. You are strongly encouraged to do Exercises 12.7 and 12.8 using the parameter values in Table 12.1 to see what this model predicts for the wavelength and speed of patterns for grass and trees.

In Figure 12.6(b), the curves filling Region IV are level surfaces of ω for the fastest growing mode. As one moves from left to right by increasing a, the value of ω on these level surfaces increases. Since the wavelength is $\Lambda = \frac{2\pi}{\omega}$, this implies that moving to the right in Region IV decreases the wavelength of the traveling waves.

This observation can be used to help understand the influence of rainfall and grazing on semiarid vegetation. As we see, the value of ω decreases with decreasing water input a. This implies that the wavelength of the regular patterns increases with decreasing water input a, as has been reported along geographic gradients in rainfall in natural striped vegetation [70] and suggested as an indicator of ecosystem degradation [67]. Increased grazing can also be considered an additional source of mortality, increasing the nondimensional parameter m through the dimensional parameter M.

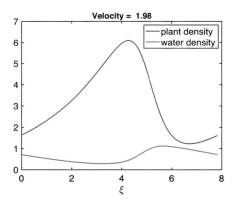

Figure 12.7. Traveling wave solution of the equations (12.22)–(12.23) with $m = 2$, $a = 7$, $v = 20$ on a domain of length $L = \Lambda = 7.85$. Profile is traveling to the right (i.e., uphill) with velocity 1.98 in dimensionless units.

As with decreasing a, increasing m causes a transition from homogeneous vegetation (Region II) to striped vegetation of increasing wavelength (Region IV), to no vegetation (Region I). This explains the (not surprising) observations that intense grazing can cause striped vegetation to be replaced by bare ground [**43**],[**72**] and that herbivore exclosures can cause mosaics to be replaced by homogeneous vegetation [**6**].

12.3. Cell Polarity

Cell polarization occurs when a cell (for example, a neutrophil = white blood cell) detects a chemical gradient and orients itself to move up the gradient, thereby enabling it to follow the secreter of the chemical signal (say, a bacterium) and ultimately capture it. An enjoyable movie of this process can be seen at many sites on the internet, including the website

https://www.youtube.com/watch?v=MgVPLNu_S-w

In a series of elegant and informative papers [**48**],[**33**],[**17**], Edelstein-Keshet and her collaborators have used mathematical models to explore the process of cell polarization. In particular, they have shown how a cell can respond to a spatial gradient of signal.

Cell polarization has at its core the activation and inactivation of a protein called a Rho-GTPase. In its inactive form, the protein is in the cytosol, bound to GDP. In its active form, the protein is membrane bound and is bound to GTP. The active form is capable of converting the inactive form to the active form through its own enzymatic activity. In its active form, it is also responsible to regulate cytoskeletal growth and cellular movement. The activation of Rho-GTPase is through a signaling cascade that is initiated by the binding of a signaling molecule such as cyclic AMP (cAMP) to a receptor on the cell surface. Following a sequence of activating steps, the net result is the activation of Rho-GTPase. These reactions are summarized (in highly compressed form) by Figure 12.8.

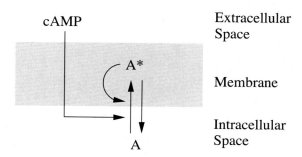

Figure 12.8. Diagram of the activation-inactivation reaction of Rho-GTPase (denoted by A) responsible for cell polarization.

A model of cell polarization needs to incorporate the following features:

- A is activated to A* by a signaling cascade;
- The active form A* is membrane bound, diffuses slowly on the membrane, and regulates actin polymerization (in other words, a pole forms anywhere the levels of A* are high);
- The inactive form A is in cytosol, and diffuses freely;
- The active form A* activates the inactive form A, recruiting it to the membrane.

To model this reaction network, we let $u = [A^*]$, $v = [A]$, and for simplicity assume that the cell is circular with its cell membrane a circle of radius R. We also assume that the A in the cytoplasm that matters lies in a circumferential band close to the membrane wall of the cell, and the diffusion of both A and A* is purely circumferential (see Figure 12.9).

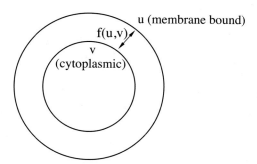

Figure 12.9. Diagram of the spatial arrangement of membrane and cytoplasm for a simplified two-dimensional circular cell.

With these assumptions, it follows that

(12.32)
$$\frac{\partial u}{\partial t} = \frac{D_u}{4\pi^2 R^2} \frac{\partial^2 u}{\partial \theta^2} + f(u, v),$$

(12.33)
$$\frac{\partial v}{\partial t} = \frac{D_v}{4\pi^2 R^2} \frac{\partial^2 v}{\partial \theta^2} - f(u, v),$$

with angular variable θ, $0 \leq \theta < 2\pi$. It is useful to scale the spatial variable, setting $\xi = 2\pi R$, so that

$$(12.34) \qquad \frac{\partial u}{\partial t} = d_u \frac{\partial^2 u}{\partial \xi^2} + f(u, v),$$

$$(12.35) \qquad \frac{\partial v}{\partial t} = d_v \frac{\partial^2 v}{\partial \xi^2} - f(u, v),$$

where ξ is a scaled perimeter variable, $0 < \xi < 1$, $d_u = \frac{D_u}{4\pi^2 R^2}$, $d_v = \frac{D_v}{4\pi^2 R^2}$. Because the membrane is a closed circle, the variables u and v are periodic with period 1. The rate of conversion of A to A^* by A^* is taken to be the Hill function of order 2, $\frac{\gamma u^2}{K^2 + u^2}$ [48], and A^* is inactivated and removed from the membrane at rate δ. Consequently,

$$(12.36) \qquad f(u, v) = (S(\xi, t) + \frac{\gamma u^2}{K^2 + u^2})v - \delta u,$$

where $S(\xi, t)$ represents the spatially dependent signaling.

Notice that because the reaction merely moves A back and forth between cytoplasm and membrane, the quantity $\int_0^1 (u + v)d\xi = V_T$ is conserved. This also follows by noting that

$$(12.37) \qquad \frac{d}{dt} \int_0^1 (u + v)d\xi = \int_0^1 (d_u \frac{\partial^2 u}{\partial \xi^2} + d_v \frac{\partial^2 v}{\partial \xi^2})d\xi = 0,$$

because of periodicity. Without loss of generality (rescale u, v, and t, see Exercise 12.9) we can take $K = 1$, $\delta = 1$, and then the two remaining parameters S and γ are dimensionless.

The first step to analyze this system is to consider the ordinary differential equation system, with no diffusion, $d_u = d_v = 0$ and S a constant. Adding the two equations together, we find that $\frac{\partial u}{\partial t} + \frac{\partial v}{\partial t} = 0$, so that

$$(12.38) \qquad u + v = V_T.$$

Substituting v into the equation for u gives the single differential equation for u,

$$(12.39) \qquad \frac{du}{dt} = (S + \frac{\gamma u^2}{1 + u^2})(V_T - u) - u = f(u, V_T - u).$$

It is relatively straightforward to understand the behavior of the solution of this equation. For example, for given values of S, V_T, and γ, the function $f(u, V_T - u)$ can have a unique positive zero, as do the lower and upper curves in Figure 12.10(a), or it can have three positive zeros, as does the middle curve in Figure 12.10(a).

The different behaviors can be organized according to their solution structure. To find the roots u as a function of S, solve $f(u, V_T - u) = 0$ for S as a function of u,

$$(12.40) \qquad S = \frac{u}{V_T - u} - \frac{\gamma u^2}{1 + u^2},$$

and then exploiting the wonders of Matlab (code cell_polarization_ode_system.m), plot u vs. S. Three such curves are shown in Figure 12.10(b) for three different values of V_T, each representing a different region in the V_T-γ parameter space, shown in Figure 12.11. In Region I, solutions are as the lower curve in Figure 12.10(b) $(V_T = 1.1)$.

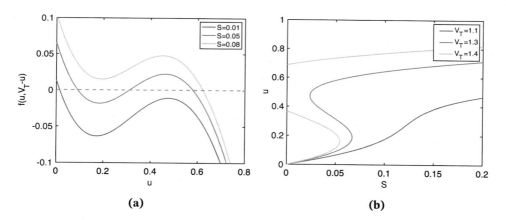

Figure 12.10. (a) Plot of the right hand side of (12.39), $f(u, V_T - u)$, for several values of S with $V_T = 1.3$, $\gamma = 3$. (b) Steady state solutions of equation (12.39) plotted as a function of S, for $\gamma = 3$, and $V_T = 1.1, 1.3, 1.4$.

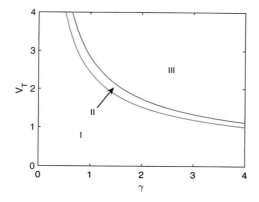

Figure 12.11. Regions in V_T-γ parameter space for which there is different qualitative behavior for the right hand side of (12.39).

In Region II, solutions are as for the middle curve of Figure 12.10(b) ($V_T = 1.3$), and in Region III, the solutions are as in Figure 12.10(b) ($V_T = 1.4$).

The boundary between Region II and Region III is where the function $S(u)$ in (12.40) has double zeros, i.e., $S(u)$ and $S'(u)$ have simultaneous zeros. This occurs on the curve

(12.41) $$V_T = \frac{2}{\gamma}\sqrt{\gamma - 1}.$$

The boundary between Regions I and II is where the functions $S'(u)$ and $S''(u)$ have simultaneous zeros. This occurs where

(12.42) $$27V_T^4\gamma^2 - 2(4\gamma^3 - 3\gamma^2 + 48\gamma + 32)V_T^2 + 27\gamma^2 = 0,$$

a quadratic equation for V_T^2, which is readily solved and plotted.

What we see from this is that for V_T and γ large enough, the differential equation system has bistable behavior, which means that there is the possibility of switching between low and high levels of u in response to the signal S. However, this switching is for a spatially uniform stimulus and gives a spatially uniform response. The important question to address next is how diffusion of u and v lead to a spatially localized response to a spatially localized stimulus.

We begin to answer that question by numerically simulating the partial differential equation system. This is easily accomplished using Crank–Nicolson steps for the diffusion operators and forward Euler steps for the reaction terms. The Matlab code for this is titled cell_polarization_f.m. For this simulation, $\gamma = 0.5$, $V_T = 4.2$, $d_u = 0.001$, and $d_v = 1$. The simulation starts with $v = V_T$ and $u = 0$ and with a stimulus

$$(12.43) \qquad S(\xi, t) = \alpha(t)\Big(\frac{1 - \cos(2\pi\xi)}{2}\Big)^{10},$$

where $\alpha(t)$ is a slowly varying function of time, starting at $\alpha = 0$, increasing to $\alpha = 0.1$ and then decreasing back to zero.

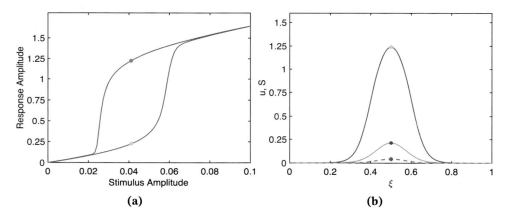

(a)   **(b)**

Figure 12.12. (a) Stimulus-response curve. (b) Amplitude of stimulus and response as functions of time. Dots denote the amplitudes of the solutions shown in Figure 12.13.

A movie of what happens can be seen by running the Matlab code cell_polarization_f.m. What happens is shown in Figure 12.12(a) with a plot of the amplitude of the response of the system to a stimulus of given amplitude following a very slow increase and then decrease of the stimulus amplitude $\alpha(t)$. This response is obviously hysteretic, with a large amplitude response when the stimulus is sufficiently large and a small response when the stimulus is small, but a bistable response for intermediate amplitudes. Figure 12.13 shows the two profiles of u for a single value of stimulus ($\alpha = 0.04$) in the bistable range.

Clearly this bistable, hysteretic response is a good thing for the organism. This is because if it detects a signal which it decides to follow, then even if the signal decreases a bit it makes sense to continue to follow the signal and not squander the investment of resources that was made after the initial decision.

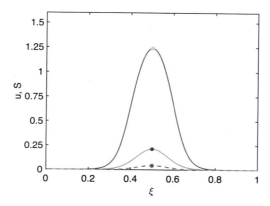

Figure 12.13. Steady state solution profiles for fixed stimulus profile with amplitude 0.04 (shown dashed).

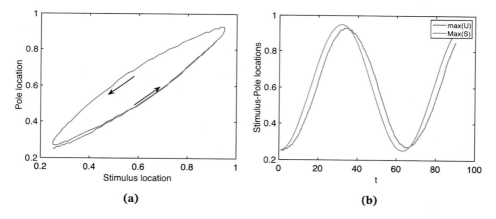

(a)   (b)

Figure 12.14. (a) Location of the polarization response vs. stimulus location for a moving stimulus. (b) Spatial location of the stimulus and response as a function of time.

The results of a second simulation (using the Matlab code polarization_moving_target.m) shown in Figure 12.14 shows the location of the maximum of the response plotted against the location of a moving stimulus. (Run this code for yourself and see a movie of the response to a moving stimulus.) Here we see another useful feature of this system in that it can track a moving target.

These simulations give insight into how polarization works, although running more simulations for different parameter values is a valuable exercise (see Exercise 12.11). What we learn is that polarization is by an activation-recruitment mechanism. That is, the initial signal converts A to A*, thereby locally depleting A and enhancing A*. The local depletion of A means that A will diffuse down its gradient to fill in where it was previously depleted, thus recruiting more A to the site of the signal. Simultaneously, A* should diffuse away from the site of the signal, but because its diffusion coefficient is much smaller than that of A, a localized aggregation builds up and is

maintained at the site of the signal. Notice that there is no violation of physical principles here. The molecules move down their concentration gradients, as they must.
However, energy must be expended to convert A to A*, in order to form the aggregate.

This is exactly how recruitment of proteins to certain sites *must* work. Unless there
is some form of energy being expended to transport the molecules, proteins can only
move down their concentration gradient. Thus, to recruit a large number of proteins
to a particular site, it must be that they are converted to a different form that does not
diffuse away, depleting the diffusing form, so that they can continue to move down
their gradient toward the aggregation site.

Exercises

12.1. Consider the system of equations

$$\frac{\partial u}{\partial t} = \alpha f(u, v) + D_u \nabla^2 u,$$

$$\frac{\partial v}{\partial t} = \alpha g(u, v) + D_v \nabla^2 v,$$

with no-flux boundary conditions on the one dimensional interval $0 < x < \pi$,
$D_u = 1$, $D_v = 10$. Suppose the Jacobian matrix of the linearization of the
system about its spatially uniform steady state solution is given by

$$J = \alpha \begin{pmatrix} 2 & -4 \\ 4 & -6 \end{pmatrix}.$$

(a) Derive conditions for instability of the nth mode;
(b) For values of α, $0 < \alpha \leq 10$, find all the bifurcation values of α, i.e., the
values where one of the modes changes its stability.

12.2. Make a plot of the curve $k = \frac{\sqrt{\rho}}{2} - \rho$, and give an interpretation of why it is
necessary that $k < \frac{\sqrt{\rho}}{2} - \rho$ and $0 < \rho < \frac{1}{4}$ in order that the Gray–Scott model
have nontrivial homogeneous steady solutions. What happens to the the phase
portrait in Figure 12.2 if either of these conditions is not satisfied?

12.3. For the Gray–Scott model with parameter values $\rho = \frac{1}{16}$, $k = 0.02$, $D_u = 1.0$,
$D_v = 0.025$, and $L = 30$, how many different unstable modes are there? How
many different stable patterns can you find?

12.4. (a) Verify that the system (12.22)–(12.23) has one stable equilibrium if $a < 2m$ and three equilibria if $a > 2m$.
(b) Show that the equilibrium with $n = 0$ is a stable node and the equilibrium
with intermediate value of n is a saddle point. Under what conditions on
m and a is the equilibrium with largest value of n stable?
(c) Show that the region $n \geq 0$, $w \geq 0$, $w + n < \alpha$, with $\alpha > a$ is an invariant
region provided $m > 1$.

12.5. Verify the statements made in the text concerning the system of equations
(12.22)–(12.23):

(a) The steady state solution $n = 0$, $w = a$ exists for all parameter values and is linearly stable.

(b) If $a > 2m$, there are two additional equilibria, one of which is a saddle point, and one of which is a node.

(c) The node is an unstable spiral point if $a < \dfrac{m^2}{\sqrt{m-1}}$ and $m > 2$, and is stable otherwise.

(d) If the node is unstable, the only stable steady state is the no vegetation state. All trajectories starting from points other than the two unstable equilibria converge to the no vegetation state.

12.6. How does the stability diagram Figure 12.6 change if v is increased or decreased?

12.7. (a) Use the parameters in Table 12.1 to determine the wavelength, speed, and spatial profile of periodic stripes for grass.

    (b) Suppose climate conditions change so that the evaporation rate E increases. At what value of E will there be no vegetation?

12.8. Use the parameters in Table 12.1 to determine the wavelength, speed, and spatial profile of periodic stripes for trees.

12.9. Find the rescaling of u, v, and t that renders $K = \delta = 1$ in equation (12.36).

12.10. Verify that the boundary between Regions II and III in Figure 12.11 is given by (12.41) and that the boundary between Regions I and II in Figure 12.11 is given by (12.42).

12.11. What happens in the polarization model to the amplitude response curve Figure 12.12(b) if:

    (a) the diffusion coefficient d_u is increased?

    (b) the diffusion coefficients d_u and d_v are equal?

    (c) V_T is reduced?

Chapter 13

Dispersal-Renewal Theory

13.1. Invasive Species

We can use what we have learned so far to study an interesting and important problem, namely the dynamics of invasive species. It is estimated that the cost of damage and control of invasive species in the United States alone amounts to well over $100 billion annually.

One invasive species that currently has my attention is the balsam woolly adelgid (BWA). BWA are small wingless insects (about 1mm long) that infest and kill firs, most noticeably (to me) the subalpine fir. Because there is no natural predator for BWA in the US, and the trees have no natural defense against them, the mortality rate is over 90%, leading to large areas of dead and dying trees. BWA have two generations of egg laying per year (although in some regions of the US there are three or even four generations), with 100–250 eggs laid per hatch. The eggs hatch as crawlers, the only stage that is able to disperse. They are dispersed primarily by the wind, and when they land on a fir tree, they seek a feeding site at which they will mature and begin the next cycle.

While invasive species come in many forms and can mount an invasion by many different means, in this chapter we consider the spread of a plant with air-borne seeds, or equivalently, BWA. Plants typically have an annual cycle in which they grow from seeds, flower and release their seeds which are then spread, carried by the wind, by insects or birds and deposited on the ground where they germinate the following spring, repeating the cycle. Examples of invasive species that have my attention (because they are prevalent near my home) include Scottish thistle, myrtle spurge, and stinging nettle.

A simple model for seed dispersal is to assume that when they are airborne, they spread by a diffusion process (which could be mediated by birds or insects). Thus, a basic model for the density of airborne seeds $u(x,t)$ and for grounded seeds $q(x,t)$ is,

Figure 13.1. Depiction of three of my least favorite invasive species, Scottish thistle, myrtle spurge and stinging nettle. Image credit: Johanna Bossart.

in one spatial dimension,

$$(13.1) \qquad \frac{\partial u}{\partial t} = D\frac{\partial^2 u}{\partial x^2} - ku, \qquad \frac{\partial q}{\partial t} = ku,$$

where k represents the drop-out rate. Of course, this does not take into account any possible effects of advection which might occur if there were a steady wind.

Suppose a seed pod containing a large number of seeds is released at position $x = 0$ at time $t = 0$. What will be the eventual distribution of seeds on the ground?

This problem is not particularly difficult to solve. We already know from Chapter 6 that the distribution of airborne seeds satisfies

$$(13.2) \qquad u(x,t) = \frac{u_0}{\sqrt{4\pi Dt}} \exp(-\frac{x^2}{4Dt} - kt),$$

so the distribution of seeds on the ground is

$$(13.3) \qquad q(x,\infty) = k \int_0^\infty u(x,\tau)d\tau.$$

Now, we use the fact that

$$(13.4) \qquad \int_0^\infty \frac{1}{\sqrt{t}} \exp(-\frac{a^2}{t} - t)dt = \sqrt{\pi} \exp(-2|a|)$$

to calculate that

$$(13.5) \qquad q(x,\infty) = \frac{1}{2}\sqrt{\frac{k}{D}} \exp(-\sqrt{\frac{k}{D}}|x|).$$

A plot of the function $q(x,\infty)$ is shown in Figure 13.4(a) (made using the Matlab code invasion_profile.m). An important feature of this function is that

$$(13.6) \qquad \int_{-\infty}^{\infty} q(x,\infty)dx = 1.$$

This calculation enables us to build a model of population spread as follows: We assume that $u_n(x)$ represents the population density of seeds on the ground in the nth generation. We also assume that there is some function $f(u)$ which represents the

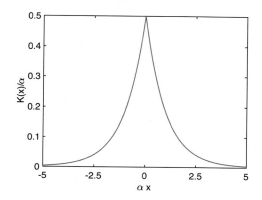

Figure 13.2. Plot of the dispersal kernel $\frac{K(x)}{\alpha} = \frac{q(x,\infty)}{\alpha}$.

seed productivity of a seed. By seed productivity we mean the density of seeds that are produced after germination and maturation from a density of seeds on the ground. Then, the population density of seeds on the ground in the $(n + 1)$-st generation will be

$$(13.7) \qquad u_{n+1} = \int_{-\infty}^{\infty} K(x - y) f(u_n(y)) dy,$$

where the function $K(x) \equiv q(x, \infty)$ is called the *dispersal kernel*. This equation represents the fact that the next generation of seeds are produced by the "parent" seeds that germinate, produce more seeds, and then are dispersed via the dispersal kernel K.

As is our custom, we begin with a numerical simulation of this process. The direct way to do this is to discretize the equation (13.7) by setting $x_j = jh$, $y_j = jh$, so that (13.7) is replaced by

$$(13.8) \qquad u_{n+1}(x_j) = \sum_k K_{jk} f(u_n(y_k)) h,$$

where $K_{jk} = K(x_j - y_k)$. Then, simulation is a straightforward matrix multiplication, as in the Matlab code dispersal_renewal.m.

The result of a simulation with seed production function and $f(u) = \frac{u}{A+u}$ with $A = 0.5$ is shown in Figure 13.3(a) with the $u(x, t) = 0.5$ level surface shown in Figure 13.3(b).

This simulation shows that, starting from a small initial profile, an invasion occurs, developing into a wave that progresses with constant speed. One can show (see Exercise 13.2) that an invasion occurs only if $A < 1$.

An interesting question to ask is if a speed of spread can be determined analytically. This is a difficult question in general, but it can be answered readily for a simple, but informative, example. Suppose we take the production function $f(u)$ to be the piecewise constant function

$$(13.9) \qquad f(u) = \begin{cases} 0 & u < u_0 \\ A_0 & u \geq u_0. \end{cases}$$

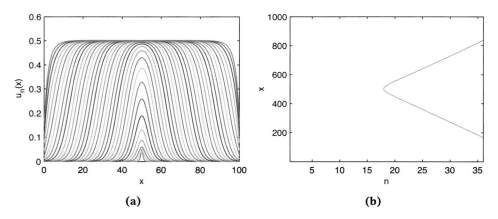

(a)   (b)

Figure 13.3. (a) Solution profiles for seed production function $f(u) = \frac{u}{0.5+u}$. (b) Contour plot of $u_n(x) = 0.25$ level surface, both with $\alpha = \sqrt{\frac{k}{D}} = 1$.

This function is a simplification of a function such as $f(u) = A_0 \frac{u^2}{u_0^2 + u^2}$, which has zero slope at the origin, reaches half its maximum at $u = u_0$, and levels out to the constant A_0 as $u \to \infty$. It is relatively easy to calculate the solution of (13.7). In particular, suppose $u_n(x)$ is a function with

$$(13.10) \qquad u_n(x) \begin{cases} > u_0 & x \le 0 \\ < u_0 & x > 0. \end{cases}$$

Then, for $x < 0$,

$$u_{n+1}(x) = \frac{A_0\alpha}{2} \left(\int_{-\infty}^{x} \exp(-\alpha(x - \xi)) d\xi + \int_{x}^{0} \exp(-\alpha(\xi - x)) d\xi \right)$$

$$(13.11) \qquad\qquad = A_0 \left(1 - \frac{1}{2} \exp(\alpha x) \right),$$

where $\alpha = \sqrt{\frac{k}{D}}$. On the other hand, for $x > 0$,

$$u_{n+1}(x) = \frac{A_0\alpha}{2} \int_{-\infty}^{0} \exp(-\alpha(x - \xi)) d\xi$$

$$(13.12) \qquad\qquad = \frac{A_0}{2} \exp(-\alpha x).$$

A plot of the function $\frac{u_{n+1}(x)}{A_0}$ as a function of αx is shown in Figure 13.4. Notice that $u_{n+1}(x)$ is a monotone decreasing function of x, so that, if $A_0 > 2u_0$, there is exactly one point $x > 0$ for which $u_{n+1}(x) = u_0$, and this point is

$$(13.13) \qquad\qquad x = \sqrt{\frac{D}{k}} \ln\left(\frac{A_0}{2u_0} \right).$$

The position x represents the distance that the population of seeds has shifted during one germination dispersal cycle, so it is the speed per generation for this plant. What we learn from this is informative, if only from a simple model. Here, u_0 represents the threshold density of seeds required to have growth, and A_0 represents the carrying

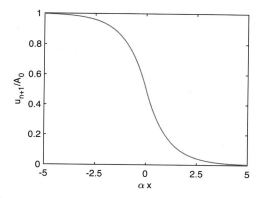

Figure 13.4. Invasion profile $\frac{u_{n+1}}{A_0}$ plotted as a function of αx, $\alpha = \sqrt{\frac{k}{D}}$.

capacity of plant density. We see that in order to have successful spread, it must be that $A_0 > 2u_0$, otherwise the seed density profile is receding. Similar features are found numerically for the function $f(u) = \frac{u^2}{A^2+u^2}$, in Exercise 13.4.

What is presented here is a relatively simple example of an integrodifference equation used to model the spread of a plant species. A very nice summary of these kinds of models and mathematical analysis can be found in the report [**12**], which you are encouraged to investigate.

Exercises

13.1. What are some examples of invasive plant species in your vicinity?

13.2. Suppose the seed productivity function is $f(u) = \frac{u}{A+u}$.
   (a) Suppose that there are two initial seed density profiles $u_0(x)$ and $v_0(x)$, with $u_0(x) > v_0(x)$. Show that $u_n(x) > v_n(x)$ for all subsequent generations.
   (b) Suppose that $u_0(x)$ is a positive constant, independent of x. Show that $u_n(x) \to 1 - A$ if $A < 1$ and $u_n(x) \to 0$ if $A \geq 1$.
   (c) Use the previous two parts to show that if $A > 1$, the plant cannot be invasive.

13.3. How does the speed of invasion depend on A for the seed productivity function $f(u) = \frac{u}{A+u}$?

13.4. Suppose the seed productivity function is $f(u) = \frac{u^2}{A^2+u^2}$. Use numerical simulation to demonstrate the following.
   (a) Show that with $A = 0.4$ there is a threshold initial population size for a successful invasion.
   (b) Estimate the speed of invasion with $A = 0.4$.

13.5. Suppose the seed productivity function is $f(u) = \frac{u^2}{A^2+u^2}$.

(a) Suppose that there are two initial seed density profiles $u_0(x)$ and $v_0(x)$, with $u_0(x) > v_0(x)$. Show that $u_n(x) > v_n(x)$ for all subsequent generations.

(b) Suppose that $u_0(x)$ is a positive constant, independent of x. Show that $u_n \to 0$ if $A > \frac{1}{2}$ and $u_n \to 0$ if $A \leq \frac{1}{2}$ and $u_0 < \frac{1}{2} - \frac{1}{2}\sqrt{1 - 4A^2}$.

(c) Use the previous two parts to show that if $A > \frac{1}{2}$, the plant cannot be invasive.

13.6. Suppose there is a steady wind with velocity V that transports airborne seeds. Calculate the dispersal kernel and the invasion speed for the piecewise constant seed production function (13.9).

Chapter 14

Collective Behavior

How do animals do things in groups? We now turn our attention to this fascinating question and in this chapter describe three examples of collective behavior.

14.1. Quorum Sensing

Quorum sensing is the ability of a bacterium to regulate its behavior through its gene expression in response to the population density of the colony in which it resides.

First discovered in the luminous bacterium *Vibrio fischeri*, quorum sensing is the process by which bacteria synchronize their gene expression based on the local cell population density [25]. Quorum sensing systems are found in several different bacterial species and are thought to be common to many, if not all, bacteria. Quorum sensing systems regulate genes associated with biofilm production, toxins, cell motility, various secretion factors, bioluminescence, and those processes essential for symbiosis.

Quorum sensing is important for the survival of many bacteria. For *Vibrio fischeri*, there is a symbiotic relationship between it and the Hawaiian bobtail squid. The bacteria grow in colonies in the light organs of the squid and become luminescent via quorum sensing when the colony size is sufficiently large. Coincidentally, this happens at night and so this provides a light source which is useful for the survival of the squid. In the morning, when the light source is no longer needed, the squid flush most of the bacteria, thereby initiating a new phase of colony growth, which, when it grows to sufficient size (the next night), once again becomes luminescent.

Pseudomonas aeruginosa is a bacterium that occurs naturally and harmlessly in many places, for example, a forest floor. In hospitals, however, it is one of the most serious causes of infection and is very difficult to treat, partly because of its quorum sensing capability. In small quantities, the bacteria are not toxic, but if a colony becomes established, quorum sensing turns on the production of a host of chemicals, including an exopolysaccharide which forms the biofilm matrix in which the colony resides and which is protected from antibiotics rendering it nearly impossible to treat.

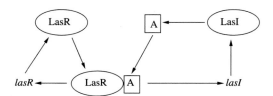

Figure 14.1. Gene regulatory network for autoinducer.

Pseudomonas aeruginosa can be present in biofilms on breathing machines, or devices such as catheters, and in patients with wounds from surgery, and often are present in the mucus lining the lungs of cystic fibrosis patients.

The fundamental ingredient of a quorum sensing system is a chemical called autoinducer, here denoted by A. A more technical description of autoinducer is that it is a homoserine lactone (HSL). A simplified diagram of the gene regulatory network for autoinducer is shown in Figure 14.1. As depicted in this diagram, autoinducer is produced by an enzyme LasI which is the protein product of the *lasI* gene. The *lasI* gene is turned on by a transcription factor, which is a dimer formed by the combination of autoinducer A and a protein LasR. LasR is the protein product of the gene *lasR*, which is also turned on by the A-LasR dimer transcription factor. The A-LasR dimer is also a transcription factor for many other downstream gene products responsible for things such as biofilm production and various toxicity factors. It is apparent from this diagram why A is called an autoinducer, since through positive feedback, A is responsible for its own induction/production.

Let's start with a simple model to see how a single cell can detect features of its environment. Suppose that a cell produces autoinducer, but autoinducer can escape from the cell into the extracellular space, where it diffuses and degrades. A mathematical model to keep track of the amount of autoinducer must take into account its production and destruction. Since autoinducer diffuses freely across the cell membrane, we have that inside the cell

(14.1)
$$\frac{\partial u}{\partial t} = D_c \nabla^2 v + f(u),$$

subject to a Robin boundary condition

(14.2)
$$-D_c \nabla u \cdot \mathbf{n} = \delta(u - v),$$

evaluated on the cell boundary $\partial \Omega$, where u is the intracellular concentration of autoinducer, v is the extracellular concentration of autoinducer, and δ is the membrane porosity, with units of velocity. The production of autoinducer is taken to be at the rate

(14.3)
$$f(u) = s_0 + \gamma \frac{u^2}{K^2 + u^2},$$

to reflect the fact that the transcription factor is a dimer, and the source s_0 allows for a small basal production of the gene products. We assume that the cell is small enough so that autoinducer has a uniform concentration throughout the cell, satisfying the identity $u = \frac{1}{V} \int_\Omega u \, dV$. Then, integrating (14.1) over the volume of the cell and applying the divergence theorem (1.17), we find

$$(14.4) \qquad \frac{du}{dt} = f(u) + \sigma\delta(v(\partial\Omega) - u).$$

Here σ is the surface to volume ratio of the cell, with units of (length)$^{-1}$.

Outside the cell, autoinducer diffuses and degrades and so satisfies a diffusion-reaction equation

$$(14.5) \qquad \frac{\partial v}{\partial t} = D_e \nabla^2 v - \alpha v,$$

with the Robin boundary condition at the boundary of the cell

$$(14.6) \qquad -D_e \nabla v \cdot \mathbf{n} = \delta(u - v),$$

where $\mathbf{n}$ is the outward unit normal vector to the cell, hence inward to the extracellular space. Clearly the flux out of the cell must match the flux into the extracellular space.

Let's look for steady solutions of this system for a one dimensional half-space. Suppose the cell is located at position $x = 0$ secreting autoinducer into the extracellular space $0 < x < \infty$. At steady state,

$$(14.7) \qquad v(x) = v_0 \exp\left(-\sqrt{\frac{\alpha}{D_e}}x\right),$$

and the Robin boundary condition at $x = 0$ implies that $-D_e \frac{dv}{dx} = \delta(u - v)$ at $x = 0$, or

$$(14.8) \qquad v_0 = \frac{u}{\sqrt{\mu} + 1},$$

where $\mu = \frac{\alpha D_e}{\delta^2}$, which when substituted into (14.4) yields the requirement

$$(14.9) \qquad f(u) - \sigma\delta\frac{\sqrt{\mu}}{\sqrt{\mu} + 1}u = 0.$$

The most convenient way to analyze the solutions of this equation is graphically. That is, rewrite equation (14.9) as

$$(14.10) \qquad \frac{f(u)}{u} = \sigma\delta\frac{\sqrt{\mu}}{\sqrt{\mu} + 1} = \frac{1}{p},$$

and realize that while we cannot solve for u as a function of p, we can easily determine p as a function of u and then plot u as a function of p by reversing the axes. According to Exercise 14.1, the function $\frac{u}{f(u)}$ is a monotone increasing function of u (for $u > 0$) if $\gamma < 8s_0$ and is triphasic if $\gamma > 8s_0$. It follows that if $\gamma > 8s_0$, the relationship between u and p exhibits hysteresis. (See Figure 14.2, made using Matlab code quorum_plots.m) What this means is that the cellular level of autoinducer responds to the values of p in a hysteretic way, with low levels of autoinducer if p is small but high levels of autoinducer if p is large. As we will see in what follows, the value of p can be influenced by a number of environmental factors (see, for example, Exercise 14.3), and this is what enables quorum sensing.

Now let's suppose that there are many cells spread throughout the domain. Because there are so many cells, we are not able to resolve the distribution of extracellular

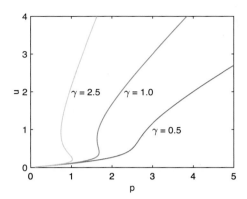

Figure 14.2. Plots of u vs. p for $p = \frac{u}{f(u)}$ with $f(u)$ given by (14.3) for $s_0 = 0.1, K = 1$ and $\gamma = 0.5, 1.0, 2.5$.

autoinducer on a fine, cellular level, scale, but are willing to track the concentration of autoinducer on a larger macroscopic scale. So, we suppose that the domain comprises intracellular space, (the cells) and extracellular space, with autoinducer concentrations u and v, respectively, Then, the equations for u and v are

$$\text{(14.11)} \qquad\qquad \frac{\partial u}{\partial t} = f(u) + \sigma\delta(v - u)$$

and

$$\text{(14.12)} \qquad\qquad \frac{\partial v}{\partial t} - D_e\nabla^2 v + \alpha v = \frac{\rho}{1 - \rho}\sigma\delta(u - v),$$

where ρ is the cellular volume fraction (i.e., the fraction of the volume occupied by cells) and $1 - \rho$ is the volume fraction of the extracellular space.

The factor $\frac{\rho}{1-\rho}$ in (14.12) can be understood as follows. The rate at which autoinducer concentration is lost from intracellular space is $\sigma\delta(u - v)$, so the rate at which the *number* of molecules of autoinducer per cell are lost from intracellular space is $\rho\sigma\delta(u - v)$. This must be the same as the number of molecules of autoinducer that are gained by the extracellular space. But since concentration is number of molecules per unit volume, the rate at which extracellular concentration of autoinducer is increased is $\frac{\rho}{1-\rho}\sigma\delta(v - u)$. A second observation is that (14.11) is written as a partial differential equation because, even though there is no explicit spatial dependence in the equation, the level of intracellular autoinducer need not be the same everywhere, and so is a function of both space and time.

To begin our analysis of this problem, we first examine the spatially homogeneous situation, for which extracellular diffusion of v can be ignored. This can be accomplished with a phase plane analysis. For the phase plane analysis, the two nullclines are

$$\text{(14.13)} \qquad\qquad \frac{du}{dt} = 0 : \quad v = u - \frac{1}{\sigma\delta}f(u),$$

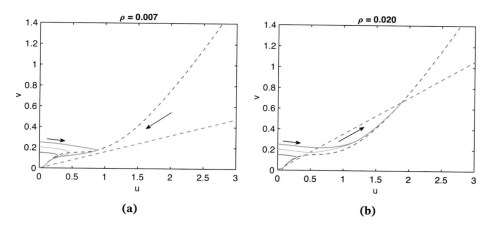

Figure 14.3. Phase plane portraits for the ordinary differential equation system (14.11), (14.12) with $D_e = 0$, shown for (a) $\rho = 0.007$ and (b) $\rho = 0.02$. For these plots, parameter values are $s_0 = 0.05, K = 1, \gamma = 1.5, \sigma\delta = 1.0, \alpha = 0.0375$. Nullclines are shown as dashed curves and trajectories are shown as solid curves.

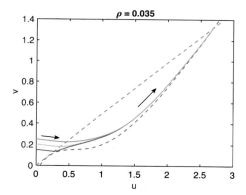

Figure 14.4. Phase plane portraits for the ordinary differential equation system (14.11), (14.12) with $D_e = 0$, shown for $\rho = 0.035$. For this plot, parameter values are $s_0 = 0.05, K = 1, \gamma = 1.5, \sigma\delta = 1.0, \alpha = 0.0375$. Nullclines are shown as dashed curves and trajectories are shown as solid curves.

and

$$(14.14) \qquad \frac{dv}{dt} = 0: \quad u = (\frac{1-\rho}{\rho}\frac{\alpha}{\sigma\delta} + 1)v.$$

The first of these is a cubic-shaped curve, and the second of these is a straight line, with slope that is dependent on the volume fraction ρ. The steady state solution can be expressed as

$$(14.15) \qquad \frac{\rho}{\alpha(1-\rho)} = \frac{u}{f(u)} - \frac{1}{\sigma\delta}.$$

This expression is convenient because, although we cannot solve for u as a function of ρ, this gives us ρ as a function of u. As already discussed above, the function $\frac{u}{f(u)}$ has

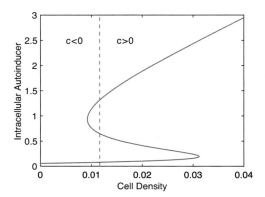

Figure 14.5. Steady state solution curve for the autoinducer quorum sensing model, showing hysteretic behavior as a function of cell density ρ. The dashed line shows the location at which the traveling wave speed sign indicator function (14.18) is zero, implying that to the right of this line there are traveling wave solutions that provide a transition from low to high autoinducer levels. For this plot, parameter values are $s_0 = 0.05, K = 1, \gamma = 1.5, \sigma\delta = 1.0, \alpha = 0.0375$.

an inflection point with zero slope if $\gamma = 8s_0$, it is a monotone increasing function of u if $\gamma < 8s_0$, and it is triphasic if $\gamma > 8s_0$. This means that if $\gamma < 8s_0$, then there is a monotone relationship between ρ and u, whereas, if $\gamma > 8s_0$, ρ is a triphasic function of u. Of course, this implies that u is a hysteretic "function" of ρ, as depicted in Figure 14.5. This gives us an understanding of how quorum sensing works. If the cell density is low, then the level of autoinducer is low and remains low. However, if the cell density becomes high, there is a switch from the low autoinducer state to the high autoinducer state.

The Matlab code to make these plots is titled quorum_pp.m.

Noticing that this system is bistable for a range of cell density ρ, we might be curious to see if there are traveling wave solutions to this system of equations. The structure of this system is similar to that of the SIR model with one diffusing species and one not diffusing, so the traveling wave analysis for this system is more difficult than for the bistable equation. However, it is easy to simulate these solutions and to observe that indeed, there are traveling wave solutions for ρ in an appropriate range. Results of such a simulation are shown in Figure 14.6 (computed using the Matlab code CN_diffusion_quorum_sensing.m).

To determine conditions under which there are traveling waves, we look for a traveling wave solution of the form $u = U(x + ct), v = V(x + ct)$, and find that the system of equations (14.11), (14.12) become the system of ordinary differential equations

$$(14.16) \qquad cU' = f(U) + \sigma\delta(V - U),$$

$$(14.17) \qquad cV' = D_e V'' - \alpha V + \frac{\rho}{1 - \rho}\sigma\delta(U - V).$$

Suppose we look for solutions that are traveling from right to left and are monotone increasing as a function of the traveling coordinate ξ (i.e., the left moving transitions

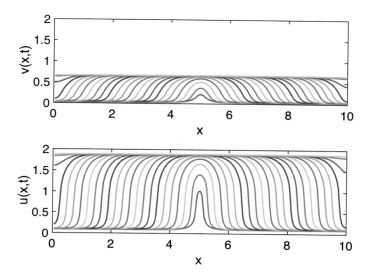

Figure 14.6. Spreading quorum sensing waves depicting a switch from low to high autoinducer concentration. Parameter values for this simulation are $s_0 = 0.05$, $K = 1$, $\gamma = 1.5$, $\sigma\delta = 1.0$, $\alpha = 0.0375$, $\rho = 0.02$, $D_e = 0.001$. $u(x,t)$ denotes intracellular autoinducer; $v(x,t)$ denotes extracellular autoinducer.

seen in Figure 14.6). This means that in the limit $\xi \to -\infty$ both $U(\xi)$ and $V(\xi)$ approach the low steady state solution, denoted U_-, V_-, while in the limit $\xi \to \infty$, they approach the high steady state solution, denoted U^+, V^+. Multiply the first of these equations by $\frac{\rho}{1-\rho}U'$ and the second by V', add, and integrate to find

$$c\int_{-\infty}^{\infty}\left(\frac{\rho}{1-\rho}(U')^2 + (V')^2\right)d\xi \; = \; \frac{\rho}{1-\rho}\int_{-\infty}^{\infty}\left(f(U)U' + \sigma\delta(V-U)(U'-V')\right)d\xi$$

$$+ \int_{-\infty}^{\infty}\left(D_e V''V' - \alpha VV'\right)\delta\xi$$

$$= \frac{\rho}{1-\rho}\int_{U_-}^{U_+} f(U)dU$$

(14.18)
$$-\frac{1}{2}\frac{\rho}{1-\rho}\sigma\delta(V-U)^2\Big|_{-\infty}^{\infty} - \frac{\alpha}{2}V^2\Big|_{-\infty}^{\infty}.$$

Clearly, the sign of the expression (14.18) is the same as the sign of the speed c, so that the traveling wave transition from low to high autoinducer can take place whenever this expression is positive.

There is no obvious, simple, interpretation of this formula, however it is relatively easy to evaluate this function numerically and to locate the value of ρ for which it is zero. For the parameter values used here, this is at $\rho = 0.0118$, and this value is shown as a dashed line in Figure 14.5. This implies that for larger values of ρ there is a traveling wave transition from low to high autoinducer levels. In other words, if the bacterial density is larger than this value, then the population can switch from low to high autoinducer levels via a traveling wave, enabling the population to thereby coordinate its behavior.

Now let's look at a (slightly) more realistic situation, in which a colony of cells has finite size (rather than infinite as above) in a larger cell-free environment. To be specific, inside the colony, autoinducer concentration is governed by (14.11)–(14.12) and outside the colony, autoinducer diffuses and degrades as described by (14.5). We would like to determine the steady state solution as a function of the colony size.

Let's look at a one-dimensional spatial domain. We assume that cells with uniform density ρ occupy the spatial region $0 < x < L$. There is a barrier at $x = 0$ preventing both the bacteria and the autoinducer from migrating to $x < 0$, consequently, there is no flux of autoinducer at $x = 0$, i.e., $v_x(0) = 0$. For $x > L$, outside the colony, the steady solution is

$$(14.19) \qquad v(x) = v_0 \exp\left(-\sqrt{\frac{\alpha}{D_e}}(x - L)\right).$$

Because the solution for $v(x)$ must be continuously differentiable at $x = L$, it must be that $D_e v_x(L) = -\sqrt{\alpha D_e} v(L)$ which gives a Robin condition for $v(x)$ at $x = L$. So, the steady state solution must satisfy the equations

$$(14.20) \qquad D_e v_{xx} - \alpha v + \frac{\rho}{1-\rho}\sigma\delta(u - v) = 0, \quad f(u) + \sigma\delta(v - u) = 0,$$

subject to the boundary conditions $v_x(0) = 0$, $D_e v_x(L) = -\sqrt{\alpha D_e} v(L)$. Introducing the variable $w = D_e v_x$, we write this as the first order system

$$(14.21) \qquad v_x \;=\; \frac{w}{D_e},$$

$$(14.22) \qquad w_x \;=\; \alpha v - \frac{\rho}{1-\rho}\sigma\delta(u - v), \quad f(u) + \sigma\delta(v - u) = 0.$$

These equations may look a little unusual, but in fact, the technique to find the solutions is exactly the same as used in Section 6.2.1.1 for Fisher's equation with Robin boundary conditions. As a review of what those solutions look like, look at Figure 6.10. Here, since we expect solutions that are decreasing as a function of x, phase plane trajectories should have w negative and v positive. Therefore, to solve this problem, we can integrate from some value of $v(0) = v_0$, with $v_x(0) = 0$ (i.e., on the $w = 0$ axis of the phase portrait, and integrate until we hit the straight line $w = -\sqrt{\alpha D_e} v$, (the left boundary condition), and by so doing, determine L as a function of $v(0)$. Unfortunately, while this is the correct idea, its implementation is quite difficult and in reality is actually a terrible idea. This is because one must eliminate u from (14.22), and this means solving the equation $f(u) + \sigma\delta(v - u) = 0$ for u as a function of v, a difficult prospect.

Here's a better idea. Let's introduce the change of variables

$$(14.23) \qquad v = u - \frac{1}{\sigma\delta}f(u), \quad v_x = (1 - \frac{1}{\sigma\delta}f'(u))u_x,$$

so that

$$(14.24) \qquad v_{xx} = (1 - \frac{1}{\sigma\delta}f'(u))u_{xx} - \frac{1}{\sigma\delta}f''(u)u_x^2,$$

and then equation (14.20) becomes

$$(14.25) \qquad D_e(1 - \frac{1}{\sigma\delta}f'(u))u_{xx} - D_e\frac{1}{\sigma\delta}f''(u)u_x^2 - \alpha u + (\frac{\alpha}{\sigma\delta} + \frac{\rho}{1-\rho})f(u) = 0$$

with boundary conditions $u_x(0) = 0$, and

$$(14.26) \qquad D_e(1 - \frac{1}{\sigma\delta}f'(u))u_x = -\sqrt{\alpha D_e}(u - \frac{1}{\sigma\delta}f(u)) \quad \text{at } x = L.$$

Written as a first order system, this is

$$(14.27) \qquad u_x = \frac{w}{D_e},$$

$$(14.28) \qquad w_x = \frac{1}{(1 - \frac{1}{\sigma\delta}f'(u))}\Big(\frac{1}{\sigma\delta D_e}f''(u)w^2 + \alpha u - (\frac{\alpha}{\sigma\delta} + \frac{\rho}{1-\rho})f(u)\Big).$$

While this may look more complicated, it is, in fact, much easier to solve this problem numerically. The idea is exactly the same as before. We pick an initial value $u(0) = u_0$ and $u_x(0) = 0$ and integrate until $(1 - \frac{1}{\sigma\delta}f'(u))w = -\sqrt{\alpha D_e}(u - \frac{1}{\sigma\delta}f(u))$. Record the value of L for this integration, and then record (and plot) L vs. $u(0)$. Of course, because of the change of variables (14.23), it is easy to find v as a function of x from knowledge of u as a function of x.

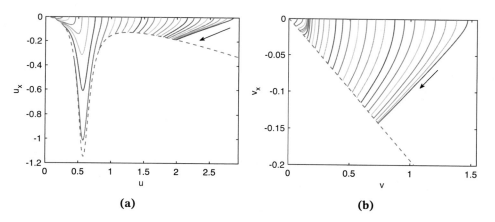

(a)   **(b)**

Figure 14.7. Phase portraits for equation (14.27)–(14.28) for (a) u_x vs. u and (b) v_x vs. v, with the curve $D_e(1 - \frac{1}{\sigma\delta}f'(u))u_x = -\sqrt{\alpha D_e}(u - \frac{1}{\sigma\delta}f(u))$ shown dashed in (a) and the curve $v_x = -\sqrt{\alpha D_e}v$ shown dashed in (b). Parameter values for this simulation are $s_0 = 0.05$, $K = 1$, $\gamma = 1.5$, $\sigma\delta = 1.0$, $\alpha = 0.0375$, $D_e = 1$, and $\rho = 0.04$.

These results, obtained using the Matlab code quorum_bounded_domain_ss_pp.m, are shown in Figures 14.7 and 14.8. What we see in Figure 14.7(a) are many $u - u_x$ trajectories that start at some value of u and $u_x = 0$ and terminate at the dashed curve, which is the boundary condition curve (14.26). Using the relationship (14.23) between the u, u_x, and v, v_x, these trajectories are plotted in Figure 14.7(b) in the v-v_x plane, starting at some value of v with $v_x = 0$ and terminating at the line $v_x = -\sqrt{\alpha D_e}v$, which is the Robin boundary condition at $x = L$ for v. These same trajectories are shown plotted in u vs. x space in Figure 14.8(a), each terminating at some value of x

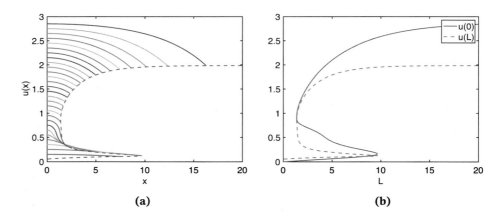

Figure 14.8. (a) Intracellular autoinducer $u(x)$ plotted as a function of x, for different values of $u(0)$, and (b) $u(0)$ and $u(L)$ (dashed) as a function of L. Parameter values for this simulation are $s_0 = 0.05$, $K = 1$, $\gamma = 1.5$, $\sigma\delta = 1.0$, $\alpha = 0.0375$, $D_e = 1$, and $\rho = 0.04$.

which represents the length of the domain for which that solution exists. Then, in Figure 14.8(b) the relationships between $u(0)$ and L and between $u(L)$ and L are shown. The most important observation, which is not unexpected, is that there is hysteretic behavior of u as a function of L, at least for these parameter values. For small values of L, the only solution has $u(x)$ relatively small, and for L large, the only solution has $u(x)$ large. For intermediate values of L there are three u profiles that satisfy the differential equation and boundary conditions.

So what have we learned from this discussion of quorum sensing? What we have seen is that the ability of a quorum sensing organism to detect features of its environment is controlled by diffusion. That is, since the rate at which autoinducer leaves the cell is governed by diffusion, if autoinducer in the extracellular space builds up, for whatever reason, then the rate of exit from the cell decreases and this causes the buildup of autoinducer inside the cell, which allows the positive feedback network to turn on. In other words, the rate at which autoinducer diffuses out of the cell contains information which is used by the cell to make a decision.

14.2. Flocking Behavior

14.2.1. On a Ring. Many organisms, including birds, fish, and insects, move in swarms or schools. Our understanding of how these swarms or schools form and are maintained is quite rudimentary, but in recent years there have been some advances in our understanding of this behavior. A fascinating description of some of these behaviors can be found in

> https://www.wired.com/2013/03/powers-of-swarms/?mbid=email_onsiteshare.

In this section, we present a simple one dimensional model of flocking behavior. We suppose that organisms (fish, birds, etc.) are moving around a circle of circumference

L. This choice is for illustrative purposes only and does not describe a particular situation. All individuals are moving with velocity v plus some small Brownian (diffusive) component, some moving clockwise and others counterclockwise. In addition, we assume that they randomly change direction. This change of direction can be represented by the reaction diagram

$$(14.29) \qquad\qquad U_+ \underset{\beta}{\overset{\alpha}{\rightleftharpoons}} U_-,$$

where U_+ represents positive (clockwise) direction movers, and U_- represents negative (counterclockwise) direction movers, and time is scaled so that $\beta + \alpha = 1$. This time scaling means that an individual that is not influenced by neighbors will have $\alpha = \beta = \frac{1}{2}$, meaning that on average the individual switches direction once every two units of time. However, for this model we assume that the direction switching *is* influenced by neighbors, so that β is a monotone increasing function of $U_+ - U_-$, with the additional feature that $\beta(0) = \frac{1}{2}$. In words, this implies that the individuals are more likely to switch to move in the direction of the majority than to switch to the direction opposite that of the majority at their present location, and the preference to switch in the direction of the majority is stronger the larger the majority. This is an entirely phenomenological model, with no mechanistic explanation for this behavior.

Now is a good opportunity to make an agent based model of this process. The basic idea is straightforward. Assign positions to a number of particles, and for each particle assign a direction of movement. Update the positions by moving them by $vdt + \sqrt{2Ddt}N(0,1)$ in their current direction of movement. Then, determine the number and direction of the nearby neighbors, and use this to determine if an individual should switch directions, with probability of switching from positive to negative being αdt and probability of switching from negative to positive being βdt.

This is a description of the Matlab code flocking_via_agents.m, and you are strongly encouraged to run this code for several different values of N, the total number of individuals, or L, the length of the ring, and make observations about the behavior.

A partial differential equation model for these dynamics is similar to one we have seen before (see (10.4), (10.5)), namely the system of equations

$$(14.30) \qquad \frac{\partial U_+}{\partial t} = \beta U_- - \alpha U_+ - v\frac{\partial U_+}{\partial x} + D\frac{\partial^2 U_+}{\partial x^2},$$

$$(14.31) \qquad \frac{\partial U_-}{\partial t} = \alpha U_+ - \beta U_- + v\frac{\partial U_-}{\partial x} + D\frac{\partial^2 U_-}{\partial x^2},$$

except that here the switching rates α and β are not constant, but are functions of $U_+ - U_-$, and the particle motion includes a diffusive component in addition to advection.

Before proceeding any further, it is worthwhile to simulate these equations to get some idea of what to look for in our analysis. The Matlab code to simulate these equations using the method of lines is titled flocking_via_MOL.m. What do you see that needs to be explained?

Let's first look for spatially uniform solutions, which satisfy the equations

$$(14.32) \qquad \frac{du_+}{dt} = \beta u_- - \alpha u_+,$$

$$(14.33) \qquad \frac{\partial u_-}{\partial t} = \alpha u_+ - \beta u_-.$$

For this, the quantity $\sigma = u_+ + u_-$, the total population size, is constant, since $\frac{d\sigma}{dt} = 0$. Eliminating u_-, we find that u_+ satisfies the equation

$$(14.34) \qquad \frac{du_+}{dt} = \left(\frac{1}{2} + f(2u_+ - \sigma)\right)\sigma - u_+,$$

since $\alpha + \beta = 1$, and $\beta = \frac{1}{2} + f(u_+ - u_-)$, for some monotone increasing, antisymmetric function f. This means that $f(-u) = -f(u)$ for all u. Now, let $u_+ = \frac{v+\sigma}{2}$, and find

$$(14.35) \qquad \frac{dv}{dt} = 2\sigma f(v) - v \equiv F(v).$$

This first order differential equation is easy to decipher. By virtue of the fact that both α and β are nonnegative, $f(u) \leq \frac{1}{2}$. We also make the simplifying assumption that $\frac{d^2 f}{du^2} \leq 0$ for $u \geq 0$. This implies that for small σ the only stable solution is $v = 0$, for which $u_+ = \frac{1}{2}\sigma$. However, when $2\sigma f'(0) > 1$, there are two stable solutions, one with $\frac{u_+}{\sigma} > \frac{1}{2}$, and one with $\frac{u_+}{\sigma} < \frac{1}{2}$, while the solution with $u_+ = \frac{1}{2}$ is unstable. It is apparent that these nontrivial solutions are stable from the fact that $F'(v) = 2\sigma f'(v) - 1 < 0$, and ranges between 0 and -1 as σ varies from 1 to ∞. In Figure 14.9(a) is shown a plot of $2\sigma f(v)$ vs. v for several values of σ, and in Figure 14.9(b) is shown the solution of $F(v) = 0$ for $f(v) = \frac{1}{2}\tanh(v)$ (made using the Matlab code flocking_plots.m).

The consequence of this is that flocking behavior is a bistable, critical phenomenon, with little collective flocking if the population is small, but bistable behavior if the

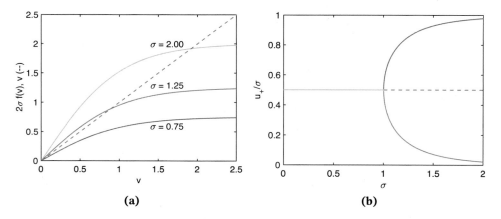

(a)　　　　　　　　　　　　　　**(b)**

Figure 14.9. (a) Plot of $2\sigma f(v)$ vs. v for several values of σ. (b) Steady state solution $\frac{u_+}{\sigma}$ as a function of σ for a spatially homogeneous flocking population. For these plots $f(v) = \frac{1}{2}\tanh(v)$.

population is sufficiently large, with most of the population moving in a single direction, and a small minority moving in the opposite direction.

This ordinary differential equation analysis gives a clue as how to proceed to study the full partial differential equation system. We introduce the change of variables $\Sigma = U_+ + U_-$, $W = U_+ - U_-$ and find that

$$(14.36) \qquad \frac{\partial \Sigma}{\partial t} = -v\frac{\partial W}{\partial x} + D\frac{\partial^2 \Sigma}{\partial x^2},$$

$$(14.37) \qquad \frac{\partial W}{\partial t} = -W + 2f(W)\Sigma - v\frac{\partial \Sigma}{\partial x} + D\frac{\partial^2 W}{\partial x^2},$$

where we have used that $\alpha + \beta = 1$ and $\beta = \frac{1}{2} + f(W)$. We suppose that Σ^* is large enough so that there is a nontrivial uniform steady state W^*, Σ^* which satisfies the equation $2f(W^*)\Sigma^* - W^* = 0$. We ask if this stable spatially homogeneous solution is stable to spatially inhomogeneous perturbations.

To address this question, we linearize the partial differential equation system about the spatially homogeneous steady state, finding

$$(14.38) \qquad \frac{\partial \sigma}{\partial t} = -v\frac{\partial w}{\partial x} + D\frac{\partial^2 \sigma}{\partial x^2},$$

$$(14.39) \qquad \frac{\partial w}{\partial t} = F'w + 2f(W^*)\sigma - v\frac{\partial \sigma}{\partial x} + D\frac{\partial^2 w}{\partial x^2},$$

where $F' = 2f'(W^*)\Sigma^* - 1 < 0$. To assess the stability of the steady state, we try a solution of this linearized system of the form

$$(14.40) \qquad \begin{pmatrix} \sigma \\ w \end{pmatrix} = \begin{pmatrix} \sigma_0 \\ w_0 \end{pmatrix} \exp(\lambda t + i\omega(x - ct)),$$

where $\omega = \frac{2n\pi}{L}$, for any integer n. This form is motivated by the observation from simulations that there may be traveling wave solutions with as yet unknown speed c. It follows that this is a solution provided

$$(14.41) \qquad \begin{pmatrix} -\lambda + ic - D\omega^2 & -vi\omega \\ 2f(W^*) - vi\omega & F' - \lambda + ic - D\omega^2 \end{pmatrix} \begin{pmatrix} \sigma_0 \\ w_0 \end{pmatrix} = \begin{pmatrix} 0 \\ 0 \end{pmatrix}.$$

This equation has a nontrivial solution only if the determinant of the matrix is zero. Since this determinant is complex, both its real and imaginary parts must be zero. Requiring the imaginary part be zero gives that

$$(14.42) \qquad c = \frac{2v\omega f(W^*)}{2D\omega^2 + 2\lambda - F'},$$

and then the real part is zero if

$$(14.43) \qquad (-\lambda - D\omega^2)(F' - \lambda - D\omega^2) - \frac{4v^2\omega^2 f^2(W^*)}{(-2\lambda - 2D\omega^2 + F')^2} + v^2\omega^2 = 0.$$

The relationship between λ, c, and ω is known as the *dispersion curve*.

The real roots of this equation determine the stability of the uniform solution, and a change of stability occurs whenever λ changes sign, i.e., at places where $\lambda = 0$. Thus,

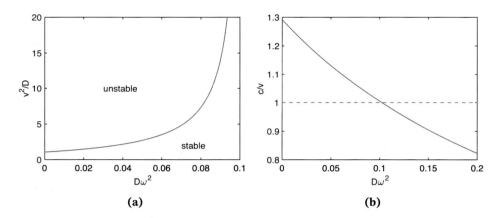

Figure 14.10. (a) Plot of the critical stability curve $\frac{v^2}{D}$ as a function of $D\omega^2$ as given by (14.44). (b) Plot of the relative speed $\frac{c}{v}$ for the neutrally stable solutions as a function of $D\omega^2$. For these curves, $W^* = 1.5$, $\Sigma^* = 1.6572$.

the critical stability curve is given by the relationship

$$(14.44) \qquad \frac{v^2}{D}\left(1 - \frac{4f^2(W^*)}{(F' - 2D\omega^2)^2}\right) = F' - D\omega^2.$$

A plot of this curve is shown in Figure 14.10(a).

  With a little more work (make a plot of the solution λ of (14.43) for different values of parameters), one can determine that the homogeneous solution is stable below and to the right of the curve (14.44), and is unstable above this curve. Since $D\omega^2$ is inversely proportional to L^2, this implies that the homogeneous solution is stable if L is small. On the other hand, if v and L are both large enough, the homogeneous solution is unstable. In addition, numerical simulation shows that if the homogeneous solution is unstable, there is a nonconstant traveling wave solution. A plot of the traveling wave

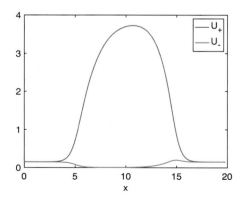

Figure 14.11. Plot of the traveling wave solution of (14.30)–(14.31) with wavespeed $c = 0.556$ for parameter values $v = 0.5$, $L = 20$, $D = 0.01$, and average population density $U_t = 1.65$.

solution is shown in Figure 14.11. (This solution was computed using the Matlab code flocking_via_MOL.m.) This wave is moving to the right, with most of the population moving to the right (i.e., U_+) and a small part of the population moving to the left (U_-). For this profile the wavespeed is $c = 0.556$ which is larger than the flight velocity $v = 0.5$. This is somewhat surprising but is suggested by Figure 14.10(b), where the relative speed $\frac{c}{v}$ of the neutrally stable wave is shown to be bigger than one for $D\omega^2$ sufficiently small.

This wave is an example of a diffusion driven pattern. It is easy to realize from (14.44) that the spatially homogeneous solution is stable for all parameter values if $D = 0$. Further, it is not difficult to show that there can be no nonconstant traveling wave solutions if $D = 0$ (see Exercise 14.10). This is actually a fascinating observation, since, as we well know by now, diffusion always spreads things out. Yet here, where there is positive feedback (since the majority is the more effective recruiter), diffusion enables the formation of an aggregate.

This also provides a simple example of what physicists like to call a phase transition. For small population density, motion is uncoordinated. However, once the population reaches a critical size there is a transition to a coordinated collective behavior and an emergent behavior. But this is only the tip of the iceberg of patterns and transitions between patterns that are seen in nature, as we will see in the next section.

14.2.2. In Two Dimensions. Now let's consider organisms (birds, or insects, for example) that are moving in a two dimensional plane. For this discussion we use an agent-based model approach with which we follow the motion of each of the individuals.

Suppose there are N flying individuals. Each of these flies with constant velocity V in the direction $d_j = (\cos(\theta_j), \sin(\theta_j))$, $j = 1, 2, \ldots, N$. The angular direction of flight θ_j is constantly changing, with a deterministic part and a stochastic part. For the deterministic part, we suppose that θ_j is moving toward a target angle θ_j^T, i.e.,

$$(14.45) \qquad \frac{d\theta_j}{dt} = \alpha(\theta_j^T - \theta_j),$$

and for the stochastic part we assume that θ_j is diffusing with diffusion coefficient D_θ, so that (recall (4.1))

$$(14.46) \qquad d\theta_j = \sqrt{2D_\theta dt}\,\mathcal{N}(0,1).$$

We combine these two into the stochastic differential equation

$$(14.47) \qquad d\theta_j = \alpha(\theta_j^T - \theta_j)dt + \sqrt{2D_\theta dt}\,\mathcal{N}(0,1).$$

In Exercise 4.10, you were given the opportunity to do an agent based simulation for which the angle θ_j changes by diffusion, but there was no deterministic part. In that exercise, you found that this process is effectively a diffusion process that has an effective diffusion coefficient proportional to $\frac{v^2}{D_\theta}$. Here we add the possibility that there is a target angle θ_j^T toward which the flyers are constantly adjusting their direction.

How should θ_j^T be determined? There are some empirical observations that help. First, it is a frequently observed behavior that individuals tend to be attracted toward other individuals (to avoid being isolated) and to align themselves with neighbors [**14**], [**55**],[**54**]. Second, it is typical that the individuals have limited peripheral vision and can see only those other individuals that are within the cone $\theta_j - \theta_p \leq \theta \leq \theta_j + \theta_p$, where $0 \leq \theta_p \leq \pi$. If $\theta_p = \pi$, there is no restriction on what the flyers can see, and if $\theta_p = 0$, the flyers cannot see anything: they are blind. Now, suppose that the vector pointing from individual j to individual k is given by v_{jk} and has length r_{jk}. This makes sense only if $j \neq k$, so to complete the definition of v, take $v_{jj} = d_j$ (the current direction of flight), and $r_{jj} = 0$. Now the criterion that flyer j can see flyer k is that the dot product of $\frac{v_{jk}}{r_{jk}}$ with d_j be greater than $\cos(\theta_p)$, i.e.,

$$(14.48) \qquad\qquad \frac{v_{jk}}{r_{jk}} \cdot d_j \geq \cos(\theta_p).$$

Denote the set of indices k within the peripheral vision of flyer j by p_j, and the number of these indices by N_p.

Suppose that the flyer j attempts to align itself with its neighbors. It can detect the direction of flight of all the flyers within its peripheral vision and takes a weighted average of those directions

$$(14.49) \qquad\qquad d_j^T = \frac{1}{N_p} \sum_{k \in p_j} d_k \exp\left(-(\frac{r_{jk}}{\rho})^2\right),$$

and then uses d_j^T to determine its target direction

$$(14.50) \qquad\qquad d_j^T = |d_j^T|(\cos(\theta_j^T), \sin(\theta_j^T)).$$

Here ρ is a parameter that measures how far the flyer can see. There are a couple of things to notice about this determination. The further away another flyer is, the less influence it has on the target direction, and if no other flyers can be seen, then the target direction is exactly the current direction θ_j.

A second way to determine a target direction is to use, rather than the direction of flight of neighboring flyers, the relative position of neighbors to determine which way to fly. So, take

$$(14.51) \qquad\qquad v_j^T = \frac{1}{N_p} \sum_{k \in p_j} \frac{v_{jk}}{r_{jk}} \exp\left(-(\frac{r_{jk}}{\rho})^2\right),$$

and then use v_j^T to determine the target direction

$$(14.52) \qquad\qquad v_j^T = |v_j^T|(\cos(\theta_j^T), \sin(\theta_j^T)).$$

With this rule, a flyer will tend to fly toward the weighted center of mass of the flyers that it can see.

Flyers that use the first rule (14.49) are identified as common direction seekers, and those that use the second rule (14.51) as center of mass seekers.

Now it is time to see what the consequences of these rules are, with simulations. There are a number of parameters to explore: Without loss of generality, we can take $V = 1$. (Why is this possible?) The other parameters are D_θ, the directional diffusion coefficient, θ_p, the angle of maximal peripheral vision, ρ, the radial scale for the weight function, α, the rate of decay of θ_j toward θ_j^T, and N, the number of flyers. All of the simulations presented here were done using the Matlab code flight_of_swarmers.m. For each simulation the initial configuration was a random distribution of flyers inside a circle of radius $r_0 = 1$ at the origin, with randomly distributed initial direction angle θ_j. The code is set up with eight different scenarios, or parameter sets, which are described below. You are encouraged to do these simulations for yourself, to see better how these flyers fly.

The range of possible patterns is intriguing. Let's explore some of these, beginning with common direction seeking flyers. In Figure 14.12(a), we see what happens when there is no limit on peripheral vision, $\theta_p = \pi$. The flyers reorient themselves and fly off as a group in some randomly chosen common direction, at least if D_θ is small. If N is small and both D_θ and α are large, the result is a meandering flight path as shown in Figure 14.12(a).

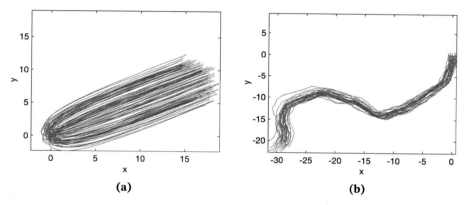

(a)   **(b)**

Figure 14.12. Particle paths for common direction seeking flyers with (a) parameters $N = 100$, $\theta_p = \pi$, $\rho = 2.5$, $D_\theta = 0.001$, $\alpha = 1.0$, and (b) parameters $N = 30$, $\theta_p = \frac{3\pi}{4}$, $\rho = 2.5$, $D_\theta = 0.5$, $\alpha = 10.0$.

It would appear from these two simulations that these flyers always form a single cluster, but such is not the case. In particular, if their peripheral vision is restricted, then they may form multiple clusters, as seen in Figures 14.13(a) and 14.13(b).

Center of mass seeking flyers form much different clusters. If D_θ is small and peripheral vision is unrestricted, they (surprisingly) fly in circles. This can be seen in Figure 14.14(a). In this, and all of the remaining figures in this section, *final position* refers to the position of the flyers at the end of the simulation. To get an understanding of the dynamics of how this pattern is formed, you need to run the Matlab code flight_of_swarmers.m with scenario 5 selected. Figure 2 of that simulation shows a movie of the flight and how this pattern forms. Cycling seems to be a fairly common feature of center of mass seekers. However, visual distance ρ matters, as is seen in Figure 14.14(b). Here is seen a pattern of flyers that are rotating roughly about the center of mass, with some cells rotating clockwise and others counterclockwise. (To get the full visual experience of this pattern, run the Matlab code flight_of_swarmers.m with scenario 6.) However, the structure of the rotating pattern is quite complicated, and is certainly not a circle, even though all of the individuals are moving in a mostly circular flight path (see Figure 5 of the simulation of scenario 6).

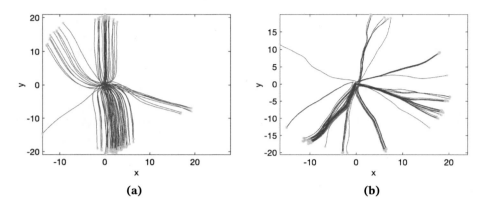

(a)   **(b)**

Figure 14.13. Particle paths for common direction seeking flyers with (a) parameters $N = 100$, $\theta_p = \frac{\pi}{2}$, $\rho = 2.5$, $D_\theta = 0.001$, $\alpha = 1.0$, and (b) parameters $N = 100$, $\theta_p = \frac{\pi}{4}$, $\rho = 3.5$, $D_\theta = 0.005$, $\alpha = 10.0$.

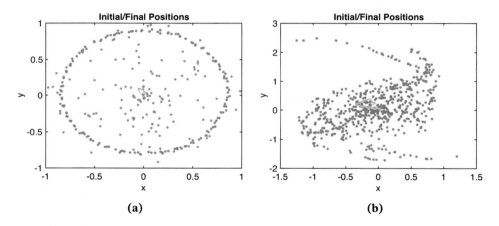

(a)   **(b)**

Figure 14.14. Initial (blue) and final (red) particle positions for center of mass seeking flyers with (a) parameters parameters $N = 300$, $\theta_p = \pi$, $\rho = 2.5$, $D_\theta = 0.0001$, $\alpha = 0.75$, and (b) parameters $N = 150$, $\theta_p = \pi$, $\rho = 1$, $D_\theta = 0.0001$, $\alpha = 0.75$.

The circular motion of the previous two cases is the result of α and D_θ being relatively small. Figure 14.15(a) shows a pattern of chaotic swarming when D_θ is substantially increased. This pattern looks to my eye (qualitatively, at least) like a swarm of flying gnats. When α is also increased the surprising pattern shown in Figure 14.15(b) emerges. In this pattern, individual flyers fly along a nearly one-dimensional path of finite extent, and reverse direction quickly when they reach the end of the path (see Figures 2 and 5 of the simulation of scenario 8).

These patterns of flight are fascinating, and it is interesting to see how changing parameters changes the resulting pattern of flight. However, for all their fascination, they don't seem to reproduce many of the features of real flight (except perhaps swarms of gnats in Figure 14.15(a)). The common direction seeking flyers form flocks that tend to separate as time progresses, and the center of mass seeking flyers form interesting

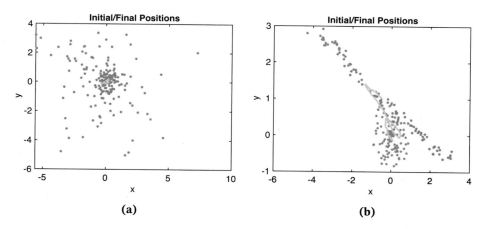

Figure 14.15. Initial (blue) and final (red) particle positions for center of mass seeking flyers for (a) parameters $N = 100$, $\theta_p = \frac{\pi}{2}$, $\rho = 2.0$, $D_\theta = 2$, $\alpha = 1.0$, and (b) $N = 100$, $\theta_p = \frac{\pi}{2}$, $\rho = 2.5$, $D_\theta = 2.0$, $\alpha = 10.0$,

patterns but don't go anywhere. Perhaps a combination of these two rules would do a better job of producing realistic patterns. The idea for such a rule is to use the weighted direction vector d_j^T specified by (14.49) if its amplitude is not too small, and to use the weighted center of mass vector v_j^T given by (14.51) if the amplitude of d_j^T is small [14]. The amplitude of d_j^T being small indicates that the neighbors that can be seen have no coordinated direction of flight or they are too far away to be accurately seen. If this is the case, it makes sense for the flyer to fly toward the center of mass of those flyers it can see, even if their direction of flight is not discernible. In this way, the model should accomplish the two things that were listed at the beginning of this discussion as common features of schooling or flocking, namely that nearby neighbors tend to align themselves, while distant flyers try to rejoin the flock. One way to accomplish this is to form a weighted direction vector w_j^T, given by

$$(14.53) \qquad w_j^T = W(d)d_j^T + (1 - W(d))v_j^T, \quad d = \frac{|d_j^T|}{\delta},$$

where $W(x)$ is a decreasing function of x with $W(0) = 1$ and $W(\infty) = 0$, for example, $W(x) = \exp(-x)$. Then, use the direction of w_j^T as the target direction θ_j^T. Here, δ is a length scale factor that determines how much of each of the two measurements to use. If $\delta \to \infty$, the model reduces to the original common direction seeker model, while if $\delta = 0$, it reduces to the original center of mass seeking model.

Rather than embarking on a detailed investigation of this model, now is a good time for you, the interested reader, to take over and pursue this investigation for yourself (see Exercise 14.14). Have fun!

Exercises

14.1. Show that the function $\frac{u}{f(u)}$ where $f(u) = s_0 + \frac{\gamma u^2}{K^2 + u^2}$ has an inflection point with zero slope when $\gamma = 8s_0$, is monotone increasing when $\gamma < 8s_0$, and is triphasic when $\gamma > 8s_0$ (all for $u > 0$).

14.2. Find the steady state solution of the autoinducer problem (14.4)–(14.5) for a spherical cell of radius R. Show that there is a parameter range for which there is a hysteretic response of autoinducer levels which is sensitive to the dimensionless parameter $\mu = \frac{\alpha D_e}{\delta^2}$.

14.3. Suppose that a cell excretes autoinducer at position $x = 0$ into a one dimensional environment with a wall at position $x = L > 0$. Show that there is a parameter range for which there is a hysteretic response of autoinducer level in response to the distance from the cell to the wall. In this way the cell is able to detect when it is close to the wall.

14.4. Show that using a rescaling of u, v, time and space, one can equivalently set $D_e = 1$, $\sigma\delta = 1$ and $K = 1$ in the autoinducer equations (14.11)–(14.12).

14.5. Make a plot of the intracellular autoinducer concentration as a function of μ, where $\mu = \frac{\alpha D_e}{\delta^2}$ satisfies (14.10). To what features of the environmental characteristics of extracellular autoinducer does the cell respond by upregulating autoinducer? (Assume $\gamma > 8s_0$.)

14.6. Find the solutions and plot the phase portrait for the equations (14.11)–(14.12) in the case that $\gamma = 0$ and $D_e = 0$.

14.7. Use the Matlab code flocking_agents.m to simulate flocking behavior for several different values of N, the total number of particles. Do you observe bistability of this system?

14.8. Use the Matlab code flocking_via_MOL.m to simulate the equations (14.30)–(14.31) for several different values of the total population size. Characterize the behavior you observe as a function of the total population size.

14.9. Show that the neutral stability curve (14.44) for the stability of the spatially homogeneous solutions of (14.36)–(14.37) is *exactly* the same as the Hopf bifurcation curve for the periodic solutions of (14.36)–(14.37) in traveling wave coordinates.

Reminder. A Hopf bifurcation for an ordinary differential equation system occurs when a pair of complex eigenvalues for a critical point changes the sign of their real parts. The critical curve for a Hopf bifurcation is the curve where a pair of eigenvalues is purely imaginary.

14.10. Show that the equations (14.36)–(14.37) cannot have nonconstant periodic traveling wave solutions if $D = 0$.

14.11. A large number of flyers are uniformly distributed, moving around a circle (as in, for example Figure 14.14(a)). Each individual moves with velocity V in the direction θ_j where θ_j is the solution of the differential equation (14.45), (i.e., $D_\theta = 0$.) Suppose the flyers determine their target direction θ_T using the center of mass formula

$$v_j^T = \frac{1}{N_p} \sum_{k \in P_j} v_{jk}.$$

(a) Suppose there is no restriction on peripheral vision, $\theta_p = \pi$. Find the radius of the circle.

(b) Suppose $\theta_p < \pi$. Find the radius of the circle. *Remark.* The radius *must* be proportional to $\frac{V}{\alpha}$. Why? (This exercise will test your trigonemetry skills.)

14.12. Use the Matlab code flight_of_swarmers.m to investigate the effect of parameters on the flight patterns of common direction seeking flyers, as follows.

(a) What is the effect of increasing or decreasing α on the flyers in Figure 14.12(a) (scenario 1)? Give an explanation for this.

(b) What is the effect of increasing or decreasing ρ on the flyers in Figure 14.12(a) (scenario 1)? Give an explanation for this.

(c) What is the effect of increasing or decreasing N on the cluster of flyers in Figure 14.12(b) (scenario 2)? Give an explanation for this.

(d) What is the effect of increasing or decreasing D_θ on the cluster of flyers in Figure 14.12(b) (scenario 2)? Give an explanation for this.

(e) What effect does increasing or decreasing ρ have on the number of clusters that are formed in Figures 14.13(a)–(b) (scenarios 3 and 4)? Give an explanation for this.

14.13. Use the Matlab code flight_of_swarmers.m to investigate the effect of parameters on the flight patterns of center of mass seeking flyers, as follows.

(a) What is the effect of increasing or decreasing α on the circular flyers in Figure 14.14(a) (scenario 5)? Give an explanation for this.

(b) What is the effect of increasing or decreasing D_θ on the circular flyers in Figure 14.14(a) (scenario 5)?

(c) What is the effect of increasing α on the rotating flyers of Figure 14.14(b) (scenario 6)? Give an explanation for this.

(d) Simulate the case of center of mass seeking flyers with parameters $N = 100$, $\theta_p = \pi/2$, $\rho = 2$, $D_\theta = 0.1$, $\alpha = 10$, and plot_paths=0. These paths are different than any seen in previous scenarios. Can you explain how and why they form? What is the effect of decreasing θ_p on these patterns? Why?

14.14. Modify the Matlab code flight_of_swarmers.m to investigate the flight patterns of flyers that use the vector w_j^T given by (14.53) with weight function $W(x) = \exp(-x)$ to determine the target direction θ_j^T. Investigate the effect of variations of the parameter δ on the patterns in Exercises 14.12 and 14.13.

Introduction to Matlab

A.1. A Matlab Primer

A primary emphasis of this text is solving equations numerically and making plots of solutions, and while there are several choices for the language in which to do these things, the choice for this text is Matlab. Consequently, all the simulations and plots shown in this text were done using Matlab, and there are a number of Matlab codes that are included in the following appendices. The purpose of this section is to give a brief introduction to those features of Matlab that are used most heavily in this text, with the hope that this will enable you, the reader, to at least understand what these codes do and how they might be modified to do slightly different tasks. There are numerous resources on the web including courses and books describing Matlab that you may wish to refer to. (Simply type "Matlab primer" into your favorite search engine.) However, to get you started, the following brief introduction is offered.

A.1.1. Basic syntax. Matlab can be used interactively, like a calculator, or by using files, always with the extension .m.

One of the first things to know is how to get help, other than by asking your classmate or professor. To get help interactively, simply type
```
help `topic'
```
where 'topic' refers to the topic about which you want help. So, for example
```
help *
```
gives information about what the operation * is, while
```
help polyfit
```
gives information about the Matlab routine 'polyfit', a routine that finds a least squares polynomial fit to data.

The command
```
help =
```
returns an error message, because Matlab thinks this is the beginning of an operational

statement. So let's begin our discussion of Matlab operations with the operation '='. As with all computer languages, '=' is an operation meaning 'is replaced by', so for example, the command

```
help = 13
```

means that the variable 'help' is replaced by or becomes the number 13. So, after entering

```
help = 13
```

forever after, typing 'help' will return the number 13. Of course, this is not a particularly good thing to do, since now the help command is conflicted, at least until the variable 'help' is cleared by typing

```
clear help
```

The next thing to know is about names. In Matlab, every combination of letters and numbers is either a variable or a function, which if it is not predefined by Matlab requires a definition. For example, typing the word

```
hello
```

will get the response from Matlab "Unrecognized function or variable 'hello' ", because Matlab thinks hello is a variable and so far it has not been assigned a value. If you type

```
hello = 'hello'
```

then Matlab creates the variable hello and gives it the value 'hello'. So forever after, or until you change the definition, when you type

```
hello
```

Matlab will respond with

```
`hello'
```

Similarly, if you type

```
A = 13
```

Matlab creates the variable 'A' and gives it the value 13, whereas the statement

```
A = [1:13]
```

creates the variable A as the row vector

$$\left(1 \quad 2 \quad 3 \quad 4 \quad 5 \quad 6 \quad 7 \quad 8 \quad 9 \quad 10 \quad 11 \quad 12 \quad 13 \right).$$

The statement

```
size(A)
```

will return

```
ans =

1 13
```

indicating that A has 1 row and 13 columns.

This definition of A uses a useful device of Matlab by which

```
[1:N]
```

creates a row vector with entries 1 through N in increments of 1, while

```
[a:b:c]
```

creates a row vector with initial element a, in increments of b, terminating with a+nb where n is the largest integer for which $n \leq \frac{c-a}{b}$.

The statement
```
A'
```
returns the transpose of A, a column vector, and the statement
```
A = A'
```
replaces the variable A with the transpose of the value of A, a column vector. The statement
```
A = [1:13]'
```
creates A as a column vector rather than a row vector.

In Matlab, numerical variables are either scalars or arrays. Two objects can be added or subtracted using the operation '+' or '−', provided their sizes are identical. Two objects can be multiplied using the operation '*', using the standard rules of linear algebra for multiplication of arrays. So, for example, if
```
A = [1:2]
B = [2:3]'
C = 13
```
then the commands
```
C*A
A*B
B*A
```
are legitimate operations, with

$$(A.1) \qquad C * A = (\begin{matrix} 13 & 26 \end{matrix}), \qquad A * B = 8, \qquad B * A = \begin{pmatrix} 2 & 4 \\ 3 & 6 \end{pmatrix}.$$

However, the commands
```
A*B'
B*A'
```
are not valid operations (and Matlab will give an error message alerting you to this fact). Notice that one *could* use the loop
```
for j = 1:2
P(j) = A(j)*B(j)
end
```
to perform the operation A*B, but one NEVER *should* do it this way. The operation A*B is both easier to write and implemented faster in Matlab.

To create the array

$$(A.2) \qquad\qquad \begin{pmatrix} 2 & 4 \\ 3 & 6 \end{pmatrix}$$

type
```
B=[2,4;3,6]
```
Here the comma separator means "move to the next element in the same row", and the semicolon means move to the next row. Other operations that can be used on arrays,

provided the sizes are appropriate, include '^' for exponentiation, and 'sqrtm' for a matrix square root. 'sqrt' and '/' make sense for scalars, but not for arrays. One convenient feature of Matlab is that one can mix variable types *if* unique sense can be made of a statement. For example, if A is a matrix and *c* a scalar, the statement

A+c

is acceptable as it adds the scalar c to every component of A, as one would hope.

The second wonderful feature of Matlab are the component-wise operations .*, ./, and .^. So for example, with A and B as defined above,

$$A.^2 = (\ 1 \ \ 4 \ ), \qquad A.*B' = (\ 2 \ \ 6 \ ), \text{ but A.*B is not defined.}$$

The third feature of Matlab is the ease with which systems of linear equations can be solved. That is, to solve the linear system $Ax = B$, where A is a matrix (a two dimensional array) and B is a column vector, one simply uses the command

x = A\B

One can also do logical operations easily, using the logical operators '<', '>', '<=', '>=', or '=='. For example, the statement

A>1

returns an array with the same size as A with zeros in the entries for which the element is less than or equal to 1, and 1 in the entries for which the element of A is greater than 1. The statement

find(A>1)

returns an array whose elements are the indices of the array A for which the element of A is greater than 1.

Matlab has a large number of commands that provide convenient shortcuts. For example, the commands

```
ones(N,M)
zeros(N,M)
rand(N,M)
randn(N,M)
```

create N × M arrays of ones, zeros, uniformly distributed random numbers, and normally distributed random numbers, respectively. The command
randn([IMIN,IMAX], N,M) returns an N×M array containing integer values drawn from the discrete uniform distribution on IMIN:IMAX.

Matlab also has a large toolbox of useful functions. Those that are used in the codes for this text include min, max, length, size, find, diag, reshape, mean, var, plot, ode23, but rather than providing a list of their usages here, it is easier to simply refer to the help feature of Matlab when you see them in code.

A.1.2. Making Plots in Matlab. A nice feature of Matlab is the ease with which plots can be made. Here is a walk through of the process of making the first plot in this text, Figure 1.1.

```
x=[-.2:0.01:1.2];
N = length(x); %  determine the length of x
al = 0.25;
```

```
A = 10; % specify the scale factor
f = A*x.*(1-x).*(x-al);
figure(1) % identify the figure to be made
plot(x,f, x,zeros(N,1),'--',[0,al,1],zeros(3,1),'*k','linewidth',2)
axis([-0.2 1.2 -1 1])
        % specify the values for the x axis tick marks
set(gca, 'XTick', -0.2 : 0.2 : 1.2);
xlabel('u','fontsize',20)
ylabel('du/dt','fontsize',20) % label the y axis % add a direction angle
annotation('textarrow',[0.35 .25],[0.7 0.7],'linewidth',2)
        % add a second direction arrow
annotation('textarrow',[0.55 .65],[0.7 0.7],'linewidth',2)
```

A.2. List of Available Matlab Codes

Here, in order of their first appearance, is a list of the Matlab codes that were used to do the simulations in this text. They are all available for download at

> http://www.math.utah.edu/~keener/books/Ugrad_PDE/matlab_codes/

Chapter 1

- de_chapt_plots.m code to make the first few plots for differential equations in the text, Figures 1.1–1.5.

- SIR_pp.m makes the SIR phase portrait Figure 1.6 and finds the relationship between $s(0)$ and $s(\infty)$.

- exponential_decay_via_Gillespie.m is code to simulate a stochastic exponential decay death process.

- stochastic_birth_death.m is code to simulate a stochastic birth-death process.

- stochastic_SIR.m is code to simulate the stochastic SIR dynamics.

- bisect_function.m provides a template to find roots of an equation using the method of bisection.

Chapter 3

- diffusion_via_MOL.m is code to simulate the method of lines approximation to the diffusion equation.

- discrete_random_walk.m is code to simulate a random walk on a discrete grid.

Chapter 4

- single_particle_diffusion.m is code to simulate the diffusion process of single particles (i.e., Brownian motion).

- first_exit_times.m is code to determine the first exit time for a diffusing particle on a line.

- splitting_probability.m calculates the splitting probability for a particle diffusing along a line and exiting at either $x = 0$ or $x = 1$.

- two_d_diffusion.m is code to simulate two dimensional diffusion for a large number of particles and calculate the mean squared displacement.
- two_d_mean_first_exit_time.m is code to simulate the diffusion of a particle on a two dimensional circular region and estimate the first exit time.
- discrete_diffusion_via_Gillespie.m is code to simulate the diffusion of particles on a discrete grid, using the Gillespie algorithm.
- one_d_direction_switcher.m is code to simulate the motion of a particle on a one dimensional line that randomly switches the direction of its ballistic motion.
- one_d_run_and_pause.m is code to simulate the motion of a particle that randomly switches between motion with constant velocity and pausing.
- agent_based_run_and_tumble.m is code to simulate an agent-based run and tumble process along a one-dimensional line.

Chapter 5

- tube_diffusion.m is the code used to make plots in Figure 5.1.
- steady_state_solutions.m is the code used to make Figure 5.2.
- diffusion_NR_via_MOL.m is code to simulate the diffusion equation with Neumann or Robin boundary conditions using the method of lines.
- Diffusion_Dirichlet_via_MOL.m is code to simulate the diffusion equation with Dirichlet boundary conditions using the method of lines.
- FEuler_diffusion_NR.m is code to simulate the diffusion equation with Neumann or Robin boundary conditions using the forward Euler method.
- BEuler_diffusion_NR.m is code to simulate the diffusion equation with Neumann or Robin boundary conditions using the backward Euler method.
- CN_diffusion_NR.m is code to simulate the diffusion equation with Neumann or Robin boundary conditions with Dirichlet boundary conditions using the Crank–Nicolson method.
- FEuler_diffusion_Dirichlet.m is code to simulate the diffusion equation with Dirichlet boundary conditions using the forward Euler method.
- BEuler_diffusion_Dirichlet.m is code to simulate the diffusion equation with Dirichlet boundary conditions using the backward Euler method.
- CN_diffusion_Dirichlet.m is code to simulate the diffusion equation using the Crank–Nicolson method.
- The code Diffusion_2D_via_MOL.m solves the diffusion equation on a circular region with uniform initial data and Dirichlet boundary conditions, the FRAP problem.

Chapter 6

- The code decay_probability.m was used to simulate a spatial decay process and make Figure 6.1.
- The code CN_diffusion_w_growth.m was used to simulate the diffusion equation with linear growth or death, and to make Figure 6.2.

- agent_SIR_2d.m is code to simulate the spread of an SIR disease using an agent-based approach in two spatial dimensions.
- agent_SIR_one_d.m is code to simulate the spread of an SIR disease using an agent-based approach in one spatial dimension and was used to make Figure 6.4.
- CN_Fisher.m is code to simulate the Fisher's equation on a large domain using the Crank–Nicolson method for diffusion and forward Euler method for the reaction.
- Fisher_waves_plot.m is code to plot the Fisher traveling wave phase portrait and wave profiles in Figure 6.6.
- CN_Fisher_w_Dirichlet.m is code to simulate Fisher's equation on a one-dimensional region of length Y with homogeneous Dirichlet boundary conditions.
- The code Fisher_ss_pp.m is used to create Figures 6.8–6.12.
- CN_Fisher_w_Dirichlet_2d.m is code to simulate Fisher's equation on a two-dimensional square region, with homogeneous Dirichlet boundary conditions.
- CN_diffusion_gluc_micro_X.m is code to simulate the growth of bacteria in a limited glucose environment.
- The code resource_consumption_profiles.m computes the profiles of the traveling wave solution for the resource consumption problem.
- CN_diffusion_SIR.m is code to simulate the diffusional spread of rabies using an SIR model.
- SIR_wave_pp.m is code used to make the phase portrait Figure 6.16.
- facilitated_diff_plots.m is code used to make the plots for Figures 6.17–6.18.
- CN_Fisher_w_Dirichlet_radial.m is code to simulate the Fisher equation on a two dimensional circular domain and is useful for Exercise 6.14.

Chapter 7

- spruce_budworm_rhs.m is code used to plot the reaction function for spruce budworm kinetics.
- HH_upstroke_rhs.m is code to plot the ion currents for the Hodgkin–Huxley upstroke model.
- calcium_CICR_rhs.m is code to plot $J_{IPR} - J_{SERCA}$, the calcium release function in (7.29).

Chapter 8

- bistable_threshold_simulation.m is code to simulate the bistable equation with different initial data, demonstrating threshold behavior.
- bistable_waves_pp.m is code to make the phase portrait and profiles for traveling waves of the bistable equation shown in Figure 8.2.
- bistable_thresholds.m and threshold_plotter.m are codes used to calculate the thresholds for the bistable equation and make the plots Figure 8.3(a).
- bistable_threshold_integral.m is code used to calculate the threshold stimulus area for the bistable equation on a one-dimensional domain.

- bistable_two_d_threshold.m is code used to calculate the threshold stimulus area for the bistable equation on a two-dimensional domain.

- bistable_two_d_threshold_number.m is code used to calculate the threshold stimulus population number for the bistable equation on a two-dimensional domain.

- CN_Bistable.m is code to simulate the bistable equation using the Crank–Nicolson method for diffusion and forward Euler method for the reaction.

- TBI_block.m is code used to make the plot of critical curves for TBI standing blocked waves.

- discrete_bistable_via_MOL.m is code used to look for traveling waves for the discrete bistable equation and to make Figure 8.10.

- discrete_failure_plot.m is code used to make Figure 8.12.

- fdf_plots.m is code used to make plots of the solution of the fire-diffuse-fire model.

- barrier_block.m is code used to calculate the size of regions of block for the bistable equation.

Chapter 9

- rbc_plots.m is code to plot steady state solutions, the critical stability curve and time dependent solutions of the red blood cell production model.

- pde_upwind_MoL.m is code that implements upwinding for a general advection equation in conservation form.

- pde_by_moc.m is code that can be used to simulate equations using the method of characteristics.

- double_sums.m is code used to make the plots illustrating change of summation order for double sums.

- gelation.m is code to simulate the Burgers' equation with initial data (9.90).

- co_counter_currents.m is code to make plots of the transfer fraction for cocurrents and countercurrents shown in Figure 9.10.

- sliding_friction.m is code to solve the equations for the force velocity relationship for a cell with protein binders.

- muscle_load_velocity.m is code used to make plots of the load-velocity curves for the Huxley model.

Chapter 10

- one_d_direction_switcher_w_drift.m simulates a direction switching process with unequal left-right direction switching rates.

- OU_process.m is code to simulate the Ornstein–Uhlenbeck equation (10.15).

Chapter 11

- chemotax_agents.m is code to do an agent based simulation of chemotactic run and tumble bacteria in two dimensions.

- CN_upwind_chemotax.m is code to simulate the chemotactic motion of amoebae by solving a partial differential equation model.

- The code dd_chemotax_ss_pp.m does the phase portrait analysis to find the *D. discoideum* steady state profiles.

Chapter 12

- Gray_Scott_Turing_via_MOL.m is code to analyze the Turing instability for the Gray–Scott model.
- The code tiger_bush_pp.m is used to make the phase portrait and stability diagram Figure 12.5.
- The code tiger_bush_dispersion_critical_crv.m calculates the tiger bush dispersion curve and stability diagram.
- The code tiger_bush_via_MOL.m simulates traveling wave solutions of the tiger bush equations using the method of lines.
- The code cell_polarization_ode_system.m is used to explore the behavior of equation (12.39) and to make the plots in Figures 12.10 and 12.11.
- cell_polarization_f.m is code to simulate cell polarization dynamics with hysteresis.
- polarization_moving_target.m is code to show the cell polarization response to a moving stimulus.

Chapter 13

- invasion_profile.m is the code used to make plots of the dispersion kernel and invasion profile.
- dispersal_renewal.m is code to simulate a dispersal-renewal process.

Chapter 14

- quorum_plots.m is the code used to make the plots in Figure 14.2,
- quorum_pp.m is code used to make phase portrait plots for the quorum sensing dynamics.
- CN_diffusion_quorum_sensing.m is code to simulate quorum sensing spatial dynamics.
- The code quorum_bounded_domain_ss_pp.m computes the steady state profile for quorum sensing on a bounded domain and was used to produce Figures 14.7 and 14.8.
- flocking_via_agents.m is code for an agent-based simulation of flocking behavior on a ring.
- flocking_via_MOL.m is code to simulate the equations (14.30)–(14.31) on a ring using the method of lines.
- flocking_plots.m is code used to make the plots in Figure 14.9.
- flight_of_swarmers.m is code to simulate swarming of two dimensional flyers, and to make the plots for Figures 14.12, 14.13, 14.14, and 14.15.

Constants, Units, and Functions

B.1. Physical Constants

Quantity	Name	Symbol	Units
amount	mole	mol	
electric charge	coulomb	C	
mass	gram	g	
temperature	kelvin	K	
time	second	s	
length	meter	m	
force	newton	N	$kg \cdot m \cdot s^{-2}$
energy	joule	J	$N \cdot m$
pressure	pascal	Pa	$N \cdot m^{-2}$
capacitance	farad	F	$A \cdot s \cdot V^{-1}$
resistance	ohm	Ω	$V \cdot A^{-1}$
electric current	ampere	A	$C \cdot s^{-1}$
conductance	siemen	S	$A \cdot V^{-1} = \Omega^{-1}$
potential difference	volt	V	$N \cdot m \cdot C^{-1}$
concentration	Molar	M	$mol \cdot L^{-1}$
atomic mass	Dalton	D	$g\,N_A^{-1}$

Physical Constant	Symbol	Value
Boltzmann's constant	k_B	1.381×10^{-23} J $\cdot$ K^{-1}
Planck's constant	h	6.626×10^{-34} J $\cdot$ s
Avogadro's number	N_A	6.02257×10^{23} mol^{-1}
unit charge	q	1.6×10^{-19} C
gravitational constant	g	9.78049 m/s^2
Faraday's constant	F	9.649×10^4 C $\cdot$ mol^{-1}
permittivity of free space	ϵ_0	8.854×10^{-12} F/m
universal gas constant	R	8.315 J mol^{-1} $\cdot$ K^{-1}
atmosphere	atm	1.01325×10^5 N $\cdot$ m^{-2}

Length	Symbol	Value
Angstrom	Å	10^{-10}m
nanometer	nm	10^{-9}m
micron	μm	10^{-6}m
millimeter	mm	10^{-3}m
centimeter	cm	10^{-2}m
kilometer	km	10^3m

Concentrations	Symbol	Value
nanomolar	nM	10^{-9}M
micromolar	μm	10^{-6}M
millimolar	mM	10^{-3}M

Liter: $1 \, \text{L} = 10^{-3} \, \text{m}^3$.

ϵ: dielectric constant for water $= 80.4\epsilon_0$

Molarity of water: 55.556M=55.556 moles/Liter

Other Identities
$1 \, \text{atm} = 760 \, \text{mmHg}$
$R = k_B N_A$
$F = q N_A$
$\text{pH} = -\log_{10}[\text{H}^+]$ with $[\text{H}^+]$ in moles per liter
$273.15 \, \text{K} = 0°\text{C}$ (ice point)
$T_{Kelvin} = T_{centigrade} - 273.15$
$T_{Farenheit} = \frac{9}{5} T_{centigrade} + 32$
$\frac{RT}{F} = 25.8 \, \text{mV at } 27°C$

B.2. Functions Used in this Book

$u(t)$	Name	Definition
$\exp(t)$	exponential	$u' = u, u(0) = 1$
$\ln(t)$	natural logarithm	$\ln(\exp(t)) = t$
$\sin(t)$	sine	$u'' + u = 0, u(0) = 0, u'(0) = 1$
$\cos(t)$	cosine	$u'' + u = 0, u(0) = 1, u'(0) = 0$
$\tanh(t)$	hyperbolic tangent	$\frac{\exp(t)-\exp(-t)}{\exp(t)+\exp(-t)}$
$\mathcal{N}(0,1)$	normal distribution	$\frac{1}{\sqrt{2\pi}}\exp(-\frac{t^2}{2})$
$\operatorname{erf}(t)$	error function	$\frac{2}{\sqrt{\pi}}\int_0^t \exp(-\tau^2)d\tau$
$J_0(t)$	0th order Bessel function, first kind	$u'' + \frac{1}{t}u' + u = 0, u(0) = 1, u'(0) = 0$
$K_0(t)$	0th order modified Bessel function	$u'' + \frac{1}{t}u' - u = 0, u(0) = 1, u'(0) = 0$
$H(t)$	Heaviside function	0 for $t < 0$, 1 for $t > 0$
$\delta(t)$	Dirac delta	$\int_{-\infty}^t \delta(\tau)d\tau = H(t)$ defined formally

Selected Answers to Exercises

C.1. Selected Answers for Chapter 1

1.1. $\frac{\partial f}{\partial t} = \frac{\partial^2 f}{\partial x^2} = \frac{x^2 - 2t}{4t^{\frac{5}{2}}} \exp\left(-\frac{x^2}{4t}\right)$.

1.3. (a) $\phi = \frac{1}{2}x^2 + xy - \frac{1}{2}y^2$.

1.5. $e^x = \sum_{j=0}^{\infty} \frac{x^j}{j!}$

1.7. (a) saddle point
     (b) unstable spiral
     (c) stable spiral
     (d) stable node

1.9. $p \geq 1 - \frac{\beta}{\alpha s_0}$.

1.10. (c) The threshold for an infection is $s = \frac{\beta}{\left(\alpha - \frac{\beta}{K}\right)}$.

1.16.
$$E(x) = \frac{1}{2}, \quad \text{var}(x) = \frac{1}{12}.$$

1.17.
$$E(x) = \frac{1}{2}, \quad \text{var}(x) = \frac{1}{4}.$$

1.18.
$$E(x) = \frac{7}{2}, \quad \text{var}(x) = \frac{35}{12}.$$

1.19. (a) $p(\frac{N}{2}|N) \approx \sqrt{\frac{2}{\pi N}}$.

1.23. With $\alpha t = 4$, $p_0 = 0.018$ and $p_{\geq 8} = 0.051$.

1.25. (a) 1.15×10^{-10}
     (b) The half life is $t = 5728$ years.

1.26. $\frac{1}{3}$

1.27.

$$E(n) = \frac{\rho}{1 - \rho},$$

and

$$\text{var} = \frac{\rho}{(1 - \rho)^2}$$

where $\rho = \frac{\alpha}{\alpha + \beta}$.

1.31. vol $= 0.16 \times 10^{-20}$ liters.

1.32. (d)

$$\frac{dp_k}{dt} = -\frac{1}{2}\beta k(k - 1)p_k + \frac{1}{2}\beta k(k + 1)p_{k+1}.$$

1.33. (c)

$$\frac{dp_k}{dt} = -\gamma k(N - k)p_k + \gamma(k + 1)(N - k - 1)p_{k+1}.$$

1.34. (b)

$$\frac{dp_k}{dt} = -(\frac{1}{2}\alpha k(k - 1) + \beta k)p_k(t) + \frac{1}{2}\alpha k(k + 1)p_{k+1} + \beta(k - 1)p_{k-1}.$$

1.35. (c)

$$\frac{dp_{k,1}}{dt} = -\alpha k p_{k,1} + \beta p_{k-1,0} + \gamma p_{k,0},$$

$$\frac{dp_{k,0}}{dt} = -(\beta + \gamma)p_{k,0} + \alpha(k + 1)p_{k+1,1}.$$

1.36. (b) The deterministic differential equation is

$$\frac{du}{dt} = (k_1 s - k_2)u - k_{-1}u^2.$$

(c)

$$\frac{dp_n}{dt} = -(k_1 sn + k_{-1}n(n - 1) + k_{-2}n)p_n$$

$$+ k_1(n - 1)p_{n-1} + (k_{-1}n(n + 1) + k_2(n + 1))p_{n+1}.$$

1.37. (a) The deterministic equation for i is

$$\frac{di}{dt} = \alpha(s_0 - \frac{\beta}{\alpha} - i)i$$

since $s + i = s_0$.

(c) Suppose that the total population size is N. Let p_j be the probability that there are j i individuals at time t. Then,

$$\frac{dp_j}{dt} = -\alpha j(N - j)p_j - \beta j p_j + \alpha(j - 1)(N - j + 1)p_{j-1} + \beta(j + 1)p_{j+1}.$$

C.2. Selected Answers for Chapter 2

2.1. $\approx 1.7 \times 10^{-12}$.

2.2. $v = \frac{200}{20} = 10$ ft/min.

2.3. (a) The flow velocity is 19.4 cm/s.

(b) Concentration flux is $J = 19.4$ mM cm/s.

(c) Number of molecules is 5.5×10^{-11} moles /s.

(d) flow volume through the vein is 393 cm^3/s.

(e) The concentration flux in the vein is $J = 1.1 \times 10^{-5}$ mM cm/s.

2.5. Total flux out of the cell across the cell wall is $J_{\text{tot}} = \frac{DA}{L}(c_i - c_e)$.

2.6. (a)

$$J = k_{\text{on}} \frac{D}{D + k_{\text{on}} Ll}.$$

(b) With the parameter values provided, $J = 134$ molecules per minute.

2.7. $J = -\frac{k}{\mu} x u(x, t)$.

2.8.

$$J = Dv \frac{C_i - C_e \exp(vL)}{\exp(vL) - 1}.$$

2.9.

$$J = u(a, t).$$

2.11. (b)

$$\frac{\partial u}{\partial t} + u \frac{\partial u}{\partial x} = 0.$$

C.3. Selected Answers for Chapter 3

3.3. (d)

$$\frac{\partial p}{\partial t} = \frac{\partial}{\partial x} \left((\beta - \alpha) \frac{\Delta x}{\Delta t} p + (\alpha + \beta) \frac{\Delta x^2}{2\Delta t} \frac{\partial p}{\partial x} \right).$$

3.5.

$$\frac{\partial u}{\partial t} = \frac{\partial^2}{\partial x^2} \left(\lambda(x) u \right).$$

3.7.

$$\frac{\partial u}{\partial t} = \frac{\partial}{\partial x} \left(\lambda(x) \frac{\partial u}{\partial x} \right).$$

3.9. (a) $E(T) \approx \ln(2) \Delta T N^2$.

(c) $D(x) = \frac{x(1-x)}{\Delta T N^2}$.

3.10. $D = 4 - 5 \times 10^3$ cm^{2}s^{-1} for sciatic nerve, $D = 0.25 \times 10^3$ cm^{2}s^{-1} for squid giant axon, while D ranges between 4×10^{-4} and 2.25×10^{-2}cm^{2}s^{-1} for human brain.

C.4. Selected Answers for Chapter 4

4.2. (a) For oxygen, $T = 1.2 \times 10^{-4}$, 1.2, and 1.2×10^6 s from a circle and $T = 7.9 \times 10^{-5}$, 0.79, and 7.9×10^5 s from a sphere.

4.3. (a) For a sphere,

$$T(R) = \frac{R^2}{3D} \left(\frac{R}{\rho} + \frac{\rho^2}{2R^2} - \frac{3}{2} \right).$$

(b) For a molecule with $D = 10^{-6}\text{cm}^2/\text{s}$ in a cell with radius $R = 5\mu\text{m}$, and a binding target 0.5nm, this time is $T \approx 833\text{s}$.

4.9. The function $P(R)$ shown in Figure 4.6 in the text is $P(R) = 1 - \exp(-\frac{R^2}{4Dt})$.

4.10. $D_{\text{eff}} = \frac{v^2}{2D_\theta}$.

4.11. $D_{\text{eff}} = D\frac{k_{\text{off}}}{k_{\text{on}}+k_{\text{off}}}$.

4.12. $D_{\text{eff}} = \frac{v^2}{2k_{\text{off}}}\frac{k_{\text{on}}}{k_{\text{on}}+k_{\text{off}}}$.

4.15. $D_{\text{eff}} = \frac{v^2}{k_{\text{off}}}\frac{k_{\text{on}}}{k_{\text{on}}+k_{\text{off}}} + D\frac{k_{\text{off}}}{k_{\text{on}}+k_{\text{off}}}$.

4.18. $D_{\text{eff}} = 2\frac{\lambda^2}{\tau}$.

C.5. Selected Answers for Chapter 5

5.1. Calculate that
$$\frac{d}{dt}\int_0^\infty u(r,t)r^2dr = 0.$$

5.2. Calculate that
$$\frac{d}{dt}E(r^2) = 2dD,$$
where d is the dimension and r is the corresponding dimensional radius.

5.3. (b) The region of influence is given by
$$X^2(t) = -4Dt\ln(0.1\sqrt{4\pi Dt}).$$

5.4. Estimates are $D = 0.3\text{-}0.9 \times 10^{-4}\text{cm}^2/\text{s}$.

5.6. $u(x) = u_0$.

5.7.
$$\lambda_k = 2(\cos(\frac{k\pi}{N}) - 1).$$

5.8.
$$\lambda_k = 2(\cos\frac{k\pi}{N} - 1), \quad k = 1, 2, \ldots, N-1.$$

5.9. (a)
$$u(x,t) = 1 - \exp(-4\pi^2 t)\cos(2\pi x).$$

5.10. (a)
$$u(x,t) = 2\exp(-\pi^2 t)\sin(\pi x).$$

5.12. (b) The smallest rate of decay is $\lambda = D\frac{\pi^2}{4L^2}$.

5.13. (b) The smallest rate of decay is $\lambda = D\mu^2\pi^2$ where $a = \mu\pi\tan(\mu\pi L)$.

5.14. Keeping only the slowest decaying mode,
$$u(\theta,t) = \frac{1}{2\pi} + \frac{1}{\pi}\exp(-D_\theta n^2 t)\cos(n\theta) + \cdots.$$

5.17. For a one dimensional domain of length L, the smallest rate of decay is $\lambda = D\frac{\pi^2}{L^2}$.

5.18. For a three dimensional sphere, the slowest rate of decay is $\lambda = D\frac{\pi^2}{R^2}$.

C.6. Selected Answers for Chapter 6

6.1.
$$u(x) = \frac{\delta A}{D\lambda + \delta} \exp(-\lambda x).$$

6.2. $u = \frac{a}{r} \exp(-\lambda(r - R))$, where $\lambda^2 = \frac{\alpha}{D}$, and $a = \frac{\delta A}{D(\lambda R + 1) + \frac{\delta}{R}}$.

6.4. (c) $\pi(x) = A \cosh(\sqrt{\frac{\alpha}{D}} x)$, where $A = \frac{1}{\cosh(\sqrt{\frac{\alpha}{D}} L)}$.

6.6. Using typical numbers, the time constant is 4 ms, and the space constant is about 4 cm for sciatic nerve and 1 cm for squid giant axon.

6.5. (c)
$$v(r) = \frac{\alpha}{2\pi D} K_0(\sqrt{\frac{\alpha}{D}} r).$$

6.7. (c) The probability of reaching the boundary before degrading is
$$\pi(0) = R\sqrt{\frac{\alpha}{D}} \frac{1}{\sinh(\sqrt{\frac{\alpha}{D}} R)}.$$

6.8. $2\sqrt{\alpha S_0 D}$.

6.12. Survival is possible if $\frac{\alpha L^2}{D} > \frac{\pi^2}{4}$.

6.13. Survival is possible when
$$\frac{a^2 b^2}{a^2 + b^2} > \frac{D\pi^2}{\alpha}.$$

A square, with $a = b$, is the smallest area rectangle for survival.

6.14. (c) The critical area for a circular domain is $A = \pi R^2 = \pi \frac{D}{\alpha} \mu_1^2 = 18.17 \frac{D}{\alpha}$. For comparison, the critical area for a square is $A = 2\pi^2 \frac{D}{\alpha} = 19.73 \frac{D}{\alpha}$. Thus, the circular domain is more efficient than the square, since it requires less area.

6.15. (b) The traveling wave speed is $2\sqrt{D\alpha(S_0 - \frac{\beta}{\alpha})}$.

6.18. The traveling wave speed is $2\sqrt{\gamma D(1 - \frac{k}{\gamma} \frac{s_0}{K + s_0})}$.

6.19. The traveling wave speed is $2\sqrt{\gamma D(1 - \frac{k}{\gamma} \frac{s_0^2}{K^2 + s_0^2})}$.

6.20. (a) $g = u_0 \frac{2D}{L^2}$.

6.22. $\rho = 2.7 \times 10^8 e_0 \text{cm}^3 \text{M}^{-1}$ for carbon dioxide vs. $\rho = 4.6 \times 10^7 e_0 \text{cm}^3 \text{M}^{-1}$ for oxygen.

C.7. Selected Answers for Chapter 7

7.1.
$$R = ab^2 + (a - c)^2 = 0.$$

7.2.
$$R = 4a^3 + 27b^2 = 0.$$

7.3.
$$R = 16a^4c - 4a^3b^2 - 128a^2c^2 + 144ab^2c - 27b^4 + 256c^3 = 0.$$

7.4. (c) The boundary between monophasic and triphasic behavior is the curve
$$R = -32\kappa^6(27\kappa^2 - 1)(\kappa^2 + 1)^2 = 0.$$

(d) The dividing curve is
$$R = 4\kappa^6\sigma^3 + 8\kappa^4\sigma^3 + 12\kappa^4\sigma^2 + 4\kappa^2\sigma^3 - 20\kappa^2\sigma^2 + 12\kappa^2\sigma - \sigma + 4 = 0.$$

7.5. The wavespeed of the Fisher-like wave with $0 < u < u_0$ where u_0 is the smallest positive zero of $f(u)$ is $2\sqrt{r_B D}$.

C.8. Selected Answers for Chapter 8

8.3. $S > \frac{16}{3}\frac{\beta}{r_B K_u}$, which, using parameter values from Table 7.1, gives $S > 432.67$ branches acre^{-1}.

8.5. The speed is $\sqrt{Dk_s c}$ where
$$\frac{K_2}{c_T}\frac{\kappa}{1+\kappa} = \frac{\sqrt{c^2+1}-c}{\sqrt{c^2+1+\kappa}+\sqrt{c^2+1}},$$

where $\kappa = \frac{k_f}{k_s}$. The speed is zero when
$$\frac{K_2}{c_T} = \frac{1+\kappa}{\kappa}\frac{1}{\sqrt{1+\kappa}+1}.$$

8.6. The speed c is found implicitly through
$$\ln(\frac{\alpha}{1-\alpha}) = \frac{\mu_+\ln\left(-\frac{(\mu_++\lambda_-)}{(\mu_++\lambda_+)}\right) - \mu_-\ln\left(-\frac{(\lambda_-+\mu_-)}{(\lambda_++\mu_-)}\right)}{\mu_+ - \mu_-},$$
where
$$\lambda_\pm = \frac{1}{2}(c \pm \sqrt{c^2+4}), \qquad \mu_\pm = \frac{1}{2}(c \pm \sqrt{c^2-4}).$$
Consequently, one can readily plot α as a function of c.

8.8. (b)   (i)
$$c \approx 250\text{m/yr}.$$

(ii) The minimal nondimensional blocking distance is $Y = 0.225$, which in dimensional units is
$$L = Y\sqrt{\frac{D}{k_4 + k_1 - k_3}} = 46\text{m}.$$

(iii) $N_2 = 68.1$ so in dimensional units, the number of released mosquitoes needs to be about $N = \frac{D}{k}N_0 N_2 = 500 \cdot 40 \cdot 5 \cdot 68.1 = 6.8 \times 10^6$ mosquitoes.

8.9. (b) $R_m = 4.055$ kΩ cm^2 and $c_0 = 20.7$ in dimensionless units.

8.10. (a) $\bar{g}_{Na} = 1.50$.

(b) The critical concentration of TTX is
$$[TTX]^* = K_d(\frac{120}{1.5} - 1) = 0.395\mu\text{M}.$$

8.12. $N_3 = 607$.

8.13.
$$Y = \frac{1}{\sqrt{\kappa}}\log(\mu), \qquad \text{where } A\mu^2 - U(Y)\mu + B = 0.$$

8.14.
$$Y = \frac{\sqrt{A_r}}{2}\ln\left(\frac{\sqrt{A_r}-1\frac{\alpha}{1-\alpha}\sqrt{A_r}+1}{\sqrt{A_r}+1\frac{\alpha}{1-\alpha}\sqrt{A_r}-1}\right).$$

8.16.
$$A_r = \frac{(1+\alpha)(\alpha-1)^3}{\alpha^3(\alpha-2)}.$$

8.18. Propagation will fail if $\theta = 0.5$ and $\beta > 0.063$. Therefore, we want $L > 0.063\sqrt{\frac{D_c}{k_s}}$, and $\sigma > \frac{c^*(0.063)}{0.5}\sqrt{\frac{D_c}{k_s}}$.

C.9. Selected Answers for Chapter 9

9.1.
$$\beta > 2\mu\exp(\mu) = 1.65/\text{yr}.$$

9.2.
$$\frac{B}{\mu-\kappa} > 1.$$

9.3. (b)
$$\mu(a) = \frac{2a}{1+a^2}.$$

(c) Require
$$\frac{\beta\pi}{2} > 1.$$

9.4.
$$N = K(1 - \frac{\mu^2}{B}).$$

9.5. $u = x$.

9.6. $u = x\exp(-2t)$.

9.7. $u = \frac{x}{1+xt}\exp(-t)$.

9.9. (a)
$$\frac{\partial g}{\partial t} = (1-z)(\alpha-\beta z)\frac{\partial g}{\partial z}.$$

(c)
$$p_0(t) = g(0,t) = \left(\frac{\alpha\exp((\alpha-\beta)t)-\alpha}{\alpha\exp((\alpha-\beta)t)-\beta}\right)^N.$$

9.10.
$$p_0(t) = g(0,t) = \left(\frac{\alpha t}{\alpha t+1}\right)^N.$$

9.11.
$$u(x,t) = u_0(x\exp(kt))\exp((k-\lambda)t).$$

9.12.
$$u(0,t) = u_0 \exp(\frac{-\lambda v_b t}{v_s + v_b}).$$

9.15. For $k = 4$, the resultant of the two polynomials is

$$
\begin{aligned}
R &= 64t^2 C_0^2 (64C_0^3 t^3 + 48C_0^2 t^2 - 27C_0 t z^2 + 12C_0 t + 1) \\
&= 64t^2 C_0^2 \big((C_0 t + 1)(8C_0 t - 1)^2 - 27tC_0(z^2 - 1)\big).
\end{aligned}
$$

9.16. (a) $\frac{\partial W}{\partial t} + W\frac{\partial W}{\partial z} = kS_1(z - z^{k-1})$.
     (c) $T = \frac{\pi}{2k\sqrt{S_1}}$ is the gel time.

9.17. $W(x,t) = -\frac{x}{1+t}$.

9.18. $u(x,t) = -\frac{x^2}{1+2t}$.

9.20.
$$c = \frac{1}{2}(\alpha + \beta).$$

9.22. (b) Oxygen debt occurs at x where
$$\frac{mx}{v} = s_0 + \frac{k_+ e_0 s_0}{(k_- + k_+ s_0)}.$$

9.24. The carbon dioxide concentration in the vessel is c_v where
$$c_v = \frac{m}{v}x.$$

9.25.
$$F = \frac{kV}{\beta}\frac{\alpha N_T}{\beta + \alpha}.$$

9.27.
$$F = \frac{1}{2}\rho k h^2 (1 - (\frac{v}{c})^2)(1 - \exp(-\frac{1}{v})),$$

where $v = \frac{V}{\alpha}, c = \frac{\beta h}{\sqrt{2\alpha}}$.

C.10. Selected Answers for Chapter 10

10.2. (c)
$$u(x) = u_0 \exp(-\frac{v}{D}x).$$

10.3. Let $\tau = \kappa t$, and $x = \sqrt{\frac{D}{\kappa}}\xi$.

10.4. The expected value is $c(t)$ and the variance is $\frac{b}{2}$, where
$$\frac{db}{dt} = 4D - 2b, \qquad \frac{dc}{dt} = y(t) - c.$$

10.5. $\delta\tau$ is the solution of the equation

$$\theta = \sum_{n=1}^{\infty} \frac{1}{\sqrt{4\pi n \delta\tau}} \exp\left(-\frac{n^2(1 - v\delta\tau)^2}{4n\delta\tau} - \beta^2 n\delta\tau\right) \equiv g_\beta(\delta\tau),$$

where $\theta = \frac{c^* L}{\sigma}$ is the dimensionless threshold.

10.7. The ratio between rates λ_1 and λ_2, where λ_j is the spread rate to neighbor j, is $\frac{\lambda_2}{\lambda_1} = \exp(-3\Lambda)$.

C.11. Selected Answers for Chapter 11

11.1. The system is unstable if $D_u D_v - \chi_u \chi_v u^* v^* < 0$.

C.12. Selected Answers for Chapter 12

12.1. (b) The bifurcation values of α with $0 < \alpha \le 10$ are $\alpha = 1, \frac{5}{2}$ for $n = 1$, $\alpha = 4, 10$, for $n = 2$, and $\alpha = 9$ for $n = 3$.

12.7. (a) With $A = 300\text{kg H}_2\text{O m}^{-2}\,\text{year}^{-1}$, the wavelength for grass is 21.5 m, and the speed 2.37 m/yr.

(b) With $A = 300\text{kg H}_2\text{O m}^{-2}\,\text{year}^{-1}$, vegetation will disappear if $E > 4.34\,\text{year}^{-1}$.

12.8. With $A = 300$, the wavelength for trees is 60.4 m, and the speed 0.81 m/yr.

C.13. Selected Answers for Chapter 13

13.3. The speed of invasion is a decreasing function of A.

13.4. With $A = 0.4$, the speed of invasion is 3.33 per generation.

13.6. The displacement per cycle is

$$x = \frac{1}{\kappa_-}\left(\ln(\frac{A_0}{2u_0}) + \ln(\frac{2}{\kappa_- \sqrt{\beta^2 + 4}})\right).$$

C.14. Selected Answers for Chapter 14

14.2.

$$v(r) = \frac{\delta R^2 u}{\sqrt{\alpha D_e R} + \delta R + D_e} \frac{1}{r} \exp(-\sqrt{\frac{\alpha}{D_e}}(r - R)),$$

where

$$f(u) - S\delta \frac{\sqrt{\mu} + \frac{D_e}{\delta R}}{\sqrt{\mu} + \frac{D_e}{\delta R} + 1} u = 0,$$

and $\mu = \sqrt{\frac{\alpha D_e}{\delta^2}}$.

14.3.

$$v(x) = \frac{u}{\mu \sinh(\sqrt{\frac{\alpha}{D_e}}L) + \cosh(\sqrt{\frac{\alpha}{D}}L)} \cosh(\sqrt{\frac{\alpha}{D_e}}(x - L)),$$

where

$$f(u) - \sigma\delta \frac{\mu \tanh(\sqrt{\frac{\alpha}{D_e}}L)}{\mu \tanh(\sqrt{\frac{\alpha}{D_e}}L) + 1} u = 0,$$

with $\mu = \sqrt{\frac{\alpha D_e}{\delta^2}}$.

14.6. With $\gamma = 0$, $D_e = 0$, the unique stable steady state solution is at

$$u = s_0 \left(\frac{\rho}{\alpha(1-\rho)} + \frac{1}{\sigma\delta} \right), \qquad v = s_0 \frac{1}{\alpha} \frac{\rho}{1-\rho}.$$

14.11. (b) $R = \frac{V}{\alpha \Delta \theta_j^T}$ where

$$\Delta \theta_j^T = \theta_p - \tan^{-1} \left(\frac{1}{\theta_p} - \cot \theta_p \right).$$

Bibliography

[1] J. Adler, *Chemoreceptors in bacteria*, Science **166** (1969), 1588–1597.

[2] L. J. S. Allen, *An Introduction to Mathematical Biology*, Prentice Hall, Upper Saddle River, N.J., 2007.

[3] R. M. Anderson, B. Anderson, and R. M. May, *Infectious diseases of humans: Dynamics and control*, Oxford University Press, 1992.

[4] N. H. Barton and M. Turelli, *Spatial waves of advance with bistable dynamics: Cytoplasmic and genetic analogues of allee effects*, The American Naturalist **178** (2011), E48–E75.

[5] J. Belair, M.C. Mackey, and J.M. Mahaffy, *Age-structured and two-delay models for erythropoiesis*, Mathematical Biosciences **128** (1995), 317–346.

[6] A. J. Belsky, *Population and community processes in a mosaic grassland in the Serengeti, Tanzania*, J. Ecol. **74** (1986), 841.

[7] N. F. Britton, *Reaction-diffusion equations and their applications to biology*, Academic Press, Inc. [Harcourt Brace Jovanovich, Publishers], London, 1986. MR866143

[8] N. F. Britton, *Essential mathematical biology*, Springer Undergraduate Mathematics Series, Springer-Verlag London, Ltd., London, 2003. MR1968417

[9] R. S. Cantrell and C. Cosner, *Spatial ecology via reaction-diffusion equations*, Wiley Series in Mathematical and Computational Biology, John Wiley & Sons, Ltd., Chichester, 2003. MR2191264

[10] P. Childs and J. P. Keener, *Slow manifold reduction of a stochastic chemical reaction: exploring Keizer's paradox*, Discrete Contin. Dyn. Syst. Ser. B **17** (2012), no. 6, 1775–1794, DOI 10.3934/dcdsb.2012.17.1775. MR2924439

[11] C.-S. Chou and A. Friedman, *Introduction to mathematical biology*, Springer Undergraduate Texts in Mathematics and Technology, Springer, [Cham], 2016. Modeling, analysis, and simulations. MR3468665

[12] C. Cobbold, M. Kot, M. Lewis, and F. Lutscher, *Integrodifference equations in ecology: 30 years and counting*, `https://www.birs.ca/workshops/2016/16w5121/report16w5121.pdf`, BIRS, 2016.

[13] S. Coombes and P. C. Bressloff, *Saltatory waves in the spike-diffuse-spike model of active dendritic spines*, Phys. Rev. Lett. **91** (2003), no. 2, 028102.

[14] I. D. Couzin, J. Krause, R. James, G. D. Ruxton, and N. R. Franks, *Collective memory and spatial sorting in animal groups*, J. Theoret. Biol. **218** (2002), no. 1, 1–11, DOI 10.1006/jtbi.2002.3065. MR2027139

[15] G. de Vries, T. Hillen, M. Lewis, J. Müller, and B. Schönfisch, *A course in mathematical biology: Quantitative modeling with mathematical and computational methods*, Mathematical Modeling and Computation, vol. 12, Society for Industrial and Applied Mathematics (SIAM), Philadelphia, PA, 2006. MR2242784

[16] L. Edelstein-Keshet, *Mathematical models in biology*, Classics in Applied Mathematics, vol. 46, Society for Industrial and Applied Mathematics (SIAM), Philadelphia, PA, 2005. Reprint of the 1988 original. MR2131632

[17] L. Edelstein-Keshet, W. R. Holmes, M. Zajac, and M. Dutot, *From simple to detailed models for cell polarization*, Phil. Trans. R. Soc. B (2013), 368.

[18] S. P. Ellner and J. Guckenheimer, *Dynamic models in biology*, Princeton University Press, Princeton, NJ, 2006. MR2223451

[19] P. C. Fife, *Mathematical aspects of reacting and diffusing systems*, Lecture Notes in Biomathematics, vol. 28, Springer-Verlag, Berlin-New York, 1979. MR527914

[20] R. A. Fisher, *The wave of advance of advantageous genes*, Annals of Eugenics **7** (1937), no. 4, 355–369.

[21] R. FitzHugh, *Thresholds and plateaus in the Hodgkin–Huxley nerve equations*, The Journal of General Physiology **43** (1960), 867–896.

[22] R. FitzHugh, *Mathematical models of excitation and propagation in nerve*, Biological Engineering (H. P. Schwan, ed.), McGraw-Hill, New York, 1969.

[23] A. L. Fogelson and J. P. Keener, *Toward an understanding of fibrin branching structure*, Phys. Rev. E (3) **81** (2010), no. 5, 051922, 9, DOI 10.1103/PhysRevE.81.051922. MR2736252

[24] A. L. Fogelson and J. P. Keener, *A framework for exploring the post-gelation behavior of Ziff and Stell's polymerization models*, SIAM J. Appl. Math. **75** (2015), no. 3, 1346–1368, DOI 10.1137/140983872. MR3361446

[25] C. Fuqua, S. C. Winans, and E. P. Greenberg, *Census and concensus in bacterial ecosystems: The luxR-luxI family of quorum-sensing transcriptional regulators*, Ann. Rev. Microbiology **50** (1996), 727–751.

[26] P. Grindrod, *The theory and applications of reaction-diffusion equations: Patterns and waves*, 2nd ed., Oxford Applied Mathematics and Computing Science Series, The Clarendon Press, Oxford University Press, New York, 1996. MR1423804

[27] C. Haurie, *Modeling complex neutrophil dynamics in the grey collie*, J. Theor. Biol. **204** (2000), no. 4, 505–519.

[28] A. V. Hill, *The heat of shortening and the dynamic constants of muscle*, Proc. Roy. Soc. (Lond.) **B126** (1938), 136–195.

[29] T. Hillen and K. J. Painter, *A user's guide to PDE models for chemotaxis*, J. Math. Biol. **58** (2009), no. 1-2, 183–217, DOI 10.1007/s00285-008-0201-3. MR2448428

[30] A. L. Hodgkin and A. F. Huxley, *A quantitative description of membrane current and its application to conduction and excitation in nerve*, J. Physiol. **117** (1952), no. 4, 500–44.

[31] A. A. Hoffmann, B. L. Montgomery, J. Popovici, I. Iturbe-Ormaetxe, P. H. Johnson, F. Muzzi, M. Greenfield, M. Durkan, Y. S. Leong, Y. Dong, H. Cook, J. Axford, A. G. Callahan, N. Kenny, C. Omodei, E. A. McGraw, P. A. Ryan, S. A. Ritchie, M. Turelli, and S. L. O'Neill, *Successful establishment of wolbachia in aedes populations to suppress dengue transmission*, Nature **476** (2011), 454–457.

[32] A. F. Huxley, *Muscle structure and theories of contraction*, Progress in Biophysics **7** (1957), 255–318.

[33] A. Jilkine and L. Edelstein-Keshet, *A comparison of mathematical models for polarization of single eukaryotic cells in response to guided cues*, PLoS Comput. Biol. **7** (2011), no. 4, e1001121, 15, DOI 10.1371/journal.pcbi.1001121. MR2805372

[34] J. P. Keener, *Principles of applied mathematics: Transformation and approximation*, Revised edition, Perseus Books, Advanced Book Program, Cambridge, MA, 2000. MR1741517

[35] J. Keener and J. Sneyd, *Mathematical physiology*, Interdisciplinary Applied Mathematics, vol. 8, Springer-Verlag, New York, 1998. MR1673204

[36] J. Keizer, *Lectures on the statistical thermodynamics of nonequilibrium steady states*, Recent developments in nonequilibrium thermodynamics: fluids and related topics (Barcelona, 1985), Lecture Notes in Phys., vol. 253, Springer, Berlin, 1986, pp. 3–22, DOI 10.1007/3-540-16489-8_29. MR859893

[37] J. Keizer, G. D. Smith, S. Ponce-Dawson, and J. E. Pearson, *Saltatory propagation of Ca^{2+} waves by Ca^{2+} sparks*, Biophys. J. **75** (1998), no. 2, 595–600.

[38] E. F. Keller and L. A. Segel, *Initiation of slime mold aggregation viewed as an instability*, J. Theoret. Biol. **26** (1970), no. 3, 399–415, DOI 10.1016/0022-5193(70)90092-5. MR3925816

[39] W. O. Kermack and A. G. McKendrick, *A contribution to the mathematical theory of epidemics*, Proc. Roy. Soc. Lond. A **115** (1927), 700–721.

[40] C. A. Klausmeier, *Regular and irregular patterns in semiarid vegetation*, Science **284** (1999), 1826–1828.

[41] K. J. Lee, W. D. McCormick, Q. Ouyang, and H. L. Swinney, *Pattern formation by interacting chemical fronts*, Science **261** (1993), 192–194.

[42] D. Ludwig, D. D. Jones, and C. S. Holling, *Qualitative analysis of insect outbreak systems: The spruce budworm and forest*, J. Animal Ecology **47** (1978), 315–332.

[43] J. A. Mabbutt and F. C. Fanning, *Vegetation banding in arid western Australia*, J. Arid Environ. **12** (1987), 41.

[44] P. D. Maia and J. N. Kutz, *Reaction time impairments in decision-making networks as a diagnostic marker for traumatic brain injuries and neurological diseases*, J. Comput. Neurosci. **42** (2017), no. 3, 323–347.

[45] H. P. McKean Jr., *Nagumo's equation*, Advances in Math. **4** (1970), 209–223 (1970), DOI 10.1016/0001-8708(70)90023-X. MR260438

[46] C. J. McMeniman, R. V. Lane, B. N. Cass, A. W. C. Fong, M. Sidhu, Y.-F. Wang, and S. L. O'Neill, *Stable introduction of a life-shortening wolbachia infection into the mosquito aedes aegypti*, Science **323** (2009), 141–144.

[47] H. Meinhardt, *The algorithmic beauty of sea shells*, The Virtual Laboratory, Springer-Verlag, Berlin, 1995. With contributions and images by Przemysław Prusinkiewicz and Deborah R. Fowler; With 1 IBM-PC floppy disk (3.5 inch; HD). MR1325695

[48] Y. Mori, A. Jilkine, and L. Edelstein-Keshet, *Wave-pinning and cell polarity from a bistable reaction–diffusion system*, Biophys. J. **94** (2008), 3684–3697.

[49] J. D. Murray, *Mathematical biology. II: Spatial models and biomedical applications*, 3rd ed., Interdisciplinary Applied Mathematics, vol. 18, Springer-Verlag, New York, 2003. MR1952568

[50] J. D. Murray, *Mathematical biology. I: An introduction*, 3rd ed., Interdisciplinary Applied Mathematics, vol. 17, Springer-Verlag, New York, 2002. MR1908418

[51] J. D. Murray, E. A. Stanley, and D. L. Brown, *On the spatial spread of rabies among foxes*, Proc. Roy. Soc. B **229** (1986), 111–150.

[52] J. D. Murray and J. Wyman, *Facilitated diffusion: the case of carbon monoxide*, J. Biological Chemistry **246** (1971), 5903–5906.

[53] J. Nagumo, S. Arimoto, and S. Yoshizawa, *An active pulse transmission line simulating nerve axon*, Proc. IRE **50** (1964), 2061–70.

[54] B. L. Partridge, *The structure and function of fish schools.*, Sci. Am. **245** (1982), 90–99.

[55] B. L. Partridge and T. J. Pitcher, *The sensory basis of fish schools: relative role of lateral line and vision.*, J. Comparative Physiol. **135** (1980), 315–325.

[56] J. E. Pearson, *Complex patterns in a simple system*, Science **261** (1993), 189–192.

[57] J. E. Pearson and S. Ponce-Dawson, *Crisis on skid row*, Physica A **257** (1998), no. 1, 141–8.

[58] B. Perthame, *Parabolic equations in biology: Growth, reaction, movement and diffusion*, Lecture Notes on Mathematical Modelling in the Life Sciences, Springer, Cham, 2015. MR3408563

[59] S. Ponce-Dawson, J. Keizer, and J. E. Pearson, *Fire-diffuse-fire model of dynamics of intracellular calcium waves.*, Proc. Natl. Acad. Sci. USA **96** (1999), no. 11, 6060–3.

[60] M. H. Protter and H. F. Weinberger, *Maximum principles in differential equations*, Prentice-Hall, Inc., Englewood Cliffs, N.J., 1967. MR0219861

[61] T. T. Renault, A. O. Abraham, T. Bergmiller, G. Paradis, S. Rainville, E. Charpentier, C. C. Guet, Y. Tu, K. Namba, J. P. Keener, T. Minamino, and M. Erhardt, *Bacterial flagella grow through an injection-diffusion mechanism*, eLife **10** (2017), 26136.

[62] J. G. Schraiber, A. N. Kaczmarczyk, R. Kwok, and et al., *Constraints on the use of lifespan-shortening Wolbachia to control dengue fever*, J. Theoret. Biol. **297** (2012), 26–32, DOI 10.1016/j.jtbi.2011.12.006. MR2899014

[63] E. F. Segel and L. A. Segel, *Model for chemotaxis*, J. Theor. Biol. **30** (1971), 225–234.

[64] L. A. Segel, I. Chet, and Y. Henis, *A simple quantitative assay for bacterial motility*, J. General Microbiology **98** (1977), 329–337.

[65] D. H. Smith V. E. Johnson, W. Stewart, *Axonal pathology in traumatic brain injury*, Exp. Neurol. **246** (2013), 35–43.

[66] J. Smoller, *Shock waves and reaction-diffusion equations*, 2nd ed., Grundlehren der Mathematischen Wissenschaften [Fundamental Principles of Mathematical Sciences], vol. 258, Springer-Verlag, New York, 1994. MR1301779

[67] D. J. Tongway and J. A. Ludwig, *Principles from Australia's rangelands*, Landscape Ecology, Function and Management (J. Ludwig, D. Tongway, D. Freudenberger, J. Noble, and Eds. K. Hodgkinson, eds.), CSIRO, Collingwood, Australia, 1997, pp. 49–61.

[68] D. J. Tongway, C. Valentin, and J. Seghieri, *Banded vegetation patterning in arid and semiarid environments: ecological processes and consequences for management*, Springer, 2001.

[69] A. M. Turing, *The chemical basis of morphogenesis*, Philos. Trans. Roy. Soc. London Ser. B **237** (1952), no. 641, 37–72. MR3363444

[70] L. P. White, *Vegetation stripes on sheet wash surfaces*, J. Ecol. **59** (1971), 615.

[71] G. B. Whitham, *Linear and nonlinear waves*, Wiley-Interscience [John Wiley & Sons], New York-London-Sydney, 1974. Pure and Applied Mathematics. MR0483954

[72] G. E. Wickens and F. W. Collier, *Some vegetation patterns in the Republic of the Sudan*, Geoderma **6** (1971), 43.

[73] M. M. Williams, *Hematology*, McGraw-Hill, New York, 1990.

[74] J. B. Wittenberg, *The molecular mechanism of haemoglobin-facilitated oxygen diffusion*, J. Biological Chemistry **241** (1966), 104–114.

[75] J. Wyman, *Facilitated diffusion and the possible role of myoglobin as a transport mechanism*, J. Biol. Chem. **241** (1966), 115–121.

[76] R. M. Ziff and G. Stell, *Kinetics of polymer gelation*, J. Chem. Phys. **73** (1980), 3492–3499.

Index

actin, 196, 197
advection-diffusion equation, 207
Aedes aegypti, 134
agent-based modeling, 69, 102, 217, 263
algebraic multiplicity, 9
anemia, 174
Arzelà theorem, 41
autoinducer, 254

Balsam Woolly Adelgid, 247
basic reproduction number, 14
Bell's law, 193
Bessel function, 127
    modified, 126
    of the first kind, 90
Bessel's equation, 90
bifurcation theory
    applied to
        blood cell production, 176
bifurcations
    Hopf, 176
"Big-Oh" notation, 4
binomial distribution, 16
birth-death process, 33
bisection method, 31, 146
Boltzman equation, 60
boundary conditions, 79
    absorbing, 79
    Dirichlet, 79
    Neumann, 79
    no-flux, 79
    periodic, 79, 240
    reflecting, 79

    Robin, 79
Brownian motion, 59
Burgers' equation, 46

cable equation, 135
Calcium-Induced Calcium Release, 138,
    160
cAMP, 238
carbon dioxide
    facilitated diffusion, 129
carbon dioxide transport, 129
carrying capacity, 101
central limit theorem, 17, 51
CFL condition, 179
characteristic polynomial, 9, 118, 222
chemical potential, 42
chronic myelogenous leukaemia, 177
CICR, 138, 160
conservation equation, 40
Courant–Friedrichs–Levy condition, 179
Crank–Nicolson algorithm, 86
cumulative distribution function, 20

D. discoideum, 219
Darcy's law, 42
diffusion time, 78
dimensional analysis, 99
Dirac delta function, 160
directional derivative, 2
discrete bistable equation, 157
dispersion curve, 235, 265
divergence theorem, 2
dominated convergence theorem, 41